Physical Principles of
Semiconductor Devices

Physica
Semiconductor

HARRY E. TALLEY

The Iowa State University

Principles of Devices

/ DON G. DAUGHERTY

Press / Ames / 1 9 7 6

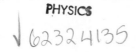
HARRY E. TALLEY is Professor of Electrical Engineering at the University of Kansas, where he received the M.S. and Ph.D. degrees. He was formerly a member of the technical staff of Bell Telephone Laboratories and a visiting professor at Lehigh University. Besides this book, he is author of several articles published in journals in the field of electronics.

DON G. DAUGHERTY is Associate Professor of Electrical Engineering at the University of Kansas. He received the M.S. and Ph.D. degrees at the University of Wisconsin. He is an industrial consultant for several firms. His current writing and research is in electronics design for automatic flight control systems.

© 1976 The Iowa State University Press
Ames, Iowa 50010.

Composed by Science Press
Printed by The Iowa State University Press

First edition, 1976

Library of Congress Cataloging in Publication Data

Talley, Harry E   1924–
  Physical principles of semiconductor devices.

  Bibliography: p.
  Includes index.
  1. Semiconductors.   I. Daugherty, Don G., 1935–
joint author.   II. Title.
TK7871.85.T18   621.3815′2   75-45182
ISBN 0-8138-1235-6

CONTENTS

PREFACE

LITTLE needs to be said to establish the impact semiconductor devices have had upon our society in general and upon the practicing electrical engineer in particular. Engineers in fact need look no farther than the scientific calculators on their desks for a symbol of the technological revolution which semiconductor electronics has brought about. At remarkably little cost engineers can hold in their hands a reliable device equal in calculating power to a roomful of expensive, unreliable computing equipment from the 1950s. The importance of semiconductor devices and the electrical engineer's need for knowledge about them are thus quite evident.

In writing this text we have in mind two goals: (1) to provide the student with a firm understanding of the physical operation of most of the semiconductor devices in use today—diodes, transistors, FETs, *pnpn*s, etc., and (2) to provide the student with a firm understanding of the physical principles which underlie the semiconductor devices of tomorrow.

Chapters 1–6 fulfill the dual role of providing the basis for the device studies in Chaps. 7, 8, 9, and 10 and the firm understanding required for dealing with the devices of tomorrow. Chapters 1, 2, and 3 are concerned with an introduction to quantum mechanics. Such an introduction is frequently part of a modern physics course in the electrical engineering curriculum; it is our belief that quantum mechanics is an important part of the electrical engineering student's education in the sciences and is sufficiently subtle as to merit study at an introductory level on more than one occasion.

Following this introduction to quantum mechanics we move on, in Chaps. 4, 5, and 6, to the energy band structure, the population of the band structure, and the conduction processes in semiconductors. This material, together with the quantum mechanics material from Chaps. 1, 2, and 3, provides the basis for the device studies in Chaps. 7, 8, 9, and 10. In Chaps. 7 and 8 we deal with the *pn* junction diode and the bipolar junction transistor both descriptively and quantitatively so that the physical principles of these devices and their mathematical representation will be understood.

In Chap. 9 we discuss the processes used in fabricating modern planar silicon devices and following this, we present in Chap. 10 discussions of a variety of semiconductor devices: field effect transistors, *pnpn* devices, Gunn and IMPATT diodes, *pin* diodes, light sensitive and light emitting devices and, very briefly, monolithic integrated circuits.

In discussing quantum mechanics, conduction in semiconductors, and the principles of the devices, we have sought to strike balances between depth and breadth and rigor and hand-waving. We have tried to limit our discussion to those topics and devices we regard as of fundamental importance and then to present sufficient discussion and analysis to allow the student to obtain a good understanding of the physical principles involved.

The material in this text is more than enough for a one-semester three-hour course, so that a variety of curricular needs can be satisfied by appropriate material selection and course pacing. It is assumed that students will have completed mathematics through differential equations, and physics through mechanics and electricity. For curricula providing exactly this background a course based on Chaps. 1–7 might be indicated. For curricula also providing a course in modern physics, Chaps. 1 and 2 can be treated briefly so that a course based on Chaps. 1–8 plus selected portions of 9 and/or 10 might be appropriate. For courses in which quantum mechanics is not to be stressed as strongly as here, Chaps. 1, 2, and 3 could be de-emphasized in favor of more complete coverage of Chaps. 8, 9, and 10.

We wish to acknowledge all those who have contributed to the completion of this text, including the many students who both criticized and encouraged us in our writing, the secretarial staff who typed the original notes and the final manuscript, and the Department of Electrical Engineering of the University of Kansas that supported and encouraged us throughout this writing project.

Harry E. Talley
Don G. Daugherty

Lawrence, Kansas
November 26, 1974

Physical Principles of
Semiconductor Devices

CHAPTER 1

Introduction

THE principal purpose of this text is to develop an understanding of the physical mechanisms underlying the behavior of semiconductor devices, especially *pn* junction diodes and transistors. This could be quite an ambitious undertaking. A detailed knowledge of substantial portions of the fields of solid-state physics, quantum mechanics, and statistical mechanics would be required if such an ambitious undertaking were done in completeness. It is possible, however, to develop an understanding of the engineering aspects of such devices in such a way that only a modest background is required. This we have attempted to do.

The material covered is divided roughly into three sections. In the first section, we discuss some elementary but important aspects of atomic and quantum physics as applied to solids. Fundamentally, the problem is to explain why materials vary in their ability to carry an electric current; the answer to the problem lies in the energy band structure of solids which we study in a qualitative fashion.

In the second section we discuss how the densities of charge carriers in a semiconductor vary with temperature and crystalline purity. We learn how the carriers move through the semiconductor and how it is possible by adding chemical impurities to a semiconductor to cause the current to be carried by either positively charged or negatively charged carriers, thus giving rise to p-type ("p" for positive) or n-type ("n" for negative) semiconductors.

In the third section we discuss those phenomena that occur when a junction is formed between p-type and n-type semiconductors. The semiconductor diode is treated in considerable detail followed by a similar discussion of the transistor. Finally, we give introductory discussions of a variety of other solid-state devices.

3

1.1 POINT CONTACT DEVICES

The first useful semiconductor devices were point contact crystal detectors. The crystal set and the early commercial radios employed such devices. The active element comprised a metal point placed in contact with a suitable crystal (galena, for example) to form a rectifying connection. This structure served as a detector of radio waves. With the development of the vacuum tube the crude point contact devices fell into disuse until the need arose in the early 1940s for high-frequency radar detectors and mixers. Because of their small size the crystal detectors could operate at substantially higher frequencies than could vacuum diodes. This stimulated experimental and theoretical studies of semiconductors and semiconductor devices culminating in 1948 in the invention of the point contact transistor by Brattain and Bardeen, and the development of junction transistor theory, notably by Shockley. The end result has been a vast new field of electronics associated with semiconductor devices that revolutionized the electronics industry.[1]

1.2 SEMICONDUCTORS

A convenient entrance to the study of semiconductors and semiconductor devices is provided by considering the electrical conductivity σ of substances found in nature. There are three more or less distinct classes of conducting materials: metals, semiconductors, and insulators. The conductivity ranges are not sharply defined, but Fig. 1.1 gives a reasonable picture of the experimental data. It is apparent that metals are very good conductors, insulators are very poor conductors, and semiconductors, as the name implies, lie somewhere between.

The fabulous range (thirty orders of magnitude) shown by the conductivity should be noted immediately. It has been remarked that σ shows a greater spread than any other commonly measured property of matter. To illustrate just how tremendous is the range, suppose we compare the radius of the earth (4.0×10^3 mi $= 6.4 \times 10^8$ cm) to the classical radius of the electron ($r_e \simeq 3 \times 10^{-13}$ cm). The result is

$$\frac{\text{radius of earth}}{\text{radius of electron}} = 2.1 \times 10^{21}$$

Thus the range of conductivities is almost nine orders of magnitude larger than this ratio! It seems important to find an explanation for this wide variation.

A second question arises from the observed relation of conductiv-

---

1. An interesting history of the study of semiconductors leading to the invention of the transistor is given by W. H. Brattain and G. L. Pearson, History of Semiconductor Research, *Proc. IRE* 90 (1955):1795.

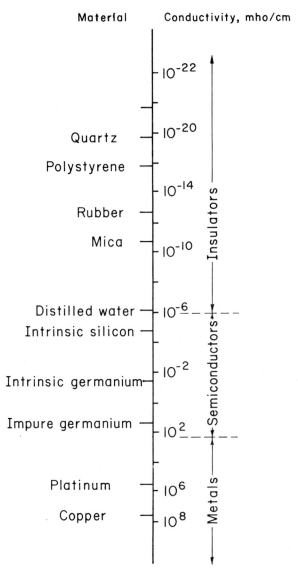

FIG. 1.1   Conductivity of various materials.

ity and temperature. In Fig. 1.2 are shown plots of the conductivities of a pure semiconductor (germanium) and a metal (copper) as functions of temperature. The coordinates require some explanation. The abscissa in Fig. 1.2a is linear, with the variable being $1/T$. The reason for this choice is that for germanium (as well as other insulators and semi-

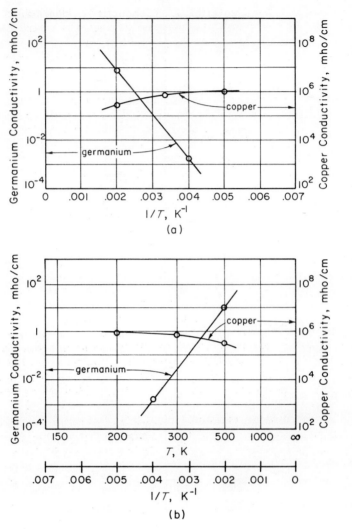

FIG. 1.2   Conductivity-temperature relationships for
germanium and copper.

conductors), ln σ is found to be approximately a linear function of $1/T$.
This scheme of plotting sometimes becomes confusing in that the numbers on the abscissa are not familiar and increasing the temperature
corresponds to moving from right to left on the graph. Accordingly in
Fig. 1.2b the $1/T$ scale is reversed and a nonlinear T scale is added. This
system retains the linear shape of the σ plot while allowing temperature

to increase from left to right on the graph. Note that the conductivity of a semiconductor increases with increasing temperature while that of the metal decreases. Evidently there is a basic difference in the two conduction processes involved. An explanation of this difference is essential to understanding the nature of semiconductors and the properties of semiconductor devices.

Another unique property of semiconductors has to do with the types of carriers responsible for their conductivity. Suppose an experiment were to be performed from which we could determine not only the conductivity of a given material, but also the concentrations of the charge carriers and the signs, positive or negative, of the charge of these carriers. Suppose this experiment were performed using several metals and semiconductors at a variety of temperatures. We would find that materials with high conductivities have high carrier concentrations and that materials with low conductivities have low carrier concentrations.

The general trend of the data would lead one to suspect that conductivity is proportional to carrier concentration, as would seem reasonable. More specifically, metals would show little variation of carrier concentrations with temperature while semiconductors would show strong changes. Plots of carrier concentration versus temperature would resemble the conductivity plots in Fig. 1.2. One other rather startling discovery would be that all the carriers in the metals have negative charges as we would expect, whereas in the semiconductors there would appear both negatively charged and positively charged carriers. The former are termed conduction electrons, the latter conduction holes. Thus the conduction mechanisms in metals and semiconductors appear to be fundamentally different. How do the two types of carriers arise?

Another property of semiconductors to be investigated is the effect of impurities on the conductivity. Consider silicon, technologically the most important semiconductor. The conductivity of pure silicon is very low, about 10^{-5} mho/cm. The density of carriers at room temperature is about $2 \times 10^{10}/cm^3$, half electrons and half holes. Now suppose 10^{16} phosphorus atoms/cm^3 are added to the crystal. It would be found, again at room temperature, that the conductivity of the silicon plus phosphorus crystal would be about 1 mho/cm. Thus the effect of the phosphorus atoms would be to increase the conductivity by five orders of magnitude. This may not seem so surprising until it is recognized that $10^{16}/cm^3$ represents only one millionth of the concentration of the host silicon atoms in the crystal. Further it would be found that virtually all of the carriers are electrons; thus the presence of a small concentration of this particular impurity results not only in a drastic increase in conductivity but a preferential increase in the electron density relative to the hole density. This type of semiconductor (i.e., one with a preponderance of electrons) is termed n-type. As would be expected there are also impurities which can preferentially increase the hole con-

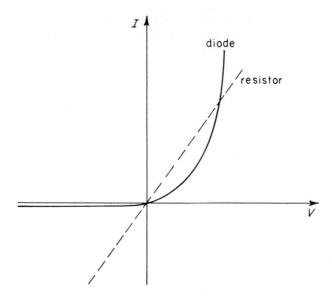

FIG. 1.3   Current-voltage characteristics of a diode
and a resistor.

centration giving rise to p-type semiconductors. What are the properties of these impurities which allow them to give rise to a specific type
of charge carrier? We shall respond to this question in Chap. 4.

Now suppose a single crystal junction is formed between an n-type
semiconductor and a p-type semiconductor and the current-voltage
characteristic of this *pn* junction diode is plotted. In contrast to a
resistor with its linear current-voltage curve, the *pn* diode has the highly
nonlinear characteristic sketched in Fig. 1.3. For one polarity of the
voltage (termed the reverse direction) the current has a very low nearly
constant value; for the other voltage polarity the current increases exponentially, yielding high currents for low voltage. It is the physical principles underlying the behavior of semiconductor diodes that are really
the heart of this text. Why do *pn* junction diodes have the properties
they do and how may these properties be used to fabricate useful electronic circuit elements?

The topics discussed in the preceding paragraphs are intended in a
rough way to chart our course in developing an understanding of the
properties of semiconductor devices. In order to develop this understanding it is necessary to begin by studying some rather basic properties in the physics of solids.

CHAPTER 2

Background of the Development of Quantum Mechanics

2.1 INTRODUCTION

The laws of classical physics are, for the most part, readily under-standable in terms of the physical laws evident from the world about us. They appear, so far as our daily existence is concerned, to be equally applicable to all parts of the universe. Newton was able to apply the same laws to explain the motion of the stars and planets as he was—we are told—to explain why an apple fell. It is perfectly under-standable that in the late nineteenth century a certain complacency arose over these apparently immutable, timeless, changeless laws of Newton. There seemed to be no reason to suspect that the concepts of classical physics would ever need revision.

And yet, as more experimental data accumulated and measuring techniques were refined, it was found that in certain areas of study either wrong answers were obtained by classical methods or no theo-retical answers were forthcoming at all. Two notable examples of this were the so-called blackbody radiation for which a wrong answer was obtained and atomic spectra for which no answers were obtained. In-vestigations of these by Planck, Einstein, and Bohr among others led to studies which gave birth to a whole new field of physics, one which con-tained classical physics as a special case and which, when applied to sys-tems of atoms and molecules, gave amazingly accurate agreement with the experimental data. This was quantum physics. But the new physics carried with it certain problems. While the laws of classical physics seemed entirely consistent with everyday experience, quantum physics predicted certain startling and almost unbelievable results. For ex-ample, according to quantum physics it is necessary to associate with each material body a wave character (what kind of a wave it does not say); and not even in principle can certain measurements be made as precise as wished. Further, the laws of quantum physics do not in general predict a unique answer to a given physical problem but rather there exists a range of possible solutions, each of which has a known probability associated with its occurrence. Such concepts as these are clearly quite different from what we would deduce from observing the macroscopic world.

2.2 BLACKBODY RADIATION

The spectrum of electromagnetic radiation spans a vast wavelength and frequency range. Such radiation (Fig. 2.1) extends from the radio waves to the far infrared (heat waves) through the narrow visible region into the ultraviolet and finally into X rays and nuclear radiation. All the radiation is characterized by the same velocity $c = 3 \times 10^{10}$ cm/s in vacuum to which the wavelength λ and the frequency ν are related by the equation

$$c = \lambda\nu \tag{2.1}$$

For the full range of radiation noted above, λ varies from approximately 10^8 cm to 10^{-12} cm. The visible region covers the small interval in λ of 0.7×10^{-4} cm to 0.3×10^{-4} cm (or in the more commonly used units, from 7000 Å to 3000 Å where Å is the ångström unit and equals 10^{-8} cm).

One form of this radiation of particular interest is that emitted by an incandescent solid. It is a well-known fact that the color of such an object is determined largely by its temperature; the optical pyrometer utilizes this principle. Thus, if measurement of radiated power versus wavelength is plotted, a curve whose shape is dependent only upon the temperature is obtained. A set of such curves for a perfect

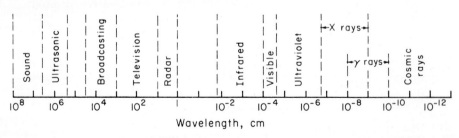

FIG. 2.1   Frequency spectrum.

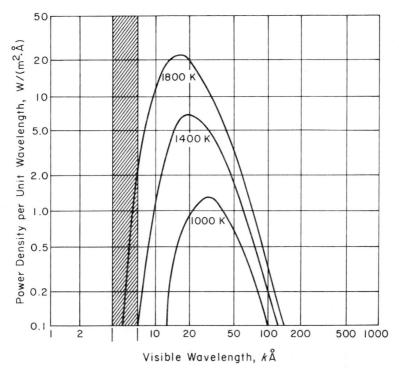

FIG. 2.2 Blackbody radiation curves.

radiator, a *blackbody,* is shown in Fig. 2.2. It is apparent from these curves that the amount of visible radiation increases with increasing temperature. The maxima occur at values such that $\lambda_{max} T$ is a constant.

The information in the above paragraph represents experimental data covering work done by Kirchhoff, Boltzmann, Wien, and others in the middle and late 1800s. Various attempts were made, with little success, to give theoretical justification to the data of Fig. 2.2. The most successful theoretical argument was proposed by Rayleigh and Jeans; it predicted the radiated power to be proportional to the inverse fourth power of the wavelength. Their expression gave an accurate description of the data for long wavelengths but was unsatisfactory at short wavelengths since it predicted a continuous increase in radiated power, contrary to experimental fact.

In order to see how this difficulty was resolved we must look briefly at the way in which the Rayleigh-Jeans Law was derived. Each atom in the solid was presumed to behave as a harmonic oscillator of frequency ν. The distribution in energy of the atomic oscillators was assumed to depend upon the frequency ν and the absolute temperature T

in the manner predicted by Newtonian mechanics. Some of the oscillators had high energy and some low, but all energies between the lowest and the highest were held to be possible. Then the number of oscillators in each frequency interval was derived and hence the energy in each frequency (or wavelength) interval was determined. This made possible a graph of radiated power versus frequency. All this led to the incorrect result described above which was termed the "ultraviolet catastrophe."

Planck, in 1901, removed the discrepancy by a rather startling hypothesis; he postulated that only those energies are possible for which the energy of the oscillator and its frequency are related by the equation

$$E_n = nh\nu \tag{2.2}$$

where E_n is the oscillator energy, n an integer equal to or greater than zero, h a constant (since named Planck's constant), and ν the frequency of the atomic oscillator. Thus, the possible energies are (for a given ν) $h\nu$, $2h\nu$, $3h\nu$,.... Further, these oscillators absorb or radiate energy by changing from one of the allowed energy states to another and thus absorb or radiate energy only in discrete amounts which are integral multiples of $h\nu$.

The units of energy in the Planck theory are multiples of the fundamental unit of energy $h\nu$. Each of these units is called a *quantum* of energy; energy is absorbed or radiated in *quanta* of $h\nu$; and the energy of the system is said to be *quantized,* that is, it can take on only a set of discrete values. In this amazing postulate was born the whole of the quantum theory of matter. Using the Planck hypothesis, the curves of Fig. 2.2 were derived in detail both for long and short wavelengths.

At first sight Planck's hypothesis may not seem strange, but some reflection shows it was, indeed, quite revolutionary. Here, for the first time, was the situation in which a property (the energy) of a system changed from one value to a different value without taking on any of the intermediate values.

Though the introduction of quantization gave a precise description of blackbody radiation it was not (as might be expected) accepted wholeheartedly, not even by Planck, it has been said. The concept seemed to depart too far from the views which had been sacred in physics for two hundred years. But as time went on more substantiating data appeared, and it became clear that the idea of quantization was not an ad hoc concept but instead was essential in describing the atomic world.

2.3   PHOTOELECTRIC EFFECT

The idea of quantization introduced by Planck lay relatively dormant for a few years. Then in 1905 Einstein used it to explain

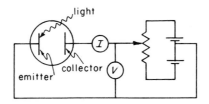

FIG. 2.3 Sketch of experimental arrangement for photoelectric measurements.

the photoelectric effect, making a contribution of profound importance to the development of quantum physics.

In order to understand Einstein's proposal, let us review the data available from photoelectric experiments. The basic experimental fact is that if light shines on certain materials, especially metals, electrons will be emitted from the surface. The emitted electrons are called *photoelectrons*. In a typical experiment the frequency and intensity of the light are varied and the number and energy of the photoelectrons are measured.

The experimental apparatus could have the form sketched in Fig. 2.3. In the simplest case there are simply two metal plates enclosed in a vacuum and surrounded by an enclosure which is transparent to the light to be used. A potential difference, either positive or negative, can be maintained between the plates by use of the potentiometer. One of the plates, the emitter, will absorb the light and (possibly) emit electrons. The other plate, the collector, will collect any emitted electrons if the bias voltage is proper.

Using our intuition, let us guess what results would be expected from various experimental conditions. One might suppose that if the intensity of the radiation is small there will be a time lag before emission occurs (one would expect the electrons to require some time to acquire sufficient energy to get out of the metal). One might also expect that as the intensity of the light increases, the energy with which the electrons leave the metal would increase (the more energy there is available, the more it might appear the photoelectrons can acquire and therefore the greater the velocity with which the electrons would emerge from the metallic surface). Finally, one would suppose that emission would occur for almost any light source if we wait long enough (regardless of how little energy is available, if we allow a long enough accumulation time, eventually an electron should acquire enough energy to break free of the metal).

As can be guessed from the way in which the "conclusions" of the preceding paragraph are presented, each of them is wrong. The experimentally obtained results are:

1. To all intents and purposes there is no time lag in the onset of emission. Such delay as exists is less than 10^{-8} s.

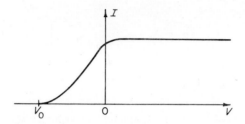

FIG. 2.4   Photocurrent as a function of collector voltage using a monochromatic light with a fixed intensity.

2. For a given metal the maximum energy of the photoelectrons is independent of the intensity of the light source.
3. For a given metal there exists a minimum optical frequency such that lower frequency light sources will cause no emission regardless of their intensity.

Thus our intuition seems to have led us badly astray. This will not be the last time in the study of quantum physics when we will find intuition to be a poor guide.

It is interesting to look at the form of the experimental data from which the above conclusions were deduced. Let us examine first the current-voltage curve for a photocell illuminated by a monochromatic light source of frequency ν and intensity L_1. So long as the collector is held positive with respect to the emitter, the current I is constant. All the electrons emitted are collected. This situation changes when the emitter-collector potential difference V is negative. As V becomes more and more negative, the current decreases steadily until at some value V_o the current is reduced to zero (see Fig. 2.4). These data are not really surprising; they only point out the reasonable fact that the photoelectrons do not all emerge from the metal with the same energy. If V is negative the photoelectrons must give up kinetic energy in going through the negative potential difference between emitter and collector. Only those electrons with sufficient energy can contribute to the current I. As V is made more and more negative this number will decrease until finally the most energetic photoelectron is stopped and the current is reduced to zero. It should be possible therefore to equate the energy lost by an electron in traversing the potential difference V_o to the kinetic energy of the most energetic photoelectron. Thus

$$-qV_o = K_{max} = (1/2)m\upsilon_{max}^2 \tag{2.3}$$

in which q is the magnitude of the charge on the electron, m is the electron mass, υ_{max} is the maximum velocity of the photoelectrons, and K_{max} is the corresponding maximum kinetic energy.

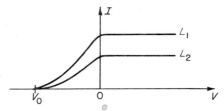

FIG. 2.5   Photocurrent as a function of collector voltage for two intensities of a monochromatic source.

Now suppose the frequency of the light source is kept the same
and the intensity is varied. Again we will plot I vs V and compare the
curves obtained using the two intensities L_1 and L_2. The result is shown
in Fig. 2.5. and is indeed startling. The stopping potential is the same
in both cases! It appears the maximum kinetic energy a photoelectron
can have is independent of the intensity of the light source. In other
words, the distribution in energy of the photoelectrons appears to be
independent of the total energy available in the light source. One other
piece of related data may be reviewed.

Suppose we were to measure experimentally the I-V curve of a
photocell using light sources of various frequencies, each having the
same intensity-to-frequency ratio. In this case we would find the dependence of I upon V illustrated in Fig. 2.6. Thus the stopping potential
is related to the frequency, increasing as ν increases, and there appears
to be some minimum frequency below which there is no photoemis-
sion. If the variation of K_{max} inferred from the appropriate value of V_o is
plotted against frequency we obtain a straight line as shown in Fig. 2.7.
If this straight line is extrapolated to zero frequency we find an energy ϕ
which appears to be characteristic of the material of the emitter. If
other materials are used as emitters, the experimental results yield a
series of parallel straight lines, each with a different intercept on the
energy axis. These are shown in Fig. 2.8.

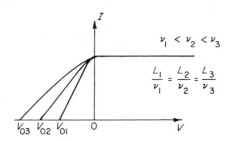

FIG. 2.6   Photocurrent as a function of collector voltage for three light sources producing equal photocur-
rents but having different frequencies.

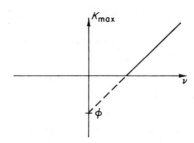

FIG. 2.7   Maximum kinetic energy of photoelectrons as a function of the frequency of the light source.

All the data presented here on the photoelectric effect were explained by Einstein (1905) by postulating the *photon* theory of light.
He assumed the following to be true:

1. Light energy is quantized in units of $h\nu$ termed *photons* where ν is
   the frequency of the associated electromagnetic wave.
2. In optical processes photons are created or absorbed as indivisible
   units.

Since the light energy is to interact with the metallic emitter to
produce photoelectrons, a model for the metal is needed. Einstein had
available to him the free electron model of metals. For such materials
it is reasonable to suppose that there is some sort of an energy barrier
at the surface of the metal to be overcome before an electron can be
freed. Thus we might picture the conduction electrons in the metal as
existing in an energy well as shown in Fig. 2.9. The energy ϕ, termed
the *work function,* represents the barrier at the surface of the metal
and is the minimum energy required by an electron to get out of the
metal. (This is not a very precise definition, but it will suffice.) If then
one of the electrons having maximum energy in the metal absorbs a
photon of energy $h\nu$, part of the acquired energy will be used in getting

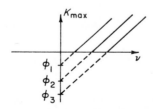

FIG. 2.8   Maximum kinetic energy of photoelectrons
as a function of frequency for materials having different work functions θ.

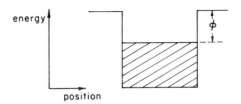

FIG. 2.9 Simplified representation of the energy of electrons in a metal as a function of position.

out of the metal and the remainder will appear as the kinetic energy of the ejected electron; for a given photon energy this type of photo-electron will be the one with maximum kinetic energy. Expressing the statements of the last sentence in equation form results in

$$K_{max} = h\nu - \phi \tag{2.4}$$

This is the famous photoelectric equation developed by Einstein in 1905; it states that the maximum kinetic energy K_{max} of a photoelectron is the difference between the energy available from a photon and the energy which must be expended by the electron in getting out of the material.

Let us look at reasonable values for the quantities involved in (2.4). Restricting our consideration arbitrarily to visible light, the wavelength range is approximately 4000–7000 Å. The corresponding frequency range is 7.5×10^{14}–4.3×10^{14} Hz. Thus the range of photon energies $h\nu$ is 5.0×10^{-19}–2.9×10^{-19} J. Values of the work function for a representative sample of materials are shown in Table 2.1. A typical value is about 4.5×10^{-19} J. It is not possible to give a typical value of K_{max} without specifying the photon energy. For the metals shown it is apparent that few if any photoelectrons would be produced using visible light as the energy source. For this reason the emitting surfaces of phototubes are rather exotic compound materials which have much lower work functions and hence do provide a photocurrent. In such materials the work functions are approximately 3×10^{-19} J giving (with visible light) photoelectrons with K_{max} values in the range 0–1.5×10^{-19} J.

Table 2.1. Work functions of metals.

Metal	$\phi(eV)$	$\phi(J)$
Cr	4.60	7.36×10^{-19}
Fe	4.48	7.17
Ni	4.61	7.37
Pt	5.32	8.51

The energy values used in the previous paragraph are a most inconvenient size. For ease in calculation and recollection it is preferable to have the fundamental measure of any physical quantity to be of the order of unity. This means that a physical unit appropriate to one class of phenomena may be inappropriate to a second class (the energy unit used to describe the capabilities of an aircraft engine would certainly not be used to measure photon energies).

Clearly 1 J is much too large in terms of energies involved in atomic processes, so a new smaller unit is sought. A quantity widely used is the electron volt abbreviated as eV. One *electron volt* is the kinetic energy an electron acquires in falling through a potential difference of 1 V. Thus

$$1 \text{ eV} = (1.6 \times 10^{-19} \text{C})(1 \text{ V}) = 1.6 \times 10^{-19} \text{ J}$$

The relationship of λ, ν, and photon energy in electron volts is shown in Fig. 2.10. Converting the several energies of interest to eV we find that photon energies in the visible region span approximately the range

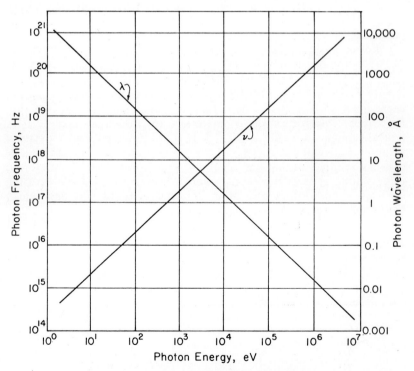

FIG. 2.10   Relation of photon energy in electron volts, photon frequency, and photon wavelength.

1.8–3.1 eV, the typical work function value is about 2 eV, and the maximum kinetic energy of the photoelectrons is in the range 0–1.0 eV.

(It cannot be emphasized too strongly that an electron volt is a unit of *energy* and not potential difference. It will be found distressingly easy to succumb to the temptation, for example, of converting an energy J to eV by dividing by 1.6×10^{-19} C, the electronic charge. The conversion factor is 1.6×10^{-19} J/eV, a ratio which is dimensionless, just as 3 ft/yd is dimensionless.)

Earlier we mentioned that if the retarding potential were just large enough, no current would flow; this value of potential was labeled V_o and termed the *stopping potential*. The magnitude of V_o must be related to K_{max}. From the conservation of energy we know that (change in potential energy) plus (change in kinetic energy) = zero. Applied to the photoelectric experiment this results in the equation

$$K_{max} = -qV_o \tag{2.5}$$

Thus the Einstein equation may be written

$$-qV_o = h\nu - \phi \tag{2.6}$$

Since $h\nu$ must be larger than ϕ to cause photoemission it is clear that V_o will be negative as indicated earlier. The magnitude of V_o can vary widely depending upon the relative magnitudes of $h\nu$ and ϕ. The quantization of light energy had an effect more profound than merely justifying the Planck hypothesis or explaining the photoelectric effect, for here was the first case of the wave-particle duality we discuss later.

The historical story is of some interest. Newton was convinced that light was corpuscular in nature rather than being a wave motion as hypothesized by his contemporary, Huygens. Newton's reasons were simple enough. All the wave phenomena known in his day (for example, sound and water waves) would, to put it crudely, go around corners whereas it was clear (to him) that light was propagated only in straight lines. Therefore light was not a wave motion, and to explain the energy propagation he postulated that light energy was carried by corpuscles, visualized as bundles of energy. He was able to carry through precise descriptions of reflection and refraction phenomena using the corpuscular notion. There was no need to look further.

Then about fifty years later it was shown that when the dimensions of a slit are comparable to the wavelength of the light illuminating it, a beam of light does not travel in straight lines. Under such circumstances the size of a shadow is not the same size as the object causing it. Light can be caused to bend around corners. These effects are termed diffraction. To explain them it was necessary to call on the Huygens principle of the wave nature of light, which also allowed correct explanations of reflection and refraction. In the late nineteenth century Maxwell, in one of the major triumphs in science, derived his theory of electromagnetism and showed that light was a special type of electromagnetic radiation. There seemed to be no doubt that light was transmitted by a wave motion and that Newton's corpuscular theory was at best incomplete and possibly incorrect.

Then along came Einstein in 1905 with an explanation of the photoelectric phenomena that required light energy to be composed of bundles of energy (quanta called photons) reverting to the Newtonian theory. The cycle was completely closed except that optical phenomena could no longer be put neatly in either a wave or a corpuscular compartment. Both types of description were necessary; some phenomena were describable in terms of wave motion, others in terms of quanta. This indeed was a curious situation; it appears several times throughout our discussion of modern physics.

2.4   COMPTON EFFECT

A second physical phenomenon which solidified the concept of particulate characteristics of electromagnetic radiation was the Compton effect. We will first describe the experimental results and then discuss the physical bases of the effect.

X rays are electromagnetic radiations having wavelengths typically in the range 0.01–10 Å. This implies x-ray photon energies of 10^3–10^6 eV. Now if an x-ray beam having a frequency ν is directed at a piece of solid material, carbon for example, it is found that emerging from the carbon are two x-ray components. One has the same frequency as the incident beam; the other, appearing at some angle γ, has a new lower frequency ν'. These results are illustrated by the sketch shown in Fig. 2.11. The presence of the photons of lower frequency in this experiment is termed the Compton effect.

Suppose we assume the x-ray photons could be treated as "particles." Could the Compton effect be explained in terms of collisions these particles suffer in traversing the carbon sample? We know that carbon is composed of atoms, each of which is composed of a small massive nucleus surrounded by six electrons. Since the electron orbits are large relative to the nucleus and the electrons are more numerous, it seems reasonable to attempt an analysis involving the interaction between photons and electrons. Probably not all the electrons in the carbon atoms would be involved; if an electron were tightly bound to the nucleus it would be unable to exchange either momentum or

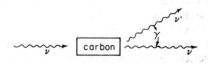

FIG. 2.11   Relation of the incident and emergent photons in the Compton effect.

energy with the x-ray photon, and therefore we would expect the interaction to depend on the more loosely bound electrons, i.e., those farther from the nucleus. In such cases there will, in general, be an exchange of energy, so it might not be unreasonable for the exiting photon to have an energy different from that which it had on entering the carbon. This could explain the presence of the lower frequency x-ray component in the output beam.

Continuing to treat this experiment as a billiard ball problem, it is easy to see how to proceed. We know that in elastic collisions such as these, the energy E and the linear momentum p of the two particles must be conserved. In equation form, where E' and p' represent quantities after collision,

$$E_{photon} + E_{electron} = E'_{photon} + E'_{electron} \qquad (2.7)$$

$$p_{photon} + p_{electron} = p'_{photon} + p'_{electron} \qquad (2.8)$$

Consider first the conservation of energy. We must equate the initial and final energies of the x-ray photon and the electron. The initial photon energy is $h\nu$ and the photon energy after collision is $h\nu'$. (We shall suppose, as is the case, that the x-ray beam emerging with frequency ν is simply due to those x-ray photons which have not suffered a collision or which have interacted with tightly bound electrons.) It is more difficult to write an expression for the electron energy. It would appear reasonable to consider the electron to be initially at rest and therefore with zero kinetic energy. After the collision the electron would have acquired some velocity v, and would have a kinetic energy $(1/2)mv^2$. The difficulty with this argument is that x-ray photons often have quite high energy (on an atomic scale) and the velocity they impart to the electron in collision can be large. As a consequence some unexpected effects must be taken into account. To examine this problem we must discuss the dependence of mass upon velocity.

The relationship between force, mass, and acceleration was first deduced by Newton who stated that the force acting on a body was equal to the time rate of change of momentum. In equation form this is

$$F = \frac{dp}{dt} = \frac{d}{dt}(mv) \qquad (2.9)$$

If m is a constant we may write

$$F = m\frac{dv}{dt} = ma \qquad (2.10)$$

Thus the important equation $F = ma$ depends for its validity upon the constancy of the mass m. In developing the special theory of relativity Einstein was able to show that the mass of a body is not constant but varies with the velocity of the body. It was shown that the mass m may be written

$$m = \frac{m_o}{(1 - v^2/c^2)^{1/2}} \tag{2.11}$$

where v is the particle velocity, c the velocity of light, and m_o is the *rest mass* (particle mass at zero velocity) of the body. Normally when we speak of the mass of a body it is m_o to which we refer. Since c has a very large value a graph of m vs v shows that m differs appreciably from m_o only when v approaches c. Thus in the macroscopic world we may surely consider m to be constant, but in the atomic domain it is quite possible that the dependence of m on v cannot be ignored.

This effect complicates our efforts to write the energy of the electron involved in the collision with the photon; we cannot simply write $(1/2)mv^2$ for the kinetic energy. Let us try to develop an expression for the kinetic energy which takes into account the relativistic variation in mass. Suppose a force F acts on a body of mass m. If the body starts from rest, then from the Newtonian force law,

$$F = \frac{d(mv)}{dt}$$

This equation may be written, using (2.11),

$$F = \frac{d}{dt}\left[\frac{m_o}{(1 - v^2/c^2)^{1/2}}\, v\right] = \frac{m_o}{(1 - v^2/c^2)^{3/2}}\frac{dv}{dt} \tag{2.12}$$

Since the body was initially at rest, we can find the kinetic energy K simply by finding the work done on the particle by the force F. If we assume that v and F are in the x-direction, then a scalar form of (2.12) can be used and we shall have

$$K = \int_0^x F\,dx' = \int_0^x \frac{m_o}{(1 - v'^2/c^2)^{3/2}}\frac{dv'}{dt}\,dx' \tag{2.13}$$

Since $v\,dt = dx$, the right side of (2.13) may be written

$$K = \int_0^v \frac{m_o}{(1 - v'^2/c^2)^{3/2}}\, v'\,dv' \tag{2.14}$$

Integrating,

$$K = c^2\left[\frac{m_o}{(1 - v'^2/c^2)^{1/2}}\right]_0^v = \frac{m_o c^2}{(1 - v^2/c^2)^{1/2}} - m_o c^2 \tag{2.15}$$

$$K = mc^2 - m_o c^2$$

This is the expression for the kinetic energy when account is taken of the variation of m with v. It is not true that we may never use $(1/2)mv^2$ for the kinetic energy; this relation is still valid so long as $m \simeq m_o$, which is another way of saying that $v \ll c$. Under this circumstance it is not difficult to show that

$$mc^2 - m_o c^2 \simeq (1/2)mv^2 \qquad v \ll c \qquad (2.16)$$

To return to the Compton effect, if we consider the electron to be a free particle at rest then its initial energy is $m_o c^2$. After collision it has an energy mc^2. The equation representing the conservation of energy thus is

$$h\nu + m_o c^2 = h\nu' + mc^2 \qquad (2.17)$$

This equation can be written in the form

$$h(\nu - \nu') = mc^2 - m_o c^2 \qquad (2.18)$$

Thus if the electron energy after the collision is larger than it was initially, the energy of the emergent photon will be less and the final photon frequency will be lower.

In this connection note a significant difference between the Compton and photoelectric effects; in the former only part of the photon energy is transferred to the interacting electron, whereas in the latter all the photon energy is lost. Even with (2.18) we cannot calculate the magnitude of $\nu - \nu'$ since we do not know the value of v and hence of m. To eliminate this variable we will have to use the second conservation law, the conservation of linear momentum. Whereas we had trouble in writing the electron energy earlier, the electron momentum may be written straightforwardly; we must look closely at the photon momentum. Consider the latter quantity.

The expression for the kinetic energy, (2.15), should apply equally well to photons or electrons. But what is the rest mass of a photon? Since the photon velocity has the constant value of c, it is clear the photon rest mass must be zero, otherwise the photon energy mc^2 would be infinite. With $m_o = 0$ in this case, then the photon mass would be determined from the energy relation $E = mc^2$. Solving for m we have

$$m = E/c^2 \qquad (2.19)$$

Then, writing the photon momentum as mc and using $h\nu$ as the photon energy, we have

$$p_{ph} = mc = (E/c^2)c = h\nu/c \qquad (2.20)$$

Equation (2.20) gives the momentum of a photon in terms of the frequency of the associated electromagnetic wave. The momentum of the electron may be written straightforwardly as

$$p_e = mv = \frac{m_o}{(1 - v^2/c^2)^{1/2}} v \qquad (2.21)$$

The statement of the conservation of linear momentum may be expressed in equation form as

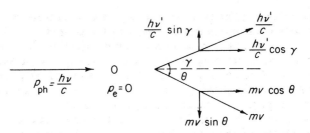

FIG. 2.12   Momentum diagram appropriate to the
Compton effect.

$$p_e + p_{ph} = p'_e + p'_{ph} \tag{2.22}$$

where p'_e and p'_{ph} represent quantities after the collision process. This
equation is a vector equation and therefore will result in a set of equations. We shall choose the direction of the original photon beam to be
the x-direction and assume that the emergent photon and electron lie
in the xy plane. Thus (2.22) will result in two equations, one describing
the conservation of the x-component and one the y-component of the
momentum. By considering the diagram in Fig. 2.12 the following
equations can be deduced.

$$h\nu/c = (h\nu'/c)\cos\gamma + m\nu\cos\theta \quad \text{for } x\text{-component} \tag{2.23}$$

$$0 = (h\nu'/c)\sin\gamma - m\nu\sin\theta \quad \text{for } y\text{-component} \tag{2.24}$$

The complete set of equations available to describe the Compton
effect is the energy conservation equation, (2.17), and the two momentum conservation equations, (2.23) and (2.24). In these three equations
there are four unknowns: the final electron velocity ν, the two angles
θ and γ made by the electron and resultant photon relative to the initial
photon direction, and the resultant photon frequency ν'. We can thus
only solve for three of the variables in terms of the fourth.

We can, for example, calculate the change in frequency and hence
the change in wavelength of the photon as a function of the exit
angle γ of the photon. The result of this calculation yields

$$(1/\nu' - 1/\nu) = (h/m_o c^2)(1 - \cos\gamma) \tag{2.25}$$

from which

$$\lambda' - \lambda = (h/m_o c)(1 - \cos\gamma) \tag{2.26}$$

Since $1 - \cos\gamma \geq 0$, we will have $\lambda' \geq \lambda$. The emerging photon, having
given some of its energy to the electron, will have a lower energy than
the incident photon. Notice that the shift in wavelength is a function
of angle, increasing as γ increases. This is readily understandable if the
electron-photon interaction is thought of as a collision process; the

larger the value of γ the more nearly the collision represents a head-on collision with a maximum loss of energy by the photon.

From the set of energy and momentum equations it is possible to calculate other important quantities: recoil angle of the electron, recoil energy of the electron, angular intensity distribution of photons, etc. The predicted results show excellent agreement with experiments, lending strong support to the theoretical approach used.

The significance of the Compton effect can be assessed as follows. The explanation of the photoelectric effect by Einstein required light energy to be discrete, the units of energy being called photons. The photoelectric experiment suggested that photons might be particulate in character, but it was not necessary to use this possibility in explaining the experimental data. The necessity for this characteristic was demonstrated by the Compton effect which showed clearly that the interaction between an electron and a photon could be treated as an elastic collision between two particles. It was thus the Compton effect that forced the concept of duality into physics. For the first time a physical phenomenon, electromagnetic radiation, could not be categorized as having either a wave nature or a particle nature. It seems necessary to consider it as a wave sometimes and as a particle at other times. This is a very puzzling situation; it is important to recognize that there is a problem. When we speak of a particle we visualize a thing which is localized in space and has a definite momentum; presumably we can find where it exists and what its velocity is. On the other hand, when we think of a wave we picture an effect which exists throughout all space and is therefore unlocalized. The two concepts seem so contradictory it is very difficult to see how we can associate them with the same physical phenomena as we must do.

2.5 DE BROGLIE HYPOTHESIS

As we have seen the seemingly contradictory wave-particle description was essential in describing completely the properties of electromagnetic radiation. The problem was complicated further by way of a conjecture made in 1925 by Louis de Broglie. If electromagnetic radiation which had been thought of as wave phenomena requires particulate properties for a complete description, is it not reasonable that those objects which we have customarily thought of as particles (electrons, for example) should also possess wave properties? His conjecture if true would thus unify the physical world by associating a wave-particle duality with all the physical universe.

In order for his supposition to be meaningful it was necessary for de Broglie to have some systematic way of associating a wavelength with a particle. From the Compton effect, the momentum associated with a photon of frequency ν and wavelength λ is $p = h\nu/c = h/\lambda$, (2.20). De Broglie hypothesized that this equation should apply equally well to all matter. He suggested, therefore, that there is associated with a particle having momentum $p = mv$ a wavelength given by

$$\lambda = h/p \tag{2.27}$$

Equation (2.27) is a symbolic statement of the de Broglie hypothesis.

It is clear that this supposition does indeed appear to make comprehension more difficult. It seems so reasonable to treat electrons or protons or baseballs as spheres of some fixed size which are localized in space that an attempt to associate wave properties with them must be incorrect. After all, you might recall we have obtained a correct description of the Compton effect by associating with the electron just such properties. But, as usual, the acceptance or denial of a physical principle cannot legitimately be made on a philosophical basis. Rather it must be judged in terms of experimental evidence.

In order to verify the de Broglie hypothesis a means was sought to detect experimentally the wave properties of matter. This search was guided by knowledge which was available from the study of physical optics. The one optical property that forced the acceptance of the wave nature of light was diffraction; diffraction occurs when the dimensions of the diffracting medium (a slit, for example) are comparable with the wavelength of the light being used. To detect the wave properties of a particle (if they exist) we should therefore try to find a diffraction grating with suitable dimensions to see whether diffraction is indeed observed.

The dimensions of the grating will be determined by the particle wavelength and therefore it is necessary to use (2.27) to find the magnitudes of the wavelengths which might be expected. As examples let us compute the de Broglie wavelength of three particles:

1. a particle having a mass of 10^{-3} kg and a velocity of 10^{-2} m/s

$$p = mv = 10^{-5} \, (\text{kg} \cdot \text{m})/\text{s}$$
$$\lambda = (6.63 \times 10^{-34})/10^{-5} = 6.63 \times 10^{-29} \, \text{m}$$

2. a proton having a kinetic energy of 10^6 eV

$$K = p^2/2m \quad p = \sqrt{2mK} = 7.34 \times 10^{-22} \, (\text{kg} \cdot \text{m})/\text{s}$$
$$\lambda = 9.05 \times 10^{-13} \, \text{m}$$

3. an electron having a kinetic energy of 50 eV

$$p = \sqrt{2mK} = 3.8 \times 10^{-24} \, (\text{kg} \cdot \text{m})/\text{s}$$
$$\lambda = 1.74 \times 10^{-10} \, \text{m}$$

A number of important conclusions can be drawn from the results of these examples. In the first example we consider a small particle (at least as viewed in the macroscopic world) traveling at a very low speed.

Under these circumstances the resultant wavelength is so short that there seems no hope of finding a medium which will permit diffraction effects to be observed. It thus appears the wave nature of matter will not be of consequence in the macroscopic world. This explains why the startling de Broglie hypothesis could be true and yet never have been observed until the atomic domain became open to inspection.

The second example above shows that even in the atomic world if the energy of a relatively massive particle is large enough the resultant wavelength may be short enough to make wavelike properties difficult or impossible to detect. There is, therefore, no guarantee that wave nature of atomic particles will be detectable.

Consider finally the example of the 50 eV electrons. The wavelength in this case is 1.74×10^{-10} m or 1.74 Å. This dimension is comparable with the separation of atoms in many crystals. This suggests the use of the atoms in the regular crystalline array of a solid as a reflecting diffraction grating; then if a beam of electrons were incident upon the crystal and the energy of the electrons and the spacing of the atoms were properly chosen, diffraction effects would be observed. By analogy with the optical case we would expect the intensity of the diffracted beam (i.e., the number of electrons/cm^2) not to be isotropic: there should be increased electron beam intensity in those directions in which there is reinforcement of the electron waves and decreased electron beam intensity in directions corresponding to cancellation of the electron waves. It should be possible to predict these directions in terms of the wavelength of the electrons and the spacing of the atoms in the crystal.

The first experimental verification of the wave properties of matter was obtained by Davisson and Germer in 1927. Basically their experiment consisted of producing a low energy (54 eV) beam of electrons which was allowed to strike perpendicularly the surface of a nickel crystal. Treating the electrons simply as hard spheres one would expect random distribution of scattered particles. That is, rebounding electrons would have no preferred direction except possibly a 180° reversal; the rough surface (on an atomic scale) of the nickel would simply reflect the electrons in all directions. Instead of this result, a strongly patterned distribution was found. Electrons appeared at preferred directions and these preferred directions could readily be explained by treating the electron as a wave in motion and the nickel surface as a diffraction grating.

To understand this, let us consider the Davisson-Germer experiment in a bit more detail. The experimental arrangement is sketched in Fig. 2.13. A thermionic filament F was used as a source of electrons. The potential difference V_a served to produce the desired electron energy (54 eV) and the electron beam was incident on single crystal sections of nickel. The intensity of the scattered electron beam was measured by a detector D whose angular orientation could be varied

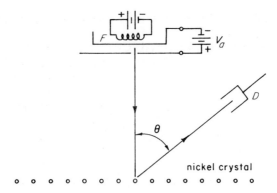

FIG. 2.13 Experimental arrangement used by Davisson and Germer to detect the wave properties of electrons.

relative to the incoming beam direction. An electron beam incident on this array of atoms would be scattered at various angles. Considering only the first row of atoms as scattering centers, the situation is sketched by Fig. 2.14. If the electrons were simply spheres suffering elastic collisions the scattered electrons would presumably be randomly distributed. If, on the other hand, the electrons possess a wave nature with wavelength λ, the circumstances are entirely different. In that case when the optical path difference Δx (see Fig. 2.14) is an integral number of wavelengths, reenforcement will occur. We would expect more electrons to be scattered at those angles for which $d \sin \theta = n\lambda$, since $d \sin \theta$ is the path difference Δx between the two waves. When the path difference is an odd multiple of a half wavelength, destructive interference will occur.

This indeed was discovered experimentally. A plot of the electron intensity as a function of angle relative to the incoming beam showed a strong maximum at 50° for 54 eV electrons. Knowing the atomic spacing for the particular orientation of the nickel crystal to be 2.15 Å, the maximum at 50° is consistent with an electron wavelength of

$$\lambda = (d \sin \theta)/n = (2.15) \sin 50°/1 = 1.65 \text{ Å} \tag{2.28}$$

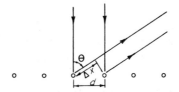

FIG. 2.14 Simplified representation of the scattering of electrons by a crystal.

This compares well with 1.67 Å, the value calculated from the de Broglie equation, (2.27).

An experiment of this type gives strong credence to the argument that we must associate wave properties with the electron. To be generally valid, of course, this behavior must not be confined to electrons. Further experimental work has shown that diffraction effects occur for many atomic particles. This, combined with all the later developments of quantum mechanics (which depend essentially upon the de Broglie hypothesis), argues persuasively that the wave-particle duality is a property common to all nature. The paradox of the wave-particle duality finds resolution in the theory unifying the description of the microscopic and macroscopic universes—quantum mechanics.

SUMMARY

- The blackbody radiation problem was one of the first cases where quantization of energy was necessary in order to obtain a theory that agreed with experimental results.

- The photoelectric effect provided elaboration of the idea of the quantization of energy. It showed that light energy must be considered as being made up of bundles of energy called photons and suggested that light, known to be a wave phenomenon, might have a particle nature as well.

- The Compton effect established that X rays, and therefore all forms of electromagnetic radiation, have both a wave nature and a particle nature and that it is often necessary to consider both in obtaining a theory to predict experimental results correctly.

- The de Broglie hypothesis suggested that things normally considered as particles might also have a wave nature characterized by the same wavelength-momentum relationship found to hold for light, namely $\lambda = h/p$.

- The Davisson-Germer experiment confirmed the correctness of de Broglie's hypothesis by demonstrating that an electron beam can be diffracted exactly as the equation $\lambda = h/p$ leads one to expect.

PROBLEMS

2.1. If a photon has an energy of 2×10^{-7} J, what is its frequency?

2.2. A beam of infrared radiation has a wavelength of 10^{-4} cm. What is the energy in electron volts of one of its photons?

2.3. A metal has a work function of 4.5 eV. What is its photoelectric threshold frequency?

2.4. What is the minimum voltage that must be applied across an x-ray tube to produce X rays with a frequency of 10^{20} Hz?

2.5. When ultraviolet light with a wavelength of 1200 Å is shone on a metal, it ejects photoelectrons with a maximum energy of 10^{-1}eV. What is the photoelectric threshold frequency of the metal?

2.6.   The work function of tungsten is 4.52 eV and that of barium is 2.50 eV. What is the maximum wavelength of light that will give photoemission of electrons from tungsten? From barium? Would either of these metals be useful in a photocell for use with visible light?

2.7.   Photoemission of electrons from calcium is being studied. The following experimental data are obtained.

λ	2536	3132	3650	4047	(Å)
V_o	-1.95	-0.98	-0.50	-0.14	(V)

Plot the data and find Planck's constant.

2.8.   What is the energy of a quantum of radiation with a frequency of 1 MHz? Suppose that the LC resonant circuit of a 1-MHz oscillator has a stored energy of 10^{-5} J (a value that might arise if the oscillator output were about 1 W). How many energy quanta are in 10^{-5} J? Energy changes of only an integral number of quanta are permitted. Does this fact cause any observable effects in this case?

2.9.   A phototube is constructed with identical emitter and collector. Because of reflection only 80% of the incoming light is absorbed by the emitter, the remaining 20% being absorbed by the collector. Sketch the I-V characteristic (analogous to Fig. 2.4) appropriate to these conditions.

2.10.   At what velocity is the mass of a particle three times its rest mass?

2.11.   What is the momentum of an electron with velocity 1.8×10^8 m/s?

2.12.   Through what potential difference in volts must an electron be accelerated from rest to achieve a velocity of $(1/2)c$?

2.13.   The cost of electrical energy supplied by a public utility company is 1/2 cent for one million J. What is the cost of 1 gm of energy?

2.14.   In a Compton scattering experiment the incident radiation had a frequency of 1.200×10^{20} Hz and the scattered electron acquired a velocity of 1.5×10^8 m/s. What is the frequency of the scattered photon?

2.15.   An electron and a photon each have a wavelength of 10^{-10} m. Find the momentum, the total energy, and the kinetic energy in each case.

2.16.   What is the kinetic energy of an electron in electron volts if its de Broglie wavelength is 10^{15} cm?

2.17.   If K is the kinetic energy of a particle with a rest mass m_o, prove that the de Broglie wavelength is $\lambda = hc/[K(K + 2m_oc^2)]^{1/2}$. Evaluate this expression in the two limiting cases:
   a) $K \ll m_oc^2$
   b) $K \gg m_oc^2$

2.18.   The momentum diagram of Fig. 2.12 is drawn for an initial photon wavelength of $\lambda_o = 0.71$ Å and $\gamma = 45°$. Use (2.26) and the conservation of momentum to calculate the angle θ of the recoil electron.

CHAPTER 3

Introduction to Quantum Mechanics

TO UNDERSTAND the operation and predict the performance of electronic devices such as transistors, integrated circuits, solar cells, etc., it is necessary to consider precisely the behavior of electrons in solids. In this situation Newton's laws are inadequate in explaining and predicting what actually happens; to obtain correct explanations and predictions we must replace Newtonian mechanics by a new variety, quantum mechanics or wave mechanics, in which wave properties are assigned to what are normally called particles. As we have remarked before, it undoubtedly seems strange that physical laws governing the world of microscopic energies and dimensions differ from those governing the world of everyday experience. Actually the same physical laws govern both worlds. The equations of quantum mechanics constitute a more universal physical law and thus apply to both cases. Newton's equations are simply approximations, very accurate in the everyday world but very inaccurate in the microscopic domain. This is not the first time Newtonian mechanics have been discovered to be approximate. In the high energy realm where velocities approach the velocity of light, relativistic mechanics are required; the relativistic equations apply at both high and moderate energies whereas Newtonian equations apply only at the moderate level.

In the same way quantum mechanics applies in both low and moderate cases (and with the inclusion of relativistic modifications in the high energy case as well) and gives the same answers that Newtonian mechanics gives for the moderate level (though not with the same ease it should be noted).

We begin the present chapter with a development of the basic equation of quantum mechanics, the Schrödinger wave equation, and discuss the meaning and properties of the wave function that quantum mechanics associates with all particles. Following that we use this equation, with generous doses of inductive reasoning and leaps of faith, to develop the energy band model for electrons in a crystalline solid. Through this model the behavior of electrons in various types of solids can be understood and predicted.

3.1   DEVELOPMENT OF THE SCHRÖDINGER EQUATION

The incorporation of the de Broglie hypothesis into a physical theory was first provided by Schrödinger. The way, in retrospect at least, seems clear. The "particle waves" should be described by the same sort of equation known to hold for commonplace wave phenomena such as acoustic waves and waves in vibrating wires, strings, membranes, etc.

Rather than considering the general wave equation, let us give a plausible deduction of the Schrödinger equation using as a vehicle the special case of a vibrating string having a mass per unit length μ and under a tension T. Suppose that the string is displaced vertically from its equilibrium position a distance y where y is a function both of x and t (see Fig. 3.1). Let the displacement be small so that we may consider T to be constant. (Strictly speaking T is constant only for zero displacement of an inextensible string.)

Consider the section of string between x and $x + \Delta x$. The net force acting on the element Δx is the difference of the downward force component at x and the upward component at $x + \Delta x$. Note that the horizontal components must be equal and opposite in order that the string be under tension. Thus at $x + \Delta x$ the vertical upward force component is $T \sin(\theta + \Delta\theta)$. The assumption of small values of the displacement y implies that θ and $\theta + \Delta\theta$ are small. For small values of

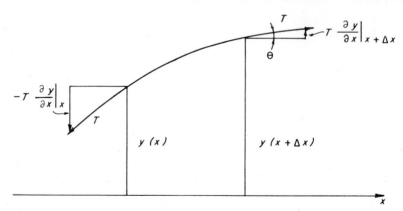

FIG. 3.1   Tensions on an element of string, from which (3.7) results.

$\theta + \Delta\theta$ it follows that

$$T\sin(\theta + \Delta\theta) \simeq T\tan(\theta + \Delta\theta) \tag{3.1}$$

But $\tan(\theta + \Delta\theta)$ is the slope of the string at $x + \Delta x$ and is equal, therefore, to the spatial derivative of y evaluated at $x + \Delta x$, that is,

$$T\tan(\theta + d\theta) = T\frac{\partial y(x + \Delta x, t)}{\partial x} \tag{3.2}$$

By similar reasoning the (downward) restoring force at x gives $T\sin\theta \simeq T\tan\theta$ and

$$T\tan\theta = T\frac{\partial y(x, t)}{\partial x} \tag{3.3}$$

The net restoring force is the difference between (3.2) and (3.3) or

$$T\frac{\partial y(x + \Delta x, t)}{\partial x} - T\frac{\partial y(x, t)}{\partial x} = F_{Net} \tag{3.4}$$

We may always equate the force acting on a body to the product of mass and acceleration (assuming no relativistic effects). In our case,

$$ma = \mu\Delta x\frac{\partial^2 y(x, t)}{\partial t^2} \tag{3.5}$$

Equating (3.4) and (3.5) and dividing by Δx and T yields

$$\frac{\mu}{T}\left[\frac{\partial^2 y(x, t)}{\partial t^2}\right] = \left[\frac{\partial y(x + \Delta x, t)}{\partial x} - \frac{\partial y(x, t)}{\partial x}\right]\bigg/\Delta x \tag{3.6}$$

Letting $\Delta x \to 0$, the right side becomes the second derivative of y with respect to x. Thus (3.6) may be written as

$$\frac{\mu}{T}\left[\frac{\partial^2 y(x, t)}{\partial t^2}\right] = \frac{\partial^2 y(x, t)}{\partial x^2} \tag{3.7}$$

Equation (3.7) is the one-dimensional form of the wave equation. It applies to a vast group of physical systems: vibrating strings, vibrating membranes, acoustic waves, electromagnetic waves, etc. It applies to essentially all classical wave phenomena with suitable reinterpretation of the quantities in the equation.

It is clear that y is, in general, a function of both x and t. In most practical problems the dependences of y on x and t are not related; i.e., the general nature of the way in which y varies with time does not depend upon where we look at y. Thus if a given wave motion were sinusoidal at $x = x_1$ we would expect it to be vibrating sinusoidally at $x = x_2$ with the same frequency, although the phase and amplitude might well be different. This behavior may be stated mathematically by writing y as the product of two functions, one dependent upon time alone and the other dependent upon position alone. Thus, in this example we may write

$$y(x, t) = R(t) f(x) \quad \text{separable}$$

(3.8)

Substituting this form of y into the wave equation we find the partial derivatives to be replaced by total derivatives because R is a function only of t and f is a function only of x. Thus

$$\frac{\partial^2 y}{\partial t^2} = \frac{\partial^2 (Rf)}{\partial t^2} = f \frac{d^2 R}{dt^2} \qquad \frac{\partial^2 y}{\partial x^2} = R \frac{d^2 f}{dx^2}$$

Substituting these into (3.7) and rearranging terms gives

$$\frac{T}{\mu f} \frac{d^2 f}{dx^2} = \frac{1}{R} \frac{d^2 R}{dt^2}$$

(3.9)

This equation has a very important property: the left side is a function only of x while the right side is a function only of t. Since x and t are independent variables, the equality expressed in (3.9) can occur only if both sides are equal to a constant, say C, and thus (3.9) can be expressed as two ordinary differential equations:

$$\frac{T}{\mu f} \frac{d^2 f}{dx^2} = C \qquad \frac{d^2 f}{dx^2} - \left(C \frac{\mu}{T} \right) f = 0$$

(3.10)

$$\frac{1}{R} \frac{d^2 R}{dt^2} = C \qquad \frac{d^2 R}{dt^2} - C R = 0$$

(3.11)

These two equations can be solved separately to find $f(x)$ and $R(t)$. Then the product of $f(x)$ and $R(t)$ can be found to give $y(x, t)$; see (3.8).

It is important to look more carefully at C. The quantity C is called the separation constant and this method of solving a partial differential equation, termed separation of variables, has wide applicability. The separation constant C is important in determining the nature of the solutions of the wave equation, (3.7). To see that this is true, solve (3.11) to obtain the time-dependent portion of $y(x, t)$. The solution can be written in several equivalent forms, one of which is

$$R(t) = A \exp(\sqrt{C}t) + B \exp(-\sqrt{C}t)$$

(3.12)

(The constants A and B are the constants of integration.) Suppose $C < 0$; then the exponents in (3.12) are imaginary, indicating that $R(t)$ is an oscillatory function and is reducible to a sum of sines and cosines. If $C > 0$ the exponents are real and $R(t)$ can be written in terms of hyperbolic sines and cosines.

If $C > 0$, $R(t)$ will increase without limit or decrease to zero as t increases; this is clearly inconsistent with the normal physical system. We know that most often those systems described by the wave equation have oscillatory properties with limited amplitude and a recurring characteristic as a function of time. This implies that C should be negative. To ensure this condition we will replace C by $-\omega^2$ which is always negative. With this substitution the solution (3.12) can be written

$$R(t) = A \exp(j\omega t) + B \exp(-j\omega t) \qquad (3.13)$$

The time-dependent portion of $y(x, t)$ will thus be, in general, an oscillating wave described by (3.13), where ω is the frequency of the wave.

Let us look at the spatial part of $y(x, t)$ described by (3.10). Written in terms of ω^2 it becomes

$$\frac{d^2 f}{dx^2} + \left(\omega^2 \frac{\mu}{T}\right) f = 0$$

This equation has exactly the same form as (3.11) and therefore it has a solution obtainable from (3.13) simply by replacing ω by $\omega \sqrt{\mu/T}$ and t by x. Thus

$$f(x) = A' \exp(j\omega \sqrt{\mu/T} x) + B' \exp(-j\omega \sqrt{\mu/T} x) \qquad (3.14)$$

While (3.14) is a valid solution, its form is not convenient and we will rewrite it in the equivalent form,

$$f(x) = A'' \sin(\omega \sqrt{\mu/T} x) + B'' \cos(\omega \sqrt{\mu/T} x)$$
$$= C' \sin(\omega \sqrt{\mu/T} x + \delta) \qquad (3.15)$$

where C' and δ are constants.

[*Exercise:* Find the values of constants A'', B'', C', and δ in terms of A' and B' such that (3.14) and (3.15) are equivalent.]

From (3.15) we see that the spatial portion of $f(x, t)$ is also an oscillatory function in the spatial variable x with amplitude of oscillation C' and phase angle δ. The wavelength or distance of periodicity is an interesting and important quantity. An examination of (3.15) shows that the distance between adjacent nodes of $f(x)$, the points where $f(x) = 0$, is $\pi/(\omega \sqrt{\mu/T})$. The distance between nodes is a half wavelength, so the wavelength λ is $\lambda = 2\pi/\omega \sqrt{\mu/T}$. Hence we may rewrite (3.15) as

$$f(x) = C' \sin[(2\pi/\lambda) x + \delta] \qquad (3.16)$$

Thus (3.10), the differential equation for $f(x)$, may be written as

$$\frac{d^2 f}{dx^2} + \left(\frac{2\pi}{\lambda}\right)^2 f = 0 \qquad (3.17)$$

Equation (3.17) is the one-dimensional time-independent portion of the wave equation, and thus describes *standing wave phenomena*. Equation (3.17) applies equally well to vibrations of membranes, electromagnetic waves, and gas molecules even though the actual physical variables bear no relation to one another. The tremendous range of applicability of this equation suggests that it might describe the de Broglie wave effects. As always the ultimate test of a theory lies in its agreement with experiments. So we shall assume that (3.17) applies to de Broglie waves and test the validity of the assumption in the predicted results.

Note that (3.17) applies only to the spatial dependence of the wave. The wave amplitude, in general, depends on both time and space coordinates, and therefore one must in some cases look for a more general equation. Here we are concerned with physical situations where time is not a variable.

We want to deduce an equation to describe particle waves as given by the de Broglie relation. Equation (3.17) was derived with the assumption that the wavelength is constant. This is not the case for particle waves, and when λ is a variable (3.17) is much more difficult to solve although its form remains correct. The variability of λ can be taken into account by the de Broglie hypothesis and through its use we are led to the Schrödinger equation.

The de Broglie hypothesis suggests that the particle wavelength may be written in terms of the kinetic energy K, as in (2.28), and remembering that $E = K + U$ (total energy of a particle = kinetic energy + potential energy),

$$\lambda = h/p = h/\sqrt{2mK} = h/[2m(E - U)]^{1/2} \tag{3.18}$$

Note that λ is a function of the space coordinates since U generally varies from point to point. E will be a constant in all our work.

It is important to note that the dependent variable, $f(x)$ in (3.17), no longer will be a positional displacement but rather some quantity whose nature at this point is not evident. To emphasize the change in meaning we shall replace $f(x)$ by $\psi(x)$ in (3.17). Making this change and using (3.18), we obtain from (3.17) the following new wave equation describing the wave nature of a particle of mass m, energy E, and potential energy $U(x)$:

$$\frac{d^2\psi}{dx^2} + \frac{2m}{\hbar^2} [E - U(x)]\psi = 0 \tag{3.19}$$

Equation (3.19) is the one-dimensional, time-independent Schrödinger equation, the quantum-mechanical equivalent of the classical time-independent wave equation (3.17). It is written in a one-dimensional form, but it may be extended to the three-dimensional case. Note also that (3.19) is not valid when relativistic effects must be taken into account; then a modified form of the Schrödinger equation must be used.

Equation (3.19) provides the quantum-mechanical description of a particle of mass m and potential energy $U(x)$. Almost everything we can know of this particle is obtainable from (3.19). This equation is in many ways the atomic analog of Newton's law $F = ma$.

One interesting aspect of (3.19) is that the forces acting on the particle do not appear to enter the equation. They are there but are hidden in the potential energy function $U(x)$. The force F and potential energy U are related by the equation (in one dimension)

$$U(x) = - \int_{x_0}^{x} F(x)\,dx \tag{3.20}$$

where x_0 is the point at which $U(x)$ is defined to be zero. In derivative form (3.20) may be written

$$F(x) = - \frac{dU(x)}{dx} \tag{3.21}$$

These equations can, of course, be generalized to three dimensions.

Thus we see that the potential energy U in the Schrödinger equation represents the forces acting on the particle being described; the Schrödinger equation therefore does not ignore the existence of forces but incorporates them by way of U. This explains why it is essential to know the potential energy before the behavior of the particle can be found.

3.2 PROPERTIES OF THE WAVE FUNCTION

Note that the Schrödinger equation, (3.19), is a second order ordinary differential equation. Its solution is ψ, the *wave function* associated with the particle to which (3.19) applies. Equation (3.19) is one-dimensional; the three-dimensional version in rectangular coordinates is

$$\frac{\partial^2 \psi}{\partial x^2} + \frac{\partial^2 \psi}{\partial y^2} + \frac{\partial^2 \psi}{\partial z^2} + \frac{2m}{\hbar^2}\,[E - U(x, y, z]\psi = 0 \tag{3.22}$$

where now both ψ and U are functions of all three coordinates x, y, and z.

We must take a careful look at ψ, since implicit in it is almost all we can know of the particle being described: energy, velocity, position, etc. A curious characteristic of ψ is that, while it cannot be experimentally detected, many measurable properties are deducible from it.

The fact that ψ is unmeasurable relates to the fact that it in many cases has a complex value. To obtain a physically meaningful quantity we form the real product $\psi\psi^* = |\psi|^2$ and consider its significance via an analogy with electromagnetic waves. The study of electromagnetism shows that the energy density J/m^3 associated with such a wave is proportional to $\mathcal{E}^2$, the square of the electric field intensity. Since the energy is carried by photons, this says that the photon density in an electromagnetic wave is proportional to $\mathcal{E}^2$. The number of photons is thus large where $\mathcal{E}^2$ is large. If we were to carry this interpretation over to quantum mechanics, we would hypothesize that the square of the amplitude of the wave function $|\psi|^2$ is related to the particle density; if we are describing one particle then we would say that $|\psi|^2$ evaluated at (x, y, z) is somehow related to the probability of the particle being found at (x, y, z).

This hypothesis was first advanced about 1925 by the German physicist, Max Born, who postulated that the probability dP of finding a particle in a volume element dV is proportional to $|\psi|^2\, dV$, i.e., that $dP = C |\psi|^2\, dV$ where C is a constant of proportionality. This conjecture has been very well borne out by experiment and we are thus led to accept it as one of the fundamental statements about the wave function.

This statement immediately leads to certain required mathematical properties of ψ. When we speak of a probability we refer to a number between zero and one, where one represents certainty of success and zero represents certainty of failure. Since the particle is certainly somewhere in the universe V this requires that

$$\int_V dP = C \int_V |\psi|^2\, dV = 1 \tag{3.23}$$

This implies that the integral of $|\psi|^2$ must be finite.

It would be convenient, though certainly not necessary, for the constant C to be unity. From (3.23) we recognize that $C = 1$ if and only if

$$\int_V |\psi|^2\, dV = 1 \tag{3.24}$$

In this event the probability equation simplifies to

$$dP = |\psi|^2\, dV \tag{3.25}$$

Now condition (3.24) can always be met if the finite integral requirement is satisfied. The wave function always contains an arbitrary constant, such as C' in (3.16), that can be factored out of all terms comprising ψ; the value of this constant can then be chosen so that (3.24) is met (see Prob. 3.8e).

This process is known as "normalizing the wave function" or "normalization." If (3.24) is not true, i.e., if $C \neq 1$, the wave function is said to be "unnormalized." Obviously (3.25) applies only to normalized wave functions.

From (3.25) we see that $|\psi|^2 = dP/dV$, the ratio of the probability that the particle is in dV to the size of dV itself. This ratio is known as the *probability density*. Hence Born's hypothesis as applied to normalized wave functions is that $|\psi|^2$ is the probability density of the particle's location.

There are several additional requirements which the wave function must meet. It must be single valued, finite, continuous, and smooth. A multivalued wave function would imply a multivalued probability density which in turn would imply ambiguous answers for the probability of finding the particle. This would be quite unacceptable. Furthermore the integral of such a function does not exist so normalization would be impossible. The requirements of finiteness, continuity, and smoothness are conditions which the wave function must have in order to satisfy the wave equation. They also can be justified on physical grounds. The finiteness requirement ties in with the requirement that ψ be normalizable, i.e., that the integral of $|\psi|^2$ be finite. (Of course it is possible to find a function which is infinite at one or more points and yet has a finite integral; the delta function is an example. These peculiar functions can be shown to be unacceptable on other grounds.) The smoothness requirement comes from the wave equation, (3.19). We have already required that ψ be finite. The energy E is certainly finite and $2m/\hbar^2$ is a finite constant. If the potential energy $U(x)$ is finite (required in real situations) then we are forced to conclude that $d^2\psi/dx^2$ is also finite. Therefore $d\psi/dx$ is continuous and ψ is smooth. The continuity requirement is obvious; if the wave function is finite and its slope $d\psi/dx$ is continuous, then ψ is continuous.

The wave function properties may now be summarized as follows:

1. $|\psi|^2$ is the probability density of the location of the particle.
2. ψ must be normalizable, i.e., $|\psi|^2$ must have a finite integral.
3. ψ must be single-valued, finite, continuous, and smooth.

An occasional exception must be made in the smoothness requirement. We have noted that $d^2\psi/dx^2$ must be finite if $U(x)$ is finite. In certain mathematical simplifications of real problems infinite potential energy is taken as a limiting case; at those places where $U(x)$ goes to infinity, $d^2\psi/dx^2$ must also go to infinity and the wave function will not be smooth. However the continuity requirement still can and must be met at such points.

Let us now return to (3.19). The solution depends strongly on the form of $U(x)$. If the potential energy of the particle is independent of x, then $U(x)$ is a constant and a solution may be obtained with little difficulty. On the other hand if the potential energy is, say, proportional to x^2, as it is approximately for an atom vibrating about its equilibrium position in a crystal, then the solution is quite difficult even though $U(x) = Kx^2$ looks simple. We later solve (3.19) for one form of $U(x)$ and discuss qualitatively the solutions for several other forms of $U(x)$.

As we solve (3.19), we must remember the conditions which ψ must possess to be a physically meaningful solution. We shall find that these conditions can, in general, be met only by restricting (quantizing) the values the energy E can assume. We are led therefore by the Schrödinger equation to quantization of energy.

3.3 WAVE FUNCTION AND ENERGY
OF AN ELECTRON IN A SOLID

Our interest in the Schrödinger equation derives from the need to be able to describe quantitatively the allowed behavior of electrons in a solid. From this description we can proceed to identify the material properties that give metals, semiconductors, and insulators their unique electrical characteristics.

We have noted that the potential energy U and the particle mass m dictate the nature of the wave function ψ and the total particle energy E. We have also noted that the nature of U determines the ease or difficulty with which the Schrödinger equation is solved.

With these two thoughts in mind—one as a motive, the other as a warning—let us direct our attention to the potential energy of an electron in a solid.

The potential energy U of any given electron depends upon the forces exerted upon it by the atomic nuclei and all electrons in the material. Consider first the potential energy due to the nuclei. For a material of atomic number Z the potential energy due to the nucleus of a single atom located at $x = 0$ is, for one dimension, $U(x) = -Zq^2/4\pi\epsilon_o r$, where $r = |x|$, ϵ_o is the electric permittivity, and q is the electronic charge magnitude. This function is sketched in Fig. 3.2.

A piece of solid used in an electronic device is made up of a very large number of atoms. For example, a cube 0.1 cm on a side contains approximately 10^{20} atoms. The potential energy due to the nuclei of these atoms is a superposition of the individual potential energies. To see the nature of this potential energy consider just two atoms (see

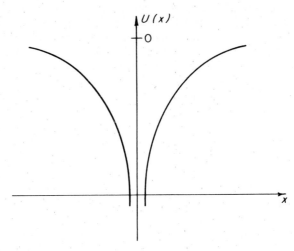

FIG. 3.2   Electron potential energy due to the nucleus of an atom.

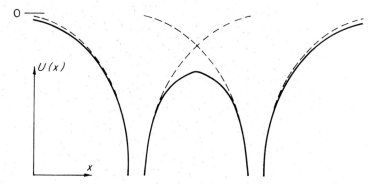

FIG. 3.3 Individual and composite electron potential
energies due to a pair of nuclei.

Fig. 3.3). Notice the sum of the two potential energies always remains
below the level designated as zero. If we extend this idea to a many-
atom linear array the potential energy shown in Fig. 3.4 results.

Consider solving the Schrödinger equation using the potential
energy function given in Fig. 3.4. Since $U(x)$ multiplies $\psi(x)$ in the
equation, and since $U(x)$ is not a constant, we shall be required to solve
a differential equation with a varying coefficient, and the variations of
that coefficient are not particularly "nice." Indeed the only attractive
feature of $U(x)$ is the fact that, excluding effects at the boundaries of
the solid, it has a repetitive pattern, i.e., it is a periodic function of x.
Evidently some simplifying approximation must be made to obtain a
solution by reasonable effort. Figure 3.5 shows the leading candidate
for this approximation. The function shown there is a series of discontinuous but periodic variations in the potential energy U. Each repeated
pattern in U (e.g., between the vertical dashed lines A and A') is termed
a "square-well" potential, so we have replaced the potential of Fig. 3.4
by a series of square-well potentials. (Where no confusion with electric
potential is likely, we shall shorten "potential energy" to "potential.")

FIG. 3.4 Potential energy of an electron in a linear
array of nuclei.

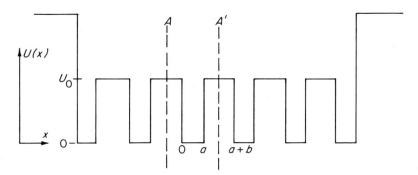

FIG. 3.5   Approximation to the potential energy of
an electron in a linear array of nuclei (see also Fig. 3.4).

The enormous advantage of this approximation is that $U(x)$ is constant almost everywhere. Within each well ($0 < x < a$, for example), $U(x)$ has the constant value zero (for convenience, zero on the energy scale has been shifted from the reference used in Figs. 3.2 and 3.3 to the bottom of the wells in Fig. 3.5), and between the wells $U(x)$ is also constant at U_0. Thus we solve the Schrödinger equation one well at a time and one mesa at a time and fit the solutions together at the well-mesa boundaries to obtain an overall wave function satisfying the general conditions of Sec. 3.3. This is still not trivial but it is much more feasible than the rigorous solution.

Rather than trying to obtain the solution for this case at once let us instead examine a series of simpler problems, using the information we obtain from these to deduce the important features we would obtain from the potential of Fig. 3.5. Each of these simpler examples involves a square-well potential of one type or another. The problems in order of appearance are:

1. *infinite square well:* a single square well in one dimension in which there is an infinite change in U at the boundaries
2. *finite square well:* a single square well in which there is a finite change in U at the boundaries
3. *double square well:* two finite square wells separated by a fixed distance
4. *periodic square well:* a one-dimensional, periodic array of finite square wells (the potential of Fig. 3.5)
5. *three-dimensional infinite square well:* the three-dimensional version of the infinite square well

3.4   INFINITE SQUARE WELL
Consider a single square well in Fig. 3.5, say the one between $x = 0$ and $x = a$ with finite height U_0. Suppose however that we wish to

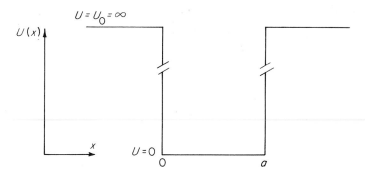

$U = U_0 = \infty$

$U(x)$

x

$U = 0$

0 a

FIG. 3.6 Potential energy for an infinite square well.

consider electron energies E much less than U_0. Mathematically it seems likely that we might have difficulty distinguishing between the actual case $U_0 \gg E$ and the limiting case $U_0 = \infty$; in any event the limiting case provides a useful starting point since it is the easiest case to solve. The potential energy being considered at present thus is as shown in Fig. 3.6.

Within the region $(0, a)$ the potential energy of the electron is zero and therefore we know that there are no forces acting on it. At the boundaries 0 and a there is an infinite and discontinuous change in the potential energy, so the electron cannot escape from that region.

With $U = 0$, the one-dimensional Schrödinger equation may be written as

$$\frac{d^2\psi}{dx^2} + \frac{2m}{\hbar^2} E\psi = 0 \qquad (0 \le x \le a)$$

The solution to this equation may be written $\psi = A \sin \alpha x + B \cos \alpha x$ where

$$\alpha = (2mE/\hbar^2)^{1/2} \qquad (3.26)$$

and A and B are the two constants of integration. To complete the solution for ψ we must evaluate A and B. To do so recall the various properties ψ must possess. Since the electron cannot be found outside of $(0, a)$, ψ must vanish for $x < 0$ and $x > a$. Also since ψ is required to be continuous it follows that ψ must vanish at both boundaries. Thus

$$\psi = 0 \quad \text{at } x = 0 \qquad (3.27)$$

$$\psi = 0 \quad \text{at } x = a \qquad (3.28)$$

These two relations are called *boundary conditions*. Using (3.27) it follows that $B = 0$ and by (3.28) it follows that

$$A \sin (\alpha a) = 0 \qquad (3.29)$$

This relation could obviously be satisfied by setting $A = 0$, but in that case $\psi(x) = 0$ and we have only a trivial solution. So we must look for another way to satisfy (3.29) to obtain a physically meaningful solution. This can be achieved if

$$\alpha a = n\pi \qquad (n = 1, 2, \ldots) \tag{3.30}$$

Since a is a constant, satisfying the boundary conditions forces us to place a restriction on the quantity α; using the defining equation for α from (3.26), (3.30) may be written as $(2mE/\hbar^2)^{1/2} a = n\pi$ ($n = 1$, 2, ...). Solving for E then yields

$$E_n = n^2\hbar^2\pi^2/2ma^2 \qquad (n = 1, 2, \ldots) \tag{3.31}$$

This equation represents a very important consequence of the Schrödinger equation. The energies specified by (3.31) form a discrete set and are the only energies the particle being described may possess; thus the energy of the particle is quantized. The quantization has appeared very naturally; application of the required boundary conditions has led directly to the quantized energies (see Fig. 3.7). Since the quantized

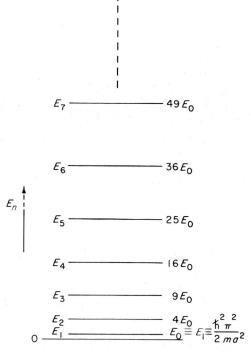

FIG. 3.7   Energy levels of a particle of mass m in an infinite square well of width a.

energies are determined by the number n, n is known as the *quantum number.*

Certainly the full power of quantum mechanics is not apparent from consideration of this simple square-well problem. Note, however, that the quantization stems naturally from the formalism. Further development of quantum mechanics would demonstrate the extension to other variables observed to be quantized.

In many cases a problem is finished when the energy spectrum is found. To obtain more insight into quantum theory it is instructive for us to continue. In the example being considered the wave function ψ is given by $\psi = A \sin (\alpha x)$. Substituting the value of α from (3.30),

$$\psi = A \sin [(n\pi/a)x] \qquad (n = 1, 2, \ldots) \tag{3.32}$$

Note that (3.32) specifies a set of sine waves with nodes (zero values) at the boundaries of the box. Thus the wave functions have the form illustrated in Fig. 3.8 and are those that "fit" in the box, i.e., those such that an integral number of half wavelengths are equal to the width of the box a. Thus

$$a = n(\lambda/2) \tag{3.33}$$

But from (3.18), since $U = 0$ in our problem and thus $E = K$, $\lambda = h/\sqrt{2mE}$. Therefore, from (3.33), $a = nh/2\sqrt{2mE}$, from which we have again (3.31),

$$E_n = n^2\pi^2\hbar^2/2ma^2$$

Thus, knowing from the nature of the problem the wavelengths the particles must have, we can, using the de Broglie hypothesis, derive the set of energy values they must possess. And these are the same as those deduced from the Schrödinger equation. (This is not, of course, a separate derivation of E; we used the de Broglie relation to obtain the Schrödinger equation.)

One undetermined constant A in (3.32) remains to be evaluated before ψ is completely specified. It can be obtained by using the normalization condition which in the present problem is

$$\int_{-\infty}^{\infty} |\psi|^2 \, dx = \int_{0}^{a} A^2 \sin^2(n\pi x/a) \, dx = 1 \tag{3.34}$$

Having determined A it is possible to determine the probability of finding the particle in any region. This is illustrated in the problems.

Now consider (3.31), the allowed energies in the infinite square well. From (3.33) we know the wavelength associated with the particle in each of these energy states is $\lambda = 2a/n$. By the de Broglie hypothesis the momentum is given by $p_n = h/\lambda = hn/2a$ and the energy relation becomes

$$E_n = (p_n)^2/2m \tag{3.35}$$

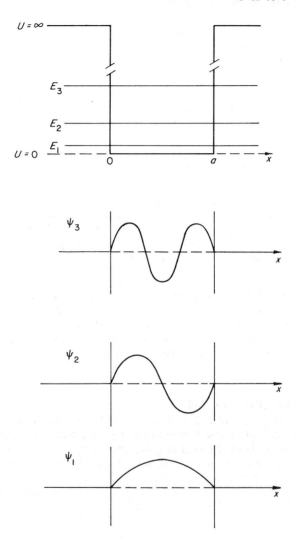

FIG. 3.8   First few allowed values of energy and wave
functions arising from infinite square-well potential of
Fig. 3.6.

the familiar classical result. Note that the momentum values of the
particle are quantized in multiples of $h/2a$. If now an E-p plot is
made, the points given by (3.35) fall on a parabola as shown in Fig. 3.9.

Some terminology associated with the Schrödinger equation and
its solutions should be given. Each of the separate wave functions given
by (3.32) specifies a *quantum state* that determines, for a particular sys-

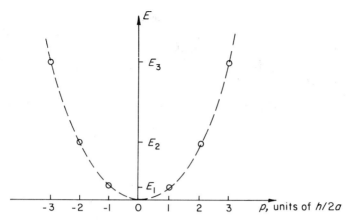

FIG. 3.9 Relation of allowed values of energy and momentum for a free particle in an infinite square well.

tem at a particular time, the system properties such as energy, momentum, position, etc. Each of the energies enumerated in (3.31) is called an *energy level*. Only one quantum state is associated with each energy level in the above problem. Later we see examples in which several quantum states correspond to the same energy.

3.5 FINITE SQUARE WELL

The infinite square well is a highly artificial case. The square-well shape itself of course is a simplifying abstraction and the infinite height of the walls of the well is quite unrealistic. Let us now consider a case somewhat closer to reality, namely, that where the well height is finite as shown in Fig. 3.10. Within the well the potential energy is again zero, and at the edges of the well there is a finite potential energy change U_0. This configuration more nearly represents the potential energy of an electron in an atom.

Finding the allowable energies in this case is quite straightforward

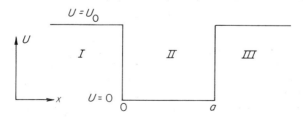

FIG. 3.10 Potential energy for a finite square well.

though tedious. We will indicate here the method of solution. First, the Schrödinger equation is written in each of the three regions of constant U: $x < 0, 0 < x < a, x > a$. Designating the three regions as *I, II,* and *III* (as shown in Fig. 3.10) the Schrödinger equations may be written as (3.36), (3.37), and (3.38), respectively.

$$\frac{d^2\psi_I}{dx^2} + \frac{2m}{\hbar^2}(E - U_0)\psi_I = 0 \qquad\qquad (3.36)$$

$$\frac{d^2\psi_{II}}{dx^2} + \frac{2m}{\hbar^2}E\psi_{II} = 0 \qquad\qquad (3.37)$$

$$\frac{d^2\psi_{III}}{dx^2} + \frac{2m}{\hbar^2}(E - U_0)\psi_{III} = 0 \qquad\qquad (3.38)$$

Solving this set of equations results in six constants of integration that (together with E) are to be evaluated using the boundary conditions and the normalization requirement. The boundary conditions here are that $\psi(x)$ and its derivative $\psi'(x)$ be continuous at $x = 0$ and $x = a$, and that $\psi(x) \rightarrow 0$ as $x \rightarrow \pm\infty$.

The nature of the restriction on the total energy E depends on the magnitude of E relative to U_0. If $E > U_0$, no restriction is placed on the values E may assume and E is not quantized since motion of the particle is not restricted by the potential well.

If $E < U_0$, then E is quantized. We can see this by considering qualitatively the solutions of (3.36), (3.37), and (3.38). Recalling our earlier discussion of the effect of the sign of the separation constant on the solution of (3.11), we can conclude that for $E < U_0$, the solutions of (3.36) and (3.38) are real exponentials of the form

$$\psi_I = A \exp(\beta x) + B \exp(-\beta x) \qquad (x < 0)$$

$$\psi_{III} = F \exp(\beta x) + G \exp(-\beta x) \qquad (x > a)$$

where $\beta = [2m(U_0 - E)/\hbar^2]^{1/2}$. Since we require the integral of $|\psi|^2$ over all x to be bounded, it must follow that $\psi_I \rightarrow 0$ as $x \rightarrow -\infty$ and $\psi_{III} \rightarrow 0$ as $x \rightarrow +\infty$. These two conditions require that $B = 0$ and $F = 0$. Thus ψ_I and ψ_{III} are decreasing exponentials in their respective regions; i.e., they decay toward zero away from the boundaries of *II*.

In *II* the solution has the same form as that of the infinite well

$$\psi_{II} = C \sin \alpha x + D \cos \alpha x \qquad (0 \leq x \leq a) \qquad (3.39)$$

where α is defined in (3.26). Thus within the well the wave function ψ_{II} is oscillatory. This function and the solutions for *I* and *III*,

$$\psi_I = A \exp(\beta x) \qquad (x \leq 0) \qquad\qquad (3.40)$$

$$\psi_{III} = G \exp(-\beta x) = H \exp[-\beta(x - a)] \qquad (x \geq a) \qquad (3.41)$$

give $\psi(x)$ for all x.

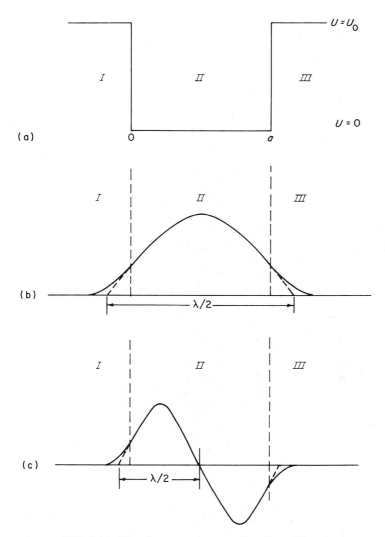

$U = U_0$

$U = 0$

(a)

0 a

(b)

$\lambda/2$

(c)

$\lambda/2$

FIG. 3.11   Two lowest order wave functions (b) and (c) for the finite square well shown in (a).

There are five conditions to be satisfied. These are

1. $\psi_I(0) = \psi_{II}(0)$ (3.42)

2. $\psi_I'(0) = \psi_{II}'(0)$ (3.43)

3. $\psi_{II}(a) = \psi_{III}(a)$ (3.44)

4. $\psi_{II}'(a) = \psi_{III}'(a)$ (3.45)

5. $\displaystyle\int_{-\infty}^{\infty} |\psi|^2\, dx = 1$ (3.46)

The first four equations are the boundary conditions and the fifth is the normalization requirement.

We have only four constants of integration and therefore to satisfy the five conditions we must use the other available constant E, and we find that E is quantized. This can be seen by applying the five conditions listed above to (3.39), (3.40), and (3.41).

Without deriving the exact values of the quantized energies we can estimate their values relative to those obtained for the infinite well. The wave function ψ_{II} in the region $(0, a)$ is an oscillatory function that must join smoothly with decreasing exponentials in I and III. The lowest value of the quantized energy E_n corresponds to ψ_{II} having maximum wavelength (see Fig. 3.11b). The rapidity of the falloff of ψ in I and III is governed by the difference $U_0 - E$; the larger the difference the more rapidly ψ_I and ψ_{III} go to zero. When the difference becomes infinitely large the wave functions do not penetrate outside the well at all. [Compare with the boundary conditions (3.27) and (3.28).] The fact that the wave functions do penetrate outside $x = 0$ and $x = a$ forces the wavelength of the oscillatory portion of this wave function to be longer than that of the corresponding wave function of the infinite well. Thus the lowest energy deduced for the finite well is lower than that obtained for the infinite well.

The second lowest energy wave function for the finite well is also sketched in Fig. 3.11c. The same arguments may be used to show that this energy, too, is lower than E_2 of the infinite well.

Two other differences between the finite and infinite square well should be pointed out. First, for a particle in the well, that is, one having a total energy less than U_0, there can exist only a finite number of allowed energies. Thus there exist only a finite number of *bound states* corresponding to $E < U_0$. In Fig. 3.12 we assume there are three such

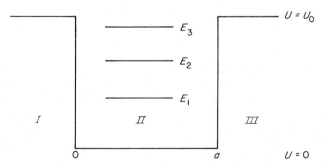

FIG. 3.12   Energy levels in a finite square well.

levels. For $E > U_0$, the allowed energies form a continuous spectrum corresponding to behavior expected of a free particle.

Secondly, there is the rather startling fact that the wave function is nonzero outside the well ($x < 0$, $x > a$) for $E < U_0$. This says that $|\psi|^2 \neq 0$ outside the well and there is thus a finite probability that the electron is in *I* and *III*. Since we are considering the case $E < U_0$, existence in *I* or *III* means a negative kinetic energy $K = E - U_0$. In classical theory this is an impossible situation since it implies a negative mass or an imaginary velocity or complex values for both. The real question of course is not "how does this situation relate to classical theory" but "how does it relate to reality?" Is this quantum-mechanical prediction in agreement with experimental results? Does one actually find the particle in *I* and *III* with $E < U_0$? If so, what behavior is associated with $K < 0$?

The answers to these questions are as follows. The quantum-mechanical prediction is not in disagreement with experimental results. It is not possible to determine experimentally whether there are particles in *I* and *III* with $E < U_0$, so it is not possible to confirm or disprove the theory or to determine what $K < 0$ means. The fact that direct experimental determination is impossible is also a quantum-mechanical prediction. We can see this by attempting to design an experiment to detect the existence of a particle in the region $x < 0$ or $x > a$. We must set up a detector somewhere in *I* or *III* and measure the electron energy to be sure that $E < U_0$. Consider a measurement made in *III*. Since the region is infinite in extent we must decide where to make the measurement. Suppose we wish to be 99% certain of finding the electron if it is in *III*. Now $|\psi|^2$ in this region is given by

$$|\psi|^2 = A \exp[-2\beta(x - a)] \qquad (x > a) \qquad (3.47)$$

and 99% of the area under this function lies between $x = a$ and $x = a + 2.3/\beta$. Hence the detector should be positioned to span this portion of *III*, and we can determine the position of a detected electron within an uncertainty of $\Delta x = 2.3/\beta$. Recall that Heisenberg recognized a fundamental principle regarding the simultaneous determination of the momentum and position of a particle. Heisenberg's principle says that the product of the uncertainties in position and momentum $\Delta x\, \Delta p$ cannot be less than a number of the order of Planck's constant, $h = 6.63 \times 10^{-34}$ J $\cdot$ s. This number is h, $h/2$, $h/2\pi$, $h/4\pi$, etc., depending upon the exact manner in which uncertainty is defined; here h itself will suffice. The position uncertainty $\Delta x = 2.3/\beta$ implies a momentum uncertainty of at least $h\beta/2.3$. The momentum uncertainty makes the uncertainty in kinetic energy larger than $U_0 - E$ so it is impossible to determine whether E is in fact less than U_0 and it cannot be verified that we are examining the properties of electrons with negative kinetic energy.

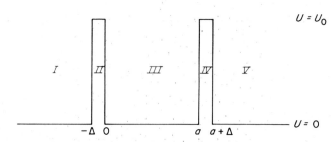

FIG. 3.13   Potential energy diagram used in describing tunneling effects.

It might appear that by increasing Δx sufficiently we could make Δp small enough to make $\Delta K < U_0 - E$. This would prove to be a false hope. Heisenberg's principle does not promise that Δp will be decreased if precision in the determination of position is sacrificed. Increasing the span of the detector does not change Δp significantly because there is a less than 1% chance that the added span will detect an electron. Thus the added span is essentially ineffective.

The situation seems to border on the ridiculous; the quantum theory predicts a result which the quantum theory says cannot be directly measured. There are ways to test the predictions of the theory. Suppose the potential energy of a particle is that shown in Fig. 3.13, the total energy of the particle is less than the potential energy ($E < U_0$), and the particle is initially in *III*. We can write the Schrödinger equation in each of the five regions shown. From our previous work we know that wave functions are oscillatory in *I*, *III*, and *V* and decreasing exponentials in *II* and *IV*. The particle is assumed to be initially in $(0, a)$. Because of the exponential tail on the wave function, the wave function is not zero in *I* and *V* and therefore there is a finite probability that the particle originally in $(0, a)$ will appear in $x < -\Delta$ or $x > a + \Delta$ even though it does not have enough energy to get over the barriers at 0 and a. The probability of this occurrence will increase as Δ decreases, as U_0 decreases, or as E increases. This phenomenon is named (appropriately) *tunneling*. It is a quantum-mechanical effect and has no classical analog.

Tunneling processes occur in many cases; of particular importance to electrical engineers are those significant in describing the behavior of Zener, backward, and tunnel diodes and that which often causes leakage currents to flow in the insulated gate field effect transistor. (We discuss briefly the operation of the diodes in Chap. 7.)

Tunneling effects then, as peculiar as they seem to be, do occur. And, while we cannot detect a particle in the negative kinetic energy state, we can inferentially determine that it has been there. This is the only means we have to explain how, with insufficient energy, the par-

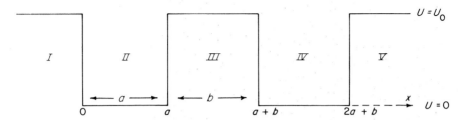

FIG. 3.14   Potential energy diagram for two coupled
finite square wells.

ticle appears in a forbidden region. Quantum mechanics is full of such
surprises.

3.6   DOUBLE SQUARE WELL

Before attempting to discuss the solution for the periodic square
well let us establish some of the features of the multiple square-well
situation by considering a pair of wells. The potential energy for this
case is indicated in Fig. 3.14. We want to look at bound states and
therefore we assume the total energy E of the particle is such that $E <
U_0$. Our discussion is qualitative.

In the case sketched in Fig. 3.14 the solution of the Schrödinger
equation can be obtained straightforwardly in each of the five regions.
The solutions and their derivatives are matched at the boundaries and
we find that the energy must be quantized to satisfy the boundary conditions. If b is very small and portions of the wave function overlap
significantly in the region $(a, a + b)$, the interaction of the *two* wells
results in a different set of quantized energies from that for either well
individually. If b is very large, the interaction between the wells is very
small and the wave functions within the wells and therefore the particle energies are like those for a single isolated well.

Consider Fig. 3.15a. If b is large compared with the characteristic
length $\hbar/[2m(U_0 - E)]^{1/2}$ $(= 1/\beta)$, then the wave functions in the
wells will be (nearly) identical to those of a single finite square well
(as in Fig. 3.11) and corresponding energy levels will thus be the same.
If b is not so large there is a region of appreciable overlap of the exponentials. To find the effect of the overlap consider the wave functions
corresponding to those of the lowest single-well energy (E_1 in Fig.
3.11b). There are two ways in which the decaying segments of the wave
functions can be joined, as sketched in Fig 3.15b. In the first way $\psi_{1.1}$,
the effective wavelength of the wave function within the wells is increased, implying a lower energy ($E_{1.1} < E_1$); in the second way $\psi_{1.2}$,
the effective wavelength is decreased, implying a higher energy ($E_{1.2} >
E_1$). Thus where in the single well we have a single quantum state and

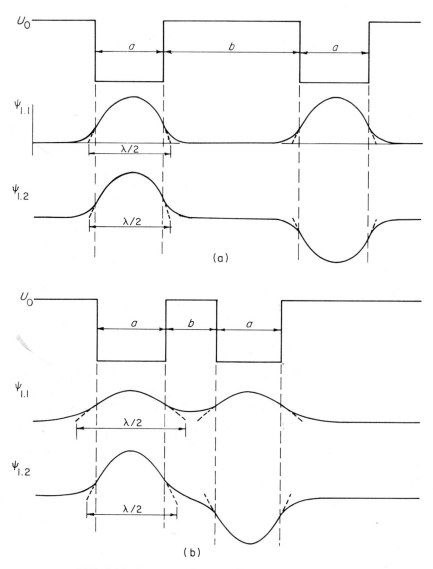

FIG. 3.15   Lowest order wave function for two coupled finite square wells: (a) negligible coupling (*b* large)
(b) appreciable coupling (*b* small).

a single energy level (E_1) we now have two quantum states and two energy levels ($E_{1.1}$ and $E_{1.2}$). From Fig. 3.15 it is easy to appreciate that the
separation between these energy levels increases as *b* decreases. In Fig.
3.15a λ is essentially the same for $\psi_{1.1}$ and $\psi_{1.2}$ so that $E_{1.1} \simeq E_1 \simeq
E_{1.2}$, whereas in Fig. 3.15b the λs are clearly different and we have

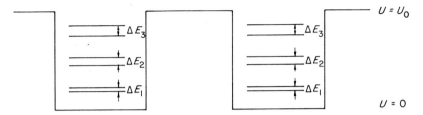

FIG. 3.16   Energy levels of two coupled finite wells.

$E_{1,1} < E_1 < E_{1,2}$. In other words, as the wells interact more and more strongly the separation of the energy levels will increase.

The argument above is made in terms of the lowest energy level. A similar argument can be made for each allowed level. The result is that for two coupled identical wells there are two energy levels for each level in the isolated well and the difference between the levels increases as the separation of the wells decreases. Figure 3.16 describes the energy spectrum of two coupled wells.

The fact that coupled systems can lead to a splitting of characteristic values is not peculiar to quantum mechanics. Similar behavior can occur in electric circuits. For example, a circuit containing an inductor and a capacitor has a resonant frequency $\omega_o = (LC)^{-1/2}$. If two such identical circuits are brought together the magnetic fields of the coils cause interaction between the circuits of an amount specified by the mutual coupling coefficient $k = M/L$. The circuit appropriate to this case is shown in Fig. 3.17b. It is left as a problem to show that there are two resonant frequencies ω_{o1} and ω_{o2} associated with this system,

$$\omega_{o1} = \omega_o/(1 + M/L)^{1/2} \qquad \omega_{o2} = \omega_o/(1 - M/L)^{1/2} \qquad (3.48)$$

and that the separation between the resonant frequencies increases as the coupling coefficient increases.

3.7 PERIODIC SQUARE WELL

Consider the periodic square well, the approximation to the actual periodic potential in a solid. The potential energy function is

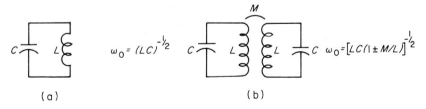

(a)   (b)

FIG. 3.17   (a) Simple LC circuit and (b) coupled LC circuits.

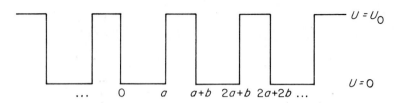

FIG. 3.18   One-dimensional square-well model of a
solid (Kronig-Penney model).

illustrated in Fig. 3.18. This model is composed of N identical square
wells each separated by the distance b. (This structure is termed the
Kronig-Penney model, named after the two men who first determined
its properties.)

To solve the Schrödinger equation appropriate to this problem,
again consider only bound states $E < U_0$. The Schrödinger equation is
written and solved for each region of the problem. The boundary conditions and the normalization condition are applied to these solutions
and their derivatives. Again the boundary conditions can be satisfied
only by quantizing the total energy of the electron.

We shall not attempt to derive in detail the nature of the energy
levels of the N interacting square wells. Instead we shall state the results
which would be obtained.

1. The energy spectrum is composed of allowed bands of energies separated by forbidden bands of energies.
2. The number of energy levels within a band is equal to the number N
   of wells considered.
3. The widths of the allowed energy bands increase as the total energy
   increases while the widths of the forbidden energy bands decrease as
   the total energy increases.
4. The widths of the allowed bands increase as the separation between
   wells b decreases.

These results are summarized in Fig. 3.19, which shows the way the
(assumed) five bound states of the individual isolated square wells become an equal number of bands.

It is especially important to examine the consequences of the
second result. The normal atomic density in the solid state is about 10^{22}
atoms/cm^3; thus the number of energy levels within a band is of this
order of magnitude. A representative width of an energy band might
be 1 eV. With 10^{22} levels within a band of the width 1 eV, the average
separation between levels would be about 10^{-22} eV. This extremely
small separation implies that for our purposes we may consider an energy band in a solid to represent a continuous distribution of energy
levels.

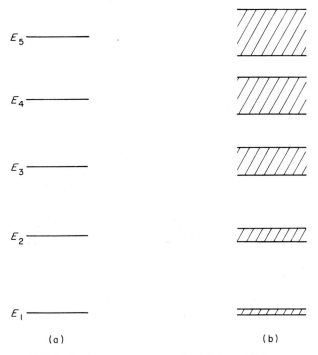

E_5

E_4

E_3

E_2

E_1

(a)   (b)

FIG. 3.19   Energy spectrum of (a) isolated finite
square well and (b) N interacting finite square wells.

The energy spectrum in Fig. 3.19 is valid for a particular well separation b in Fig. 3.18. Let us plot the energy spectrum versus separation between wells. If the separation is very large, the wells are (nearly) independent and we simply have N coincident levels corresponding to the levels of a single well. As the wells are brought closer together the higher energy levels are affected first since the exponential tails of the wave functions increase in length as the energy increases. Then as the separation continues to decrease the lower levels are also affected. The broadening associated with the higher levels is always greater than that of the lower levels. This behavior is summarized in Fig. 3.20. (In Sec. 4.2 of Chap. 4 we discuss the significance of b_1, b_2, b_3, and b_4.)

In Fig. 3.21 we superimpose the band structure of Fig. 3.19 upon the potential energy diagram of Fig. 3.4. The shaded regions are the allowed bands; they are shown only where the kinetic energy is positive because the wave functions become vanishingly small in the regions where $K < 0$. At energy E_1, for example, the line is drawn between the sides of the wells surrounding each atom. This does not mean that a given state at E_1 is confined to a given atom; each state is defined for all values of position both inside and outside the wells.

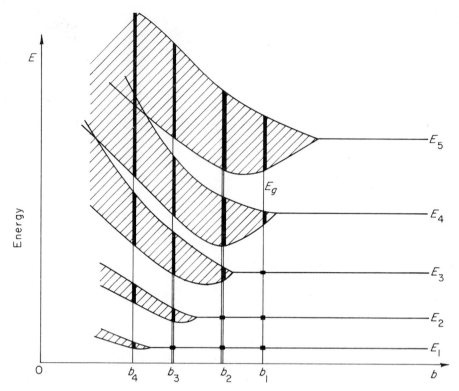

FIG. 3.20   Idealized energy spectrum of a large group of atoms plotted as a function of the interatomic spacing.

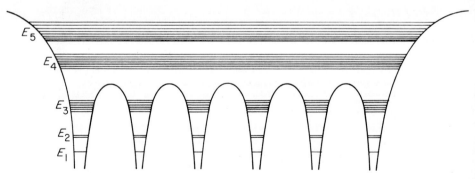

FIG. 3.21   Potential energy and band structure of a solid.

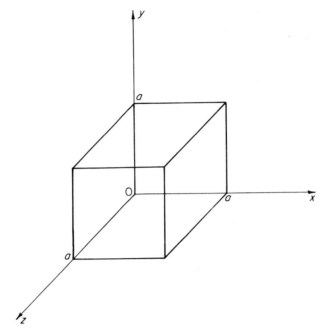

FIG. 3.22   Model for three-dimensional infinite square-well problem ($\Delta U = \infty$ at each bounding plane).

3.8   THREE-DIMENSIONAL INFINITE SQUARE WELL

Before leaving the square-well type of potential energy it is important to consider a three-dimensional problem. Three-dimensionality is a characteristic of the real world and this characteristic leads to an important feature of the energy spectrum, namely, several wave functions associated with the same energy E.

We assume a potential energy function such that an electron is completely confined to the cubic region specified by the rectangular coordinates $x = (0, a)$, $y = (0, a)$, $z = (0, a)$ (see Fig. 3.22). Within the cube the potential energy of the electron is zero and there is an infinite discontinuity in potential energy at each bounding plane. Thus the problem is a three-dimensional infinite square well. The Schrödinger equation applicable to this case is, for positions inside the cubic region,

$$\frac{\partial^2 \psi}{\partial x^2} + \frac{\partial^2 \psi}{\partial y^2} + \frac{\partial^2 \psi}{\partial z^2} + \frac{2m}{\hbar^2} E\psi = 0 \qquad (3.49)$$

To solve (3.49) we use the method of separation of variables. We assume that $\psi(x, y, z)$ can be written as the product of three functions, each dependent on only one variable.

$$\psi(x, y, z) = X(x)\, Y(y)\, Z(z) \tag{3.50}$$

Substituting this in (3.49), performing the differentiations, and dividing by (3.50) gives

$$\frac{1}{X(x)}\frac{d^2X}{dx^2} + \frac{1}{Y(y)}\frac{d^2Y}{dy^2} + \frac{1}{Z(z)}\frac{d^2Z}{dz^2} + \frac{2m}{\hbar^2}\,E = 0 \tag{3.51}$$

We have here a situation similar to that discussed earlier in the development of the Schrödinger equation. The first three terms are functions of single independent variables. It must follow that each of these terms is a constant, and that the sum of the three constants is $-(2m/\hbar^2)E$. Thus we have

$$\frac{1}{X}\frac{d^2X}{dx^2} = -\alpha_x^2$$

$$\frac{1}{Y}\frac{d^2X}{dy^2} = -\alpha_y^2$$

$$\frac{1}{Z}\frac{d^2Z}{dz^2} = -\alpha_z^2$$

$$-\alpha_x^2 - \alpha_y^2 - \alpha_z^2 + (2m/\hbar^2)\,E = 0 \tag{3.52}$$

Each of the above differential equations has the form of the one-dimensional Schrödinger equation. The boundary conditions appropriate to each of these functions are precisely those of the infinite square well in (3.27) and (3.28). Therefore, we may immediately write down the solutions,

$$X(x) = A \sin \alpha_x x + B \cos \alpha_x x$$
$$Y(y) = C \sin \alpha_y y + D \cos \alpha_y y$$
$$Z(z) = F \sin \alpha_z z + G \cos \alpha_z z$$

Application of the boundary conditions places restrictions on the constants α_x, α_y, and α_z such that

$$\alpha_x = n_x \pi/a \qquad \alpha_y = n_y \pi/a \qquad \alpha_z = n_z \pi/a \tag{3.53}$$

where n_x, n_y, and n_z are positive integers. Note that in this case we find three quantum numbers, one from each of the independent coordinates entering the Schrödinger equation. This is a general result.

The constants shown in (3.53) may be substituted into (3.52) to give the quantized energies of the electron,

$$E = (\hbar^2\pi^2/2ma^2)(n_x^2 + n_y^2 + n_z^2) = E_0(n_x^2 + n_y^2 + n_z^2) \tag{3.54}$$

This expression shows how the total energy depends upon the quantum numbers. It is the sum of their squares $(n_x^2 + n_y^2 + n_z^2)$ that is important and not n_x, n_y, and n_z individually. Various combinations of

Table 3.1. Quantum numbers and associated energies for three-dimensional infinite square well.

n_x	n_y	n_z	E
1	1	1	$3E_0$
2	1	1	$6E_0$
1	2	1	$6E_0$
1	1	2	$6E_0$
2	2	1	$9E_0$
2	1	2	$9E_0$
1	2	2	$9E_0$
3	1	1	$11E_0$
1	3	1	$11E_0$
1	1	3	$11E_0$
2	2	2	$12E_0$
3	2	1	$14E_0$
2	3	1	$14E_0$
1	2	3	$14E_0$
3	1	2	$14E_0$
2	1	3	$14E_0$
1	3	2	$14E_0$

n_x, n_y, and n_z can lead to the same energy. This can best be appreciated by constructing a table of the allowed energies for the electron being considered. Using E_0, implicitly defined in (3.54), gives the results shown in Table 3.1. The energy level diagram is shown in Fig. 3.23.

From Table 3.1 we see that there may be several quantum states with the same energy level. An energy level for which this is true is said to be a *degenerate* level, and the *order of degeneracy* is the number of states corresponding to that energy. Thus the $6E_0$ level is said to be threefold degenerate while the $14E_0$ level is sixfold degenerate. A moment's thought should make clear that the order of degeneracy increases as the energy E increases. It may not be so obvious that the distribution of quantum states (the number of quantum states per unit energy interval) approaches a continuous function as the energy increases so that the electron being considered has an infinite number of energies available. We later derive a function that describes the density of quantum states and we make important use of this function in determining the numbers of charge carriers in a semiconductor. For the moment, however, it is sufficient to note that the quantum states are distributed throughout all energy values.

With this discussion we are essentially finished with the solving of square-well problems. We must now concern ourselves with how the electrons may occupy the states predicted from Schrödinger's equation, and how the electrons modify these allowed states by the forces they exert on one another. Before we can discuss the occupation of states we

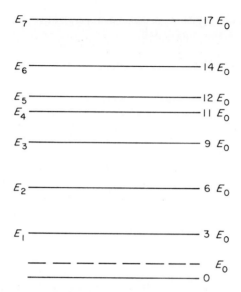

E_7 ——————————————— $17\,E_0$

E_6 ——————————————— $14\,E_0$

E_5 ——————————————— $12\,E_0$
E_4 ——————————————— $11\,E_0$

E_3 ——————————————— $9\,E_0$

E_2 ——————————————— $6\,E_0$

E_1 ——————————————— $3\,E_0$

— — — — — — — — E_0
——————————————— 0

FIG. 3.23   Energy levels for the three-dimensional infinite square-well problem.

must define precisely what we mean by the term state. This we do in the next section. Following that we shall consider the effects of the electron-electron forces.

3.9   QUANTUM STATES AND THE PAULI PRINCIPLE

A *quantum state* is an allowed condition for a particle (electron) in a system (the array of atoms comprising a solid). A value of electron energy is associated with each quantum state. As noted earlier, several wave functions can have the same energy, hence specification of an energy E does not specify a particular quantum state. A wave function ψ is also associated with each quantum state and this association is one to one. The quantum numbers that define the wave function thus define the quantum state. It would therefore seem that specification of the three quantum numbers n_x, n_y, and n_z should uniquely define a quantum state. Not so, however! The Schrödinger equation does not include one subtlety of the wave function, a property known as *electron spin*.

In 1925 two Dutch physicists, Uhlenbeck and Goudsmit, were able to explain certain details of the radiation and absorption spectra by postulating the existence of electron spin. They suggested the electron could be treated as a sphere having finite radius with the electronic charge distributed over the surface of the sphere. Since the sphere could be rotating about its own axis, this rotation of charge would constitute a current. From electromagnetism it is known that a current loop of this type has associated with it a magnetic moment given by the product of the current and the area of the current loop.

If such a magnetic moment were present in a magnetic field there would be an interaction energy between the field and the current loop. Here this implies that the existence of the electron spin would influence the energy an electron has in a magnetic field and would, therefore, affect the spectrum of the atom of which the electron was a part. To explain observed spectral results Uhlenbeck and Goudsmit hypothesized that the magnetic moment of the spinning electron (a vector) is quantized in a way such that its magnitude has a fixed value and its direction is either parallel or antiparallel to the magnetic field (that is, at an angle of 0° or 180° relative to the magnetic field) so two possible spin quantum states are associated with the electron. The spin vector is given by $m_s \hbar a_B$, where a_B is a unit vector in the direction of the applied magnetic field and m_s is the spin quantum number, taking on the value $\pm 1/2$. (The spin quantum number comes out of a relativistic formulation of quantum mechanics conceived by P.A.M. Dirac in 1928). Thus we must say that a quantum state is completely specified by four quantum numbers: n_x, n_y, n_z, and m_s.

Because of the introduction of the electron spin the concept of degeneracy must be reexamined. We know that several combinations of n_x, n_y, and n_z may lead to the same energy, and the number of combinations defines the order of degeneracy of the energy level. The spin quantum number has no effect upon energy if an external magnetic field is not applied. Thus with two possible values of m_s available the degeneracy of each energy level is doubled.

It should be mentioned in passing that all the so-called elementary particles have associated with them a spin quantum number, but not all have the values $\pm 1/2$. There are two broad classes of particles: those with m_s an even multiple of $1/2$ called *bosons* and those with m_s an odd multiple of $1/2$ called *fermions*. The more common particles (electrons, protons, neutrons) are fermions and have $m_s = \pm 1/2$.

Having defined precisely what constitutes a quantum state we may now ask what rules govern the placement of the electrons in the states. (For brevity we shall drop the adjective quantum and simply use the term state.) Can a state be occupied by one electron, two electrons, or any number of electrons? Surprisingly, the answer to this question was given shortly before the development of quantum mechanics. In 1925 the Swiss physicist Pauli found that atomic spectra could only be explained by assuming that no two electrons in an atom can be in the same state. This statement is called the Pauli exclusion principle. In terms of quantum mechanics this principle can be stated: no two electrons can have the same four quantum numbers n_x, n_y, n_z, and m_s.

3.10   ELECTRON INTERACTION

We can now add electrons to the array of atomic nuclei and thereby obtain a description of a complete solid. If one electron is introduced into the array it radiates away its excess energy and settles into the state with the lowest energy. Referring to Fig. 3.21 this would be the lowest of the states with $E \simeq E_1$. What happens as a second electron is introduced? The presence of the first electron means that U is not quite the same as before; therefore the states available to the second electron are slightly different from those originally available to the first electron. In addition the presence of another electron modifies U for the first one so that its allowed states also change slightly. Both electrons take up low energy states with $E \simeq E_1$; neither state is exactly one of those originally available to the first one but the differences are slight. Qualitatively the situation is unchanged. As each additional electron is introduced, minor adjustments occur in all the available states. The final energy band structure is quantitatively different from the initial one but unchanged in form, and now Fig. 3.21 may be regarded as depicting the energy band structure for a solid with the electrostatic forces of both the nuclei and all the electrons accounted for.

The essential features of this band structure are:

1. There are several broken-up bands at low energy levels (three in Fig. 3.21). Electrons residing in these bands are very tightly bound to the atomic nuclei and almost never penetrate the energy barriers separating one atom from the next. (The bands correspond to the innermost shells in the atomic model used in introductory studies of chemistry.)
2. Above the broken-up bands there are unbroken bands, i.e., bands continuous through the array of atoms. Electrons in these bands can move from one atom to the next. The highest band containing electrons is known as the valence band because it contains the valence electrons. (The valence band corresponds to the valence shell.)
3. At the edges of the array of atoms, the outer boundaries of the solid, the bands are terminated by a rising potential energy; thus there is an energy barrier at the surface of the solid.

SUMMARY

- A particle is characterized not only by its mass m but also by a wave function $\Psi(x, t) = \psi(x) f(t)$.
- The wavelength of the particle wave function is given by the de Broglie hypothesis.
- The Schrödinger equation is the differential equation from which $\Psi(x, t)$ is found. The one-dimensional time-independent form of this equation is

$$\frac{d^2\psi}{dx^2} + \frac{2m}{\hbar^2}[E - U(x)]\psi = 0$$

where E is the particle energy and $U(x)$ is the particle potential energy.

• The wave function ψ must be single-valued, finite, continuous, and smooth. Its magnitude squared $|\psi|^2$ when normalized is the probability density of the location of the particle. The integral of $|\psi|^2$ over all space must thus be finite.

• The above conditions force a constraint on the allowed values of the energy E when the particle is bound by its potential energy to a finite region of space. More specifically, the energy is quantized; i.e., only discrete values are allowed.

• The wave function of an electron (the particle of interest here) defines an allowed *quantum state* for the electron.

• Wave functions derived from the Schrödinger three-dimensional equation are characterized by three quantum numbers; when rectangular coordinates are used the numbers are n_x, n_y, and n_z. The wave function depends also on the spin quantum number m_s. Thus a quantum state is defined by these four quantum numbers.

• In orderly arrays of atoms the energies corresponding to the allowed quantum states are grouped into densely packed bands of energy. The number of quantum states corresponding to the energies in a given band is an integer times the number of atoms in the array.

• The occupation of quantum states is governed by the Pauli principle that says no two electrons may be in the same quantum state at the same time, or equivalently, no more than one electron may be in a given quantum state at a given time.

PROBLEMS

3.1. The one-dimensional wave equations for the electric and magnetic fields in an electromagnetic wave traveling in a vacuum are

$$\frac{\partial^2 E}{\partial x^2} = \frac{1}{c^2}\frac{\partial^2 E}{\partial t^2} \qquad \frac{\partial^2 H}{\partial x^2} = \frac{1}{c^2}\frac{\partial^2 H}{\partial t^2}$$

where E and H are the amplitudes of the field intensities and c is the speed of light.

a) Select one of these equations and use the method of separation of variables to reduce the problem to solving an x-dependent differential equation and a time-dependent differential equation.

b) Solve the time-dependent equation using an angular frequency parameter ω.

c) Solve the x-dependent equation and identify the wavelength λ in terms of ω and c.

d) Rewrite the x-dependent differential equation in terms of λ rather than ω and c and verify that the result is identical with (3.17).

3.2. The current I, flowing down one conductor and back on the other conductor of a two-wire electrical transmission line, and the voltage V between conductors vary with position and time due to the series inductance and shunt capacitance of the conductors. The wave equations for I and V (assume resistanceless wires and perfect insulation) are

$$\frac{\partial^2 V}{\partial x^2} = LC \frac{\partial^2 V}{\partial t^2} \qquad \frac{\partial^2 I}{\partial x^2} = LC \frac{\partial^2 I}{\partial t^2}$$

where L and C are the inductance per meter and capacitance per meter of the pair of wires. Carry out steps a–d of Prob. 3.1 for this system.

3.3.   The propagation of sound waves through air, or any other gas in which absorption of energy is negligible, can be described by a wave equation for the pressure P of the air or other gas. This wave equation is

$$\frac{\partial^2 P}{\partial x^2} = \frac{\rho_v}{\gamma_g P_a} \frac{\partial^2 P}{\partial t^2}$$

where ρ_v is the air mass per unit volume, P_a is the average ambient air (or gas) pressure, and γ_g is the ratio of the specific heat at constant pressure to that at constant volume. Carry out steps a–d of Prob. 3.1 for this wave equation.

3.4.   Given below are several potential energy functions together with pro-

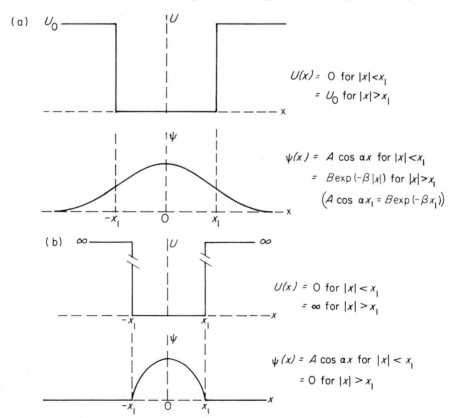

(a)
$$U(x) = 0 \text{ for } |x| < x_1$$
$$= U_0 \text{ for } |x| > x_1$$

$$\psi(x) = A \cos \alpha x \text{ for } |x| < x_1$$
$$= B \exp(-\beta|x|) \text{ for } |x| > x_1$$
$$\left(A \cos \alpha x_1 = B \exp(-\beta x_1) \right)$$

(b)
$$U(x) = 0 \text{ for } |x| < x_1$$
$$= \infty \text{ for } |x| > x_1$$

$$\psi(x) = A \cos \alpha x \text{ for } |x| < x_1$$
$$= 0 \text{ for } |x| > x_1$$

(c)

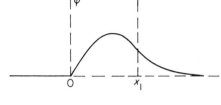

$U(x) = \infty$ for $x < 0$

$= 0$ for $0 < x < x_1$

$= U_0$ for $x > x_1$

$\psi(x) = 0$ for $x < 0$

$= A \sin \alpha x$ for $0 < x < x_1$

$= B \exp(-\beta x)$ for $x > x_1$

(d)

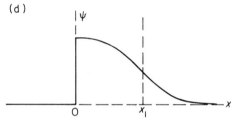

$\psi(x) = 0$ for $x < 0$

$= A \cos \alpha x$ for $0 < x < x_1$

$= B \exp(-\beta x)$ for $x > x_1$

posed wave functions for the potential energies. Determine in each case whether the proposed wave function is proper. [Part d has same $U(x)$ as c.]

[Ans.: a) yes; b) yes, function is not smooth at $x = \pm x_1$ but this is all right since $U(x)$ changes from 0 to ∞ at x_1; c) yes; d) not proper, function should be continuous at $x = 0$]

3.5. The wave function for some particular situation is

$\psi(x) = 0$ for $x < -d$

$= A \cos(\pi x/2d)$ for $-d < x < d$

$= 0$ for $x > d$

a) Normalize this wave function if $d = 10^{-8}$ cm. [Ans.: $A = 10^4$ cm$^{-1/2}$]

b) Calculate the probability the particle is in the range $x = 0$ to $x = 0.5d$. [Ans.: $0.25 + 1/2\pi$]

3.6. Show by explicit algebraic steps that (3.27), the left-hand boundary condition for the infinite square well, leads immediately to the fact that the coefficient B of the cosine term of $\psi(x)$ must be zero.

3.7. a) Normalize the wave functions for the infinite square well, i.e., apply (3.34) to (3.32). [Ans.: $A = \sqrt{2/a}$]

b) For the lowest order wave function of the infinite square well, i.e., (3.32) with $n = 1$, calculate the probability that the electron is between $x = 0$ and $x = 0.1a$.

c) Repeat b for the interval from $x = 0.45a$ to $x = 0.55a$. [Ans.: slightly less than 0.2]

3.8.   In calculating allowed energies for the finite square well and evaluating coefficients in the wave functions it is helpful to recognize that $U(x)$ is symmetric around its midpoint and each wave function is either symmetric or antisymmetric around this midpoint. For example, the wave function in Fig. 3.11b is symmetric, whereas that in Fig. 3.11c is antisymmetric. Because of these properties it is convenient to move $x = 0$ to the center of the well and define a quantity $d = a/2$. With these changes we have

$$\psi_I = A \exp[\beta(x + d)] \qquad \psi_{III} = \pm A \exp[\beta(x - d)]$$
$$\psi_{II} = C \sin \alpha x \quad \text{for the antisymmetric wave functions}$$
$$\quad = D \cos \alpha x \quad \text{for the symmetric wave functions}$$

a)   Rephrase the boundary conditions, (3.42), (3.43), (3.44), and (3.45), in terms of the new x-axis.

b)   Show that application of the boundary conditions leads to $\beta = \alpha \tan(\alpha d)$ for the symmetric wave functions and to $\beta = -\alpha \cot(\alpha d)$ for the antisymmetric wave functions.

c)   Recognizing that β and α are functions of energy E, devise numerical methods for finding values of E that satisfy the above equations.

d)   Implement these numerical methods in a computer program and determine the first six allowed energies together with the corresponding values of α and β. Use $m = 9.1 \times 10^{-31}$ kg, $d = 10^{-10}$ m, and $U_0 = E_6$ of the infinite square well.

e)   Normalize the wave functions. To do this, temporarily assume that C or D is unity and evaluate the integral of $|\psi|^2$ over all x. The proper value of C or D is then the square root of the reciprocal of this integral. (The integrations should be done analytically rather than numerically; evaluation of the expressions resulting from these integrations could then be done on the computer.)

3.9.   In the left-hand side of the coupled LC circuit of Fig. 3.17b insert a series switch which closes at $t = 0$. Let the left-hand capacitor have an initial voltage V_0. The right-hand capacitor is initially uncharged and the initial current is zero in each loop. Evaluate the current in either loop as a function of time; there is a sinusoidal component of current at each of two frequencies. Verify that these frequencies are given by (3.48).

3.10.   Carefully sketch the lowest and next lowest order wave functions for the potential energy given below. Assume $E < U_0$.

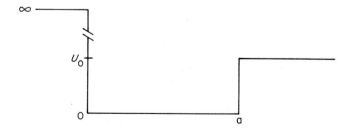

3.11. Consider the triple square well whose potential energy is given below. Assume b is large enough that there is negligible overlap of the exponential tails between wells. There are two possible wave functions (not three) corresponding to the lowest order function for the isolated square well. Sketch these wave functions. [Note: Since $U(x)$ is a symmetric function around its center, the wave functions must exhibit either cosine symmetry (be an even function of x) or sine symmetry (be an odd function of x) around the center of $U(x)$.]

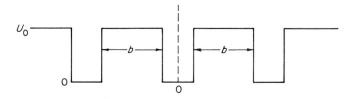

3.12. a) Draw the potential energy for a quadruple square well.
   b) Assuming the well separation b is large, sketch the four wave functions corresponding to the lower order function of the isolated square well.

3.13. a) Solve the Schrödinger equation using the potential energy in Prob. 3.4c. Why is it necessary to assume $E < U_o$?
   b) Sketch $\psi(x)$ for the second lowest allowed energy. How will this energy compare with E_2 in an infinite square well of width x_1? Explain. [Note: It is not possible to solve analytically for the energy E. The methods used in Prob. 3.8 do apply however.]

3.14. When the Schrödinger equation is written for an electron the mass appears explicitly but the electronic charge q does not. Surely the charge is important in determining the motion of the electron. Explain.

3.15. Again for an infinite square well, find the energy levels for a particle of 1-gm mass in a well of width 1 cm. What must n be so the kinetic energy is 1 J? What is the separation in joules between E for n and E for $n + 1$? Will the discreteness of energy levels be apparent in laboratory experiments?

3.16. Compute the kinetic energy of an electron in the ground state of an infinite square well of width 3 Å. What fraction is this of the rest energy $m_o c^2$? Is relativity important in calculations with well width of this order of magnitude typical of the outer electrons in atoms and molecules?

3.17. Compute the ratio of the probability of finding the particle in a small range δx of x at a distance Δx outside the edge of the finite square well to the probability of finding it in the same range δx at the edges of the well ($x = 0$ or $x = a$); that is, compute $|\psi(a + \Delta x)|^2/|\psi(a)|^2$ and $|\psi(0 - \Delta x)|^2/|\psi(0)|^2$. Use values of Δx and $U_o - E$ typical of atomic problems, namely, $\Delta x = 1$ Å and $U_o - E = 1$ eV. Solve the problem for both electrons and protons.

3.18. The potential energy for an electron in a system is given by the following sketch.

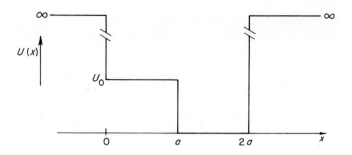

The energy is $E = 9(\hbar^2/2m)(\pi/a)^2$ while $U_0 = 5(\hbar^2/2m)(\pi/a)^2$.

a) Apply the Schrödinger equation to each of the four regions, $(-\infty, 0)$, $(0, a)$, $(a, 2a)$, and $(2a, \infty)$ and find the form of ψ in each region.

b) State and apply the boundary conditions at 0, a, and $2a$. From these determine whether ψ is larger in region $(0, a)$ or in region $(a, 2a)$ and explain how you reach your conclusion.

c) Sketch the complete wave function.

CHAPTER 4

Implications of Quantum Theory for the Conduction Characteristics of Solids

IN Chap. 3 discussion of the time-dependent Schrödinger equation led to a result of principal significance to the study of conductive properties of solids: the energy levels available to electrons in solids are a series of bands of allowed energies separated by bands of forbidden energies (see Fig. 3.21). The result is analogous to the discrete energy levels of an electron in an isolated atom.

The conduction characteristics of solids are implicit in this energy band structure. In this chapter we shall show that knowledge of the occupancy of the various energy bands permits us to distinguish between the three types of conductors—metals, insulators, and semiconductors. We shall show, too, that this model also predicts the existence of the two types of carriers (holes and conduction electrons) in semiconductors and insulators, and moreover, permits a description of the effect of impurities on the conductivity of semiconductors.

4.1 LATTICE CONSTANT

In the idealized square-well model of a solid there is no prescription for calculating the equilibrium separation of atoms. In the actual case minimum separation occurs when the total energy of the system of atoms is a minimum. Calculating the energy of a system of a large number of atoms is clearly a very complicated problem. Trying to calculate from first principles all possible interaction energies is, for practical purposes, impossible. For the simplest of solids such calculations have been made but with probable errors often larger than the differences between various possible configurations of the atoms.

Even though such calculations are difficult we know there does exist an equilibrium distribution of the atoms in a solid that corresponds to the minimum energy of the system. The atoms form a crystalline lattice which is periodic over distances of a few atomic diameters. This distance of periodicity is termed the *lattice constant* b_o. Typical lattice constants for some materials are shown.

Material	Lattice Constant (Å)
Au	4.07
Diamond	3.56
Ge	5.65
K	5.65
Pt	3.91
Si	5.42

4.2   CONDUCTION CHARACTERISTICS OF SOLIDS

Let us return to Fig. 3.20, a sketch of band structure versus interatomic separation. We have no way of predicting from that sketch the lattice constant for such a system. Because of the variations of band structure with interatomic separation, it is not surprising that the properties of the solid depend critically on the value of b_o. To see this, look at the way electrical conductivity properties of a solid depend on the lattice constant.

Consider, for simplicity, a single atomic species with energy levels $E_1, E_2, E_3, \ldots$, the first five of which are shown in Fig. 3.20. We know that as b decreases the higher lying levels are affected earliest; E_5 begins splitting long before E_1 is changed at all. Suppose the minimum total energy of the system occurs at $b = b_1$. Then b_1 is the lattice constant of the crystal and the energy bands arising from energies equal to or less than E_5 are indicated by the heavily shaded regions lying above b_1. These are redrawn in Fig. 4.1a. Note that there is no perceptible widening in the lower three levels while E_4 and E_5 lead to definite bands of energies. Further, the allowed regions are separated by regions in which there are no allowed energy levels.

Instead of b_1 suppose b_2 is the lattice constant (the separation corresponding to minimum energy). The band structure for this case is shown in Fig. 4.1b. Compared with the previous case E_3 has broadened slightly and the forbidden energy gaps are smaller due to the increased interactions. If b_3 is the lattice constant, E_2 is split slightly and the energy gaps are further decreased (see Fig. 4.1c). Finally, if b_4 is the lattice constant (Fig. 4.1d), all levels show some broadening, with the important result that E_4 and E_5 are so wide that they now overlap, and become one large band with no forbidden gap between them.

To appreciate the significance of these results it is necessary to digress to discuss certain aspects of conduction in solids. (Conduction

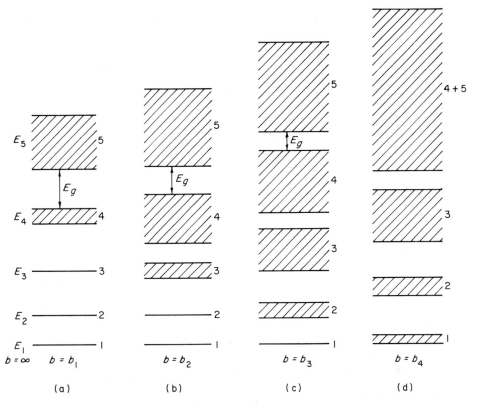

FIG. 4.1   Energy band structure for various lattice
constants as deduced from Fig. 3.20.

processes are considered in greater detail in Chaps. 5 and 6.) A potential difference placed across a specimen results in an electric field equal to the gradient of the potential. Thus a force is acting on any charged particles within the electric field and an electric current results if these carriers acquire a net velocity. Therefore, for a current to flow the charge carriers must acquire energy in excess of the thermal equilibrium value. The energy available from the usual voltages or fields we discuss is small, very much less than an electron volt, for example; therefore, for a current to arise there must be empty energy levels adjacent to those occupied by the electrons in their equilibrium state. In the case of a filled band there are no such available levels and therefore the electrons in a full band can carry no current.

Let us now develop some nomenclature and further consider the types of band structure a solid may exhibit. The terms valence band and conduction band refer to those bands which are important in electrical conduction. The *valence band* is the energy band where the

Insulator & semi-conductors.

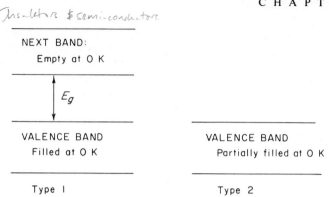

FIG. 4.2　Two general types of energy band structure.

valence electrons are found at $T = 0$ K (it corresponds to the valence shell of an atom). The *conduction band* is the band in which electrons move as essentially free particles, giving rise to appreciable electrical conduction.

Consider now the possible band structures. We need consider only the valence band and the first band above it. As we said, the valence band is the highest energy band containing electrons at 0 K. Since electrons always seek the lowest available energy levels, all energy bands and levels below the valence band are completely filled at 0 K (and at all other temperatures of interest). Thus no electrical conduction arises from electrons in these low lying bands and levels and we need consider only the valence electrons. Thus there are only two general band structures to consider, insofar as a qualitative description of conduction is concerned. These are shown in Fig. 4.2.

The Type 1 structure has only filled and empty bands at 0 K. The highest occupied band is completely filled; all higher bands are empty. Solids of this type exhibit no electrical conduction at 0 K since all electrons are in a filled band. When the temperature is above absolute zero the electrons each have an average thermal energy of $3kT/2$. On occasion the thermal energy of a valence electron exceeds its average value by an amount sufficient for the electron to transfer from the valence band to the next higher band. This means the next band contains a small number of essentially free electrons that can provide electrical conduction; in other words the next band is a *conduction band*. The two classes of materials in this category are insulators and semiconductors.

What about the Type 2 structure? Here the valence band is partially filled both at and above 0 K. The band contains a large number of valence electrons and an even larger number of quantum states so the valence electrons can acquire energy within the band. Thus the valence band and the conduction band are one and the same. Materials having this band structure are conductors, i.e., metals.

Let us return to Figs. 3.20 and 4.1a, again assuming b_1 is the lattice constant. Suppose the band corresponding to E_4 is the valence band and the number of valence electrons completely fills this band at 0 K. This material is evidently Type 1. The energy gap E_g is large so the material is a very good insulator at all temperatures of interest.

For lattice constants $b = b_2$ and $b = b_3$, the picture is unchanged qualitatively; the materials are both Type 1. However, E_g for $b = b_2$ is smaller than for $b = b_1$ so this material might be described as a fair rather than very good insulator. For $b = b_3$, E_g is even smaller. In this material the number of electrons excited thermally ($T > 0$ K) from the valence band to the conduction band arising from E_5 is sufficient for a significant amount of conduction to occur (less than in conductors but much more than in insulators). This material is a semiconductor.

Next consider the case of lattice constant $b = b_4$. Here the bands arising from E_4 and E_5 have overlapped to form a single composite band. Assuming the number of valence electrons is just sufficient to fill the states arising from E_4 it is clear that the composite band is only partially filled at any temperature. The valence band is therefore the conduction band for this material and the material is a conductor or metal.

If the number of valence electrons only partially fill the levels corresponding to E_4 at 0 K, then all the band structures in Fig. 4.1 are Type 2 and the materials are all conductors.

Let us summarize by reiterating the properties of insulators, semiconductors, and metals (conductors).

1. *Insulator:* The valence band at absolute zero is completely full and separated from the conduction band by a band of forbidden energies of width E_g sufficiently large to allow very few carriers to get into the conduction band at reasonable temperatures. (We shall see later that this implies a value of E_g of several electron volts.) Such a material might have a band structure corresponding to a lattice constant of b_1 or b_2 in Fig. 4.1. In later sections we shall describe more quantitatively terms such as "sufficiently large," "very few," "reasonable," etc.

2. *Semiconductor:* The semiconductor is a better conductor than insulator, but it is a relative rather than an essential difference. At room temperature a somewhat larger number of electrons appears in the conduction band and the conductivity is thereby larger. Figure 1.1 compares insulator and semiconductor conductivities. The semiconductor differs from the insulator in having a smaller value of E_g, in the range of 0.3 eV to 1.5 eV (in silicon $E_g = 1.1$ eV and in germanium $E_g = 0.67$ eV). Such a material might have a band structure arising from a lattice constant b_3 (Fig. 4.1c), where again E_4 in the isolated atoms is normally completely filled and E_5 empty.

→ due to overlap

3. *Metal:* In metals the valence band is only partially filled at any temperature so the valence band is also the conduction band. This partially filled band arises when either (1) there is a simple valence band (a band arising from a single level in an isolated atom) and the material has fewer valence electrons than there are quantum states in the band, or (2) there are enough valence electrons to fill a simple band but two simple bands overlap to yield a partially filled composite band.

4.3   HOLE CONDUCTION

There is one particularly important feature of conduction in semiconductors or insulators which so far has been ignored. Figure 4.3 shows the valence and conduction bands of a semiconductor. (This will be the general practice in our future work, since only these two energy bands of the energy spectrum enter into conduction processes.) Suppose there exist n electrons in the conduction band. These electrons must have come from the valence band and therefore some levels in that region are empty. Because of this the remaining electrons in the valence band can acquire an energy increment and therefore a net velocity with the result that current arises not only from electrons in the conduction band but also from electrons in the valence band. The current carried by electrons in the conduction band is proportional to the number of electrons in the conduction band. The current carried by the electrons in the valence band is proportional to the number of vacancies in the valence band rather than to the number of valence electrons.

Because the number of vacancies determines the valence electron current, we can regard this current as being carried by the vacancies. These vacancies behave like positively charged particles and are named,

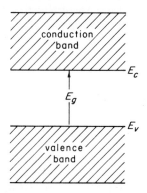

FIG. 4.3   Energy bands significant in semiconductor conduction processes.

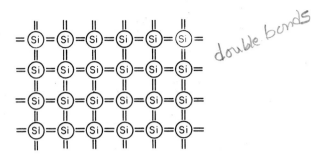

FIG. 4.4   Valence bond model of silicon.

appropriately enough, *holes*. Thus the current in the valence band is considered to result from the motion of holes in a band almost empty of holes. This concept results in simpler calculations and a clearer physical model.

In semiconductors and insulators, therefore, the conductive processes may be described in terms of two particles, one positively charged (the hole) and the other negatively charged (the conduction electron). In pure semiconductors or insulators the number of electrons and holes must be equal.

To study the properties of the hole let us examine the so-called valence bond model of the substance. We can represent the lattice atom by an ion core containing the nucleus and all the electrons except the valence electrons; surrounding the ion core are the valence electrons which are shown connecting the atoms in the crystal lattice. For example, in the crystalline structure of pure silicon each atom in the lattice shares four valence electrons with its four nearest neighbors (see Fig. 4.4).

No electric current can be carried in such a lattice since there are no available mobile charges. All valence electrons are tied into valence bonds. It requires about 1.1 eV, the gap energy, to break an electron loose from such a covalent bond in silicon, and reasonable electric fields cannot provide this amount of energy. But for all temperatures greater than absolute zero some valence electrons acquire thermal energy greater than 1.1 eV. These energetic electrons will break loose from the valence bond and carry current if an electric field exists. Consider the bond vacated by the electron. This region now has a negative charge deficiency and is thus positively charged. This changes the local energy structure so that another nearby bound electron may, with small energy expenditure, move into the vacancy. The electron filling the vacancy leaves a positive charge at the bond where it originated. Thus the deficient bond or hole seems to migrate through the crystal in a direction opposite to that of the electrons giving rise to its motion and it may be considered to carry current as though it were a positively charged particle. This process is illustrated in Fig. 4.5.

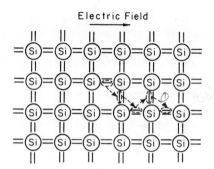

FIG. 4.5   Migration of a hole in silicon under the
influence of an electric field directed as shown.

Note that the hole is a "construct," that is, a fabrication offering a
simple way to explain a physical occurrence. Actually, electrons are the
only charge carriers which move through the lattice. The two types of
conducting electrons are free electrons (which have broken free of their
valence bonds) and bound electrons (which are still involved in valence
bonds).

The concept of the hole simplifies the problem by allowing the
conduction due to bound electrons to be treated similarly to that due to
free electrons. The conduction band is a band of energy levels almost
empty of electrons while the valence band is a band almost empty of
holes. Since only a small percentage of the conduction band levels are
occupied, the conduction electrons may be treated as free and noninteracting particles. The free particle problem is relatively easy to
solve compared with the situation where interaction of the conduction
electrons must be taken into account.

In the valence band, on the other hand, almost all energy levels
are normally filled with electrons, thus leading to a problem of great
complexity if we were to attempt to derive their behavior. By considering only the empty levels or holes it is possible to treat the problem as a
free particle problem analogous to that of the free (conduction) electron. Thus the valence band is considered as a band containing a great
many hole energy levels with only a small percentage normally occupied. The holes may be considered as free and noninteracting particles
with the resulting simplification in the analysis.

We thus will consider the current in semiconductors—and insulators—to be carried by two different types of particles, electrons and
holes, one being negatively charged, the other positively charged. The
total carrier density is the sum of the hole density p in the valence band
and the electron density n in the conduction band. In intrinsic (pure)
semiconductors these densities are equal. In silicon this number is $n_i =
p_i = 1.5 \times 10^{10}/cm^3$ at 300 K (where the subscript i means intrinsic).

In metals there is normally a single type of carrier—electrons. This arises from the nature of the metallic bond. A metallic crystal can be thought of as consisting of two substances, a large number of free electrons and the immobile positively charged ion cores. Only the former can move and carry current. Their number (about one per atom) is relatively insensitive to temperature.

4.4 EFFECT OF IMPURITIES ON SEMICONDUCTOR CONDUCTIVITY

Early research devoted to the study of semiconductors was inhibited by the extreme variability in the conductivity of such materials. Samples of a semiconductor, all presumably pure, showed drastically different behavior. After much labor it was recognized that the presence of very small concentrations of certain impurities could cause large changes in semiconductor conductivities. It was not until the metallurgist developed methods to reduce impurity concentrations to very low levels (of the order of one part in 10^{10}) and then to add impurities in a reproducible and controllable fashion, that semiconductor devices truly became technically feasible. It is important, therefore, that we examine the effects of such impurities.

Consider a sample of pure silicon. Suppose we substitute a phosphorous atom for one of the host silicon atoms. (When we talk of device fabrication we will discuss how this can be done.) Phosphorus is an element from Group V of the periodic table and therefore has five valence electrons. In the silicon lattice four of these electrons are required to satisfy the covalent bonds with the four nearest neighbors. The fifth electron is not needed to fill a bond. This situation is illustrated in Fig. 4.6.

The fifth electron is weakly bound to the phosphorous ion, requiring only about 0.04 eV to break free, thereby making an additional electron available for conduction. Comparing this energy with that

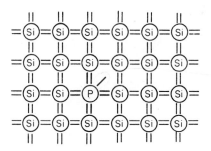

FIG. 4.6   Valence bond model of silicon containing a Group V element (phosphorus).

needed to free an electron from a Si—Si bond (equal to E_g of 1.1 eV) we see that free electrons from the Group V impurities are produced at much lower temperatures than those from broken silicon bonds. Remembering the small numbers of intrinsic carriers in silicon it is easy to show that very small concentrations of impurities can greatly affect its conductivity.

To illustrate, consider the following example. Intrinsic (pure) silicon at room temperature (300 K) contains about 10^{10} free carriers/cm³. Since the atomic density of silicon in the solid state is about 10^{22} atoms/cm³, this implies about one intrinsic carrier/10^{12} silicon atoms. Suppose to this pure material were added 10^{16} phosphorous atoms/cm³. This represents a small impurity concentration, only about one part per million. If (as is the case) each of these phosphorous atoms gives up its fifth electron by 300 K, the carrier concentration increases by a factor of 10^6 and conductivity increases by about the same factor. One part of impurity per million host atoms leads to a millionfold increase in conductivity! It is easy to see why the early efforts to study semiconductor properties were frustrated by trace impurities.

When an electron is taken from a Si—Si bond, a free electron and a hole are always created; thus intrinsic generation always involves equal numbers of each carrier type. In impurity generation this is no longer the case. The ionization of the phosphorous atom gives rise to a (mobile) free electron and an immobile positive phosphorous ion; there is no hole involved. Such impurities give rise to conduction by only one charge type. In a semiconductor containing only Group V impurities the charge carriers are predominantly negatively charged and hence such a semiconductor is said to be *n-type*. The type of impurity exhibiting this behavior is termed a *donor* atom since it donates an electron to the conduction process. Other Group V atoms with the same properties in germanium and silicon are arsenic and antimony.

In an n-type semiconductor the electron concentration is larger than the hole concentration; in this case the electrons are termed *majority carriers* and holes are termed *minority carriers*. We shall use n_n to denote the electron concentration (number per unit volume) in n-type material and p_n to symbolize hole concentration in n-type material.

There are also impurities that lead to dominantly hole conduction. To see how this situation can come about we consider substituting a Group III element such as boron into a lattice position of a silicon crystal (see Fig. 4.7). Since boron has only three valence electrons one of the bonds with the four surrounding silicon atoms is not filled. Empirically it is found that 0.045 eV is required to move a neighboring bound electron into the empty B—Si bond position, thus giving rise to a hole in the Si—Si bonds. When this has taken place the boron atom is said to be ionized and is an immobile negative charge center. (Because of the similarity of ionization energies of Group III and Group V

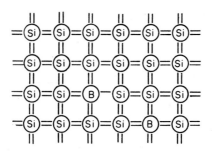

FIG. 4.7 Valence bond model of silicon containing a Group III element (boron).

impurities, the same remarks concerning temperature dependence apply.) In this case the presence of the impurity produces a *p-type* semiconductor because the majority carriers, holes, are positively charged. Electrons of course are the minority carriers. The hole and electron concentrations in this case are denoted by p_p and n_p. Other Group III atoms serving the same purpose are gallium, aluminum, and indium. The general name for these impurity atoms is *acceptor* because they accept valence electrons from Si—Si bonds, creating an increased concentration of holes, i.e., incomplete Si—Si bonds.

Except for differences in ionization energy the above remarks apply equally well to the addition of Groups III and V elements to germanium.

It is interesting to look at impurity conduction from the viewpoint of the energy band structure of the semiconductor. Prior to introducing the impurity into the lattice the crystalline potential was a smooth periodic structure (similar to that in Fig. 3.4). Solving the Schrödinger equation with this potential leads to the band structure discussed earlier and the valence and conduction bands illustrated in Fig. 4.1. The presence of an impurity atom in the lattice destroys the regularity of the potential in the crystal, leading to a different potential function in the vicinity of the impurity atom, a different solution to the Schrödinger equation, and hence a different energy spectrum for an electron in the crystal. If the density of impurity atoms added is not too large compared to the density of the host Ge or Si atoms ($10^{22}/cm^3$), the presence of the Group III or Group V elements introduces a discrete energy level in the forbidden energy gap. The density of states in the level is equal to the density of impurity atoms added.

Let us consider adding N_d Group V donor atoms/cm³ into a silicon lattice. We know empirically that with the expenditure of only about 0.04 eV the fifth valence electron can be broken free and hence will appear in the conduction band. This means that Fig. 3.21 must be modified to include a discrete electron energy level 0.04 eV below the bottom edge of the conduction band. This energy level arises because

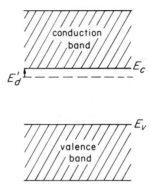

FIG. 4.8   Energy band structure of a semiconductor
containing a Group V impurity with ionization energy
E'_d.

of the impurity atom in the lattice; it is occupied by an electron at 0 K.
It donates that electron to the conduction band for temperatures
greater than 0 K (see Fig. 4.8; the dashed line just below the conduction
band indicates the presence of the N_d donor states/cm^3).

The situation is similar if N_a Group III acceptor atoms/cm^3 are
introduced into silicon. Again, the presence of the impurity atom in
the silicon lattice produces a discrete set of electron energy levels in the
forbidden energy gap. The level in this case is about 0.04 eV above the
top of the valence band and is empty. It is thus ready to accept an electron from the valence band giving rise to a hole and a negative immobile charge (see Fig. 4.9).

The dashed lines representing energy levels arising from impurities

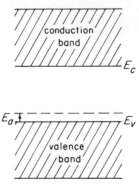

FIG. 4.9   Energy band structure of a semiconductor
containing a Group III impurity with ionization energy E_a.

are significant. A discrete set of energy levels are available to electrons in an isolated atom. The interaction of the atoms in a solid lead to these levels broadening into bands. In an analogous way, if the impurity atoms in a semiconductor are far enough apart to prevent appreciable interaction, the allowed energies arising from their presence are discrete levels in the energy gap localized near the impurity atom. When the concentration of impurities becomes large enough, the interaction between them results in a band of energies in the energy gap. Showing the levels arising from impurities as dashed lines implies that their concentration is not large enough to result in a band. We state (without proof) that this implies a concentration less than about $10^{19}/cm^3$, and that the impurity concentrations in most semiconductor devices fall below this value.

To summarize the discussion of the effect of impurities in semiconductors:

⟶ as opposed to no carriers in insulators

1. The small numbers of carriers normally present in semiconductors lead to the possibility of small concentrations of impurities having profound effects on conductivity.
2. The two types of impurities are donors, giving rise preferentially to electrons, and acceptors, giving rise to holes.
3. Group III and Group V elements are examples of acceptors and donors, respectively, in silicon and germanium.
4. We have examined the effects of the impurities in terms of both the valence band model and the energy band model.

In Table 4.1 empirical data for the ionization energies of Group III and Group V impurities are given. Since these ionization energies are

Table 4.1. Ionization energies of Group III and Group V impurities in germanium and silicon.

Impurities	Ionization Energies (eV)	
	Ge	Si
Group III		
boron	0.010	0.045
aluminum	0.010	0.057
gallium	0.011	0.065
indium	0.011	0.160
Group V		
phosphorus	0.012	0.044
arsenic	0.013	0.049
antimony	0.0096	0.039
bismuth	. . .	0.069

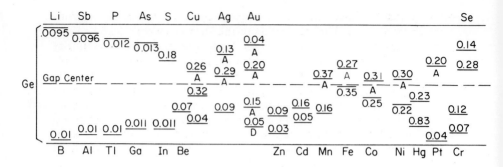

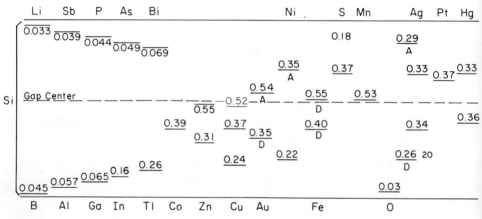

FIG. 4.10   Electron energy levels arising from the
presence of impurities in germanium and silicon. For
levels above the dashed line (gap center) energy is
measured from the conduction band edge; for levels
below, from the valence band edge.

small, we can assume that the impurities are fully ionized at all temperatures above about 200 K. This assumption is substantiated in
Chap. 5, where we see how to calculate precisely the percentage that is
ionized at any specified temperature. Nothing has been said about the
way in which impurity concentrations can be controlled. This subject
is discussed in Chap. 9.

Group III and Group V elements are not the only impurities that
serve as donors and acceptors in germanium and silicon. Many different elements can introduce energy levels in the energy gap (see Fig.
4.10). Some elements (e.g., gold in silicon) give rise to more than one

impurity level, possibly both donors and acceptors. Moreover, donor levels need not lie near the conduction band nor acceptor levels near the valence band. A donor level is an electron energy level introduced anywhere into the forbidden energy gap which is empty at 0 K. Because silicon is by far the most important semiconductor technologically, we shall be most concerned with its properties. Since the Group III and Group V elements are the most important dopants in silicon (and germanium), in the remainder of this text (unless explicitly stated otherwise) the terms "acceptor" and "donor" will refer to Group III and Group V impurities, respectively.

Group III and Group V elements occupy a unique position primarily because (1) their concentrations can be readily controlled in the range important for semiconductors; and (2) because of their small ionization energy, virtually all impurities are ionized at temperatures far below room temperature, possibly 200 K. Thus the influence of such impurities on the conductive properties of semiconductors is independent of temperature above about 200 K. The same would not be true, for example, for a donor level lying near the valence band. In that case the percentage of ionized impurities might continue to increase at and beyond room temperature with the undesirable result that the conductive properties of the semiconductor would be continuously variable.

Figure 4.11 shows qualitatively the temperature dependence of the conductivity σ of a semiconductor crystal containing a moderate number of impurities. In A the impurity atoms are being ionized. Because of the small energies involved, this takes place at low temperatures; usually the impurities are completely ionized near 200 K. The slope of $\ln \sigma$ vs $1/T$ in A is related to the ionization energy of the impurity. We develop the exact relation in Chap. 5. In B, there is no increase in σ due to impurity conduction and the temperature is not high enough to allow very many electrons to jump directly from the valence band to the conduction band; here σ remains relatively constant. In C the temperature is high enough to allow the carriers arising from the valence-to-conduction-band generation to dominate and the semiconductor behaves as an intrinsic material. The slope of the curve in C can be related to the gap energy E_g. The onset of C in germanium is about 150°C (423 K), while for silicon it is about 250°C (523 K). The σ-T behavior is only sketched here. It is treated in much greater detail in later sections.

Apart from silicon and germanium there has been no mention of other semiconductors. There are a multitude of them. Germanium and silicon from Group IV of the periodic chart are the most important elemental semiconductors. The next most important class is formed between elements from Group III and Group V of the periodic chart, the compound semiconductors referred to as III-V compounds. Important among them are GaAs, GaP, InSb, InP, and GaAsP. Numerous other semiconductors such as selenium, CdS, CuO, and SiC have also been

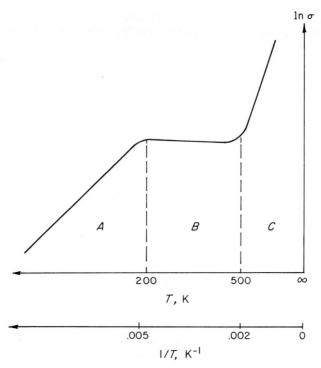

FIG. 4.11   Semiconductor conductivity as a function
of temperature.

studied and used in technology. All these materials have the common
characteristics described as belonging to semiconductors: low enough
E_g to give reasonable conductivity at room temperature, conduction by
holes and electrons, sensitivity to impurity concentration, etc. They
differ, however, in many ways; the energy gap values vary widely and
the substances which function as donor and acceptor impurities are
different, etc.

Undoubtedly silicon is technologically the most important semiconductor, and it is used in the specific examples in this text. However
germanium and gallium arsenide have important applications and
there are other useful semiconductors with properties quite different
from those of silicon in certain important respects.

4.5   CALCULATIONS OF CHARGE CARRIER
CONCENTRATIONS IN A SEMICONDUCTOR

Conduction electrons and holes in semiconductors arise from two
sources: electrons can be raised from the valence to the conduction

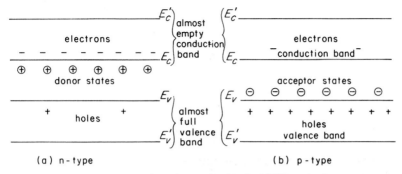

FIG. 4.12 Semiconductor energy band structure for (a) n-type material and (b) p-type material.

band usually by way of thermal energy, creating thereby a conduction electron and a hole; or the ionization of impurity atoms will result in the creation of an electron or a hole.

We have seen how donor and acceptor impurity atoms strongly affect the concentrations of holes and electrons in a semiconductor by introducing new filled or empty quantum states into the forbidden gap. The complete band structure for n-type and p-type material is illustrated in Fig. 4.12. The minus signs in the conduction band represent conduction electrons; their concentration is symbolized as n (negative). The plus signs in the valence band represent the holes; their concentration is symbolized as p (positive).

In Figs. 4.8 and 4.9 donor and acceptor states are represented by dashed lines to emphasize the fact that they exist at specific energy levels and they are localized at the impurity atom sites. In Fig. 4.12 the dashes are changed to circles to permit denoting state of ionization of the atoms. (The fact that a circle has height is not intended to suggest that the impurity states occupy a range of energies.) The plus signs in the circles indicate the donors have given up electrons, becoming positive ions; the negative signs in the circles indicate the acceptors have acquired electrons, becoming negative ions. If a donor has not donated or an acceptor has not accepted, the appropriate circle will be empty.

The conduction of current by these electrons and holes depends on their concentrations and their ability to move under the influence of an applied field. In this section we shall concern ourselves with the concentrations and the various factors which influence them. The motions of the charge carriers will be taken up in Chap. 6.

To determine carrier concentrations, consider first the situation known as thermal equilibrium (T.E.). This is a situation characterized by the following:

(*a*) The temperature is uniform in space and not varying with time.

(b) No significant electric, magnetic, or radiation fields are being impressed upon the system (the piece of semiconductor in our case) from outside.

(c) Conditions a and b have been true for a time such that the effects of any fields impressed upon the system in the past have long since become undetectable, the motions of the holes and electrons are completely random, and all concentrations are statistically constant.

Thermal equilibrium is not useful in itself in that nothing is happening. However, knowledge of T.E. concentrations of holes and electrons can be used to determine something about nonequilibrium concentrations. We designate the T.E. concentration values as n_o and p_o, the subscript o denoting the equilibrium state.

Thus far we have discussed the case where the semiconductor is *doped* (a term for the process of adding impurities) with either donors or acceptors. Consider what happens when both are present (practical semiconductors frequently contain deliberately introduced amounts of both). As one would expect, the larger impurity concentration determines the type of semiconducting material which results. Let the donor and acceptor concentrations be designated as N_d and N_a, respectively. In these terms, $N_d > N_a$ yields n-type material and $N_a > N_d$ yields p-type material. Consider the calculations of n_o and p_o in these two types of material; more specifically, consider the calculations of n_{no} and p_{no} in n-type material and of n_{po} and p_{po} in p-type material.

4.5.1   n-type Material

In this case we have $N_d > N_a$. At 300 K we may reasonably assume that all donors have donated and all acceptors have accepted. It is important to discuss where the donated electrons have gone and where the accepted electrons have come from. To determine these things it is convenient to think in a two-step sequence: (1) conditions at $T = 0$ K, and (2) the change in conditions as T is increased from 0 to 300 K.

At $T = 0$ K the electrons fill the quantum states with the lowest energies (one electron per state, of course). Since the supposedly empty acceptor states are at a lower energy than the supposedly filled donor states, the acceptor states take precedence. Thus there are N_a donor electrons/cm^3 residing in acceptor states and $(N_d - N_a)$ donor electrons/cm^3 residing in donor states. Thus all acceptors and some donors are "ionized" at $T = 0$ K. The valence band will be full and the conduction band will be empty so that n_{no} and p_{no} are both zero.

If the temperature is raised to 300 K the $(N_d - N_a)$ donor electrons are excited into the conduction band. The impurities thus contribute $(N_d - N_a)$ electrons and no holes. There will be some holes in existence at 300 K arising from hole-electron pair production, i.e., from the thermal excitation of valence electrons out of the valence band and into the conduction band. Letting n_{he} designate the concentration of these hole-electron pairs, there are $(N_d - N_a)$ electrons/cm^3 due to impurities, n_{he} electrons/cm^3 due to thermal excitation, no holes from the impurities, and n_{he} holes from thermal excitation. In equation form we thus have

$$n_{no} = (N_d - N_a) + n_{he} \qquad (4.1)$$

$$p_{no} = n_{he} \qquad (4.2)$$

Assuming that $(N_d - N_a)$ is given, there are three unknowns in this pair of equations: n_{no}, p_{no}, and n_{he}. To evaluate these three variables we need another equation involving the hole-electron pair production process that determines n_{he}. We shall consider how to obtain this equation after first examining p-type material for relationships analogous to (4.1) and (4.2).

4.5.2 p-type Material

In this case $N_a > N_d$. Again it will clarify matters to proceed from absolute zero to room temperature. At 0 K the donor electrons will seek the lowest available energy levels and since there are more acceptors than donors, all donor electrons find available acceptor states. Thus all the donors will be ionized, N_d acceptors will be ionized, and $(N_a - N_d)$ acceptors will be neutral. At 300 K these $(N_a - N_d)$ acceptors will accept electrons from the valence band thus producing $(N_a - N_d)$ holes/cm^3. No free electrons will be produced by the impurities. Hole-electron pair production however will yield n_{he} electrons and n_{he} holes. Thus we find

$$p_{po} = (N_a - N_d) + n_{he} \qquad (4.3)$$

$$n_{po} = n_{he} \qquad (4.4)$$

Again there are two equations and three unknowns so that another equation is required. To obtain this equation we turn our attention to the processes involved in hole-electron pair production, namely, *thermal generation* and *recombination*.

4.6   THERMAL GENERATION AND RECOMBINATION

Thermal generation is the process of elevating an electron from a state in the valence band to one in the conduction band. *Recombination* is the reverse of this process. Thermal generation thus produces hole-electron pairs while recombination annihilates them. In thermal equilibrium these two processes must balance; i.e., their rates must be equal. If new hole-electron pairs are produced as fast as old ones are annihilated, then n_{he} is constant and T.E. exists. Conversely, if the rates are not equal, n_{he} either grows or diminishes and the system is not in T.E. The thermal generation rate G_t is determined by the amount of thermal energy available and by the minimum energy $E_g = E_c - E_v$ required to produce a hole-electron pair. Hence G_t is a function simply of E_g and T. It does not depend upon how many impurities are present (so long as the impurity concentrations are moderate, say, $|N_d - N_a| < 10^{19}/\text{cm}^3$).

The recombination rate R depends upon how frequently an electron in the conduction band encounters a vacant state (hole) in the valence band. Clearly the rate is proportional to the concentrations of holes and electrons. The more holes there are, the sooner an electron will encounter one. Similarly, the more electrons there are, the sooner a hole will encounter an electron. In addition the rate R is influenced by temperature since the temperature determines the velocities of the holes and electrons. Thus R may be written as

$$R = rpn \tag{4.5}$$

where r is a parameter dependent on E_g and T. Since T.E. requires that $R = G_t$ it follows that

$$G_t = R|_{\text{T.E.}} = rp_o n_o \tag{4.6}$$

Note that this equation involves the two unknowns p_o and n_o (p_{no} and n_{no} in n-type material, and p_{po} and n_{po} in p-type material) together with two parameters G_t and r that depend only on the energy gap E_g and the temperature T. If (4.6) is rearranged slightly we have $p_o n_o = G_t/r$. The right side of this equation depends only on E_g and T. Taking silicon (n-type, p-type, or pure) as an example, this implies that for all samples of silicon, the product of $p_o n_o$ is constant. Symbolically

$$p_o n_o = p_{no} n_{no} = p_{po} n_{po} = p_i n_i = G_t/r \tag{4.7}$$

This result is extremely important. It states that the product of the equilibrium electron and hole concentrations is independent of impurity concentration; it depends only on the temperature and the particular semiconductor. Being independent of impurity concentration, the product must be equal to the value appropriate to intrinsic material where $p_i = n_i$. In more compact form (4.7) can be written simply as

$$p_o n_o = n_i^2 \tag{4.8}$$

This equation will be used again and again. It will be referred to as the carrier product equation (CPE).

Since n_i is a quantity found in tables of material properties, (4.8) provides the third equation required in Secs. 4.5.1 and 4.5.2. Applying (4.8) to those two specific cases we can write

$$p_{no} = n_{he}|_{\text{n-type}} = n_i^2/n_{no} \tag{4.9}$$

$$n_{po} = n_{he}|_{\text{p-type}} = n_i^2/p_{po} \tag{4.10}$$

These equations permit calculating n_o and p_o in terms of N_d, N_a, and n_i in both n-type and p-type materials (see Sec. 4.7).

Let us consider rather carefully the implications of the CPE, (4.8). The equation indicates that if the concentration of one type of carrier is increased the concentration of the other is decreased. Thus when donors are added to pure material to change n_o from, say n_i to $100\,n_i$, the CPE promises that p_o will decrease from n_i to $n_i/100$. This phenomenon is sometimes called *minority carrier suppression*. Why does it occur? This can be seen via the following thought experiment.

Imagine a pure semiconductor in thermal equilibrium so that $n_o = p_o = n_i$. Now imagine that N_d donors are suddenly added and that they immediately donate N_d electrons. Momentarily one would have

$$n = n_i + N_d \qquad p = n_i \quad \text{not T.E.}$$

The system is not in thermal equilibrium. The generation rate was, and still is, $G_t = rn_i^2$. The recombination rate however is now larger than this because, while the hole concentration is the same as before, the electron concentration is larger so that more holes recombine per second. Mathematically

$$R = rpn = rn_i(N_d + n_i) = rn_i N_d + rn_i^2 > rn_i^2 \quad \text{not T.E.} \qquad (4.11)$$

Since the recombination rate R is larger than the generation rate G_t, there will be a net recombination process proceeding at a rate $R - G_t$. This means that holes and electrons are disappearing so that

$$n = N_d + n_i - \int_0^t (R - G_t)\,dt \qquad p = n_i - \int_0^t (R - G_t)\,dt$$

As n and p continue to decrease, the difference between R and G_t shrinks until finally values of p and n are reached such that $R = G_t$. At this point thermal equilibrium will be maintained. The equilibrium values, p_o and n_o, will satisfy the CPE, (4.8). Graphically, the results of the experiment we have been imagining are sketched in Fig. 4.13. We thus see that adding one carrier type via increased doping reduces the other carrier type because the chances of recombination are increased for the other carrier.

4.7 CALCULATIONS OF n_o AND p_o.

Given the CPE as adapted in (4.9) and (4.10), we can now complete the calculations of n_o and p_o for the two types of material.

4.7.1 n-type Material

The pertinent equations here are (4.1), (4.2), and (4.9).

$$n_{no} = (N_d - N_a) + n_{he} \qquad p_{no} = n_{he} \qquad p_{no} = n_i^2/n_{no}$$

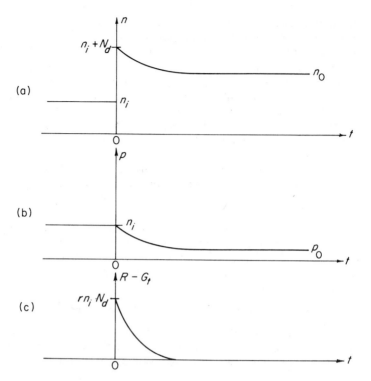

FIG. 4.13   Time variations of (a) electron concentration, (b) hole concentration, and (c) net recombination
rate for a thought experiment in which N_d donor impurities are suddenly added to pure material.

The quantity $N_d - N_a$ in (4.1) represents the number of donors left over
after all the acceptors have been ionized; thus $N_d - N_a$ is the net donor
concentration which implies n-type material. Hence we shall symbolize
it as N_n, i.e., $N_d - N_a \equiv N_n$. Using this and (4.2) permits rewriting (4.1)
as

$$n_{no} = N_n + p_{no} \tag{4.12}$$

Equation (4.12) can be solved simultaneously with (4.9); combining
them yields a quadratic in n_{no} which can be solved by the quadratic
formula. We shall consider this solution shortly.

Note the size of the terms in (4.12). Normally the doping is such
that $N_n \gg n_i$. Since the minority concentration p_{no} is always smaller
than n_i, the second term in (4.12) must be negligible compared to the
first. Thus to good approximation

$$n_{no} \simeq N_n \tag{4.13}$$

Then by (4.9) we find

$$p_{no} \simeq n_i^2/N_n \qquad (4.14)$$

In making the above approximations we should ask, How much error has been introduced? Comparing (4.12) and (4.13) the absolute error in n_{no} is seen to be simply p_{no}. The relative error then is r.e. = $p_{no}/(N_n + p_{no})$ or by using (4.9)

$$r.e. = \frac{n_i^2/(N_n + p_{no})}{N_n + p_{no}} \qquad (4.15)$$

Now if we again assume $N_n \gg p_{no}$ and write

$$r.e. \simeq n_i^2/N_n^2 \qquad (4.16)$$

we have reduced the size of both divisors; thus (4.16) overestimates the amount of the error. Therefore if (4.16) predicts an acceptably small error we can use (4.13) and (4.14). (Suppose that $N_n = 4 n_i$. In that case the relative error is $1/16$ or about 6%. Therefore the error in using (4.13) and (4.14) is less than 6% whenever $N_n > 4 n_i$.)

For cases where $N_n < 4 n_i$ we probably wish to obtain an exact solution. Substituting (4.9) into (4.12) gives $n_{no} = N_n + n_i^2/n_{no}$. Solving by the quadratic formula,

$$n_{no} = N_n/2 + [(N_n/2)^2 + n_i^2]^{1/2} \qquad (4.17)$$

To find p_{no}, use (4.9); $p_{no} = n_i^2/n_{no}$.

4.7.2 p-type Material

The pertinent equations here are (4.3), (4.4), and (4.10),

$$p_{po} = (N_a - N_d) + n_{he} \qquad n_{po} = n_{he} \qquad n_{po} = n_i^2/p_{po}$$

Defining the net acceptor concentration N_p in p-type material as $N_a - N_d \equiv N_p$ and using (4.4) in (4.3) gives

$$p_{po} = N_p + n_{po} \qquad (4.18)$$

When $N_p > 4 n_i$

$$p_{po} \simeq N_p \qquad (4.19)$$

$$n_{po} \simeq n_i^2/N_p \qquad (4.20)$$

with a relative error of no more than

$$r.e. = n_i^2/N_p^2 \qquad (4.21)$$

When $N_p < 4 n_i$, exact results are required, and solving (4.18) and (4.10) simultaneously leads to

$$p_{po} = N_p/2 + [(N_p/2)^2 + n_i^2]^{1/2} \qquad n_{po} = n_i^2/p_{po} \qquad (4.22)$$

4.8   INTRINSIC MATERIAL

The semiconductors considered in the above examples are known as *extrinsic* semiconductors. This name applies whenever impurities strongly influence the carrier concentrations n_o and p_o. When the carrier concentration is negligibly affected by impurities the semiconductor is *intrinsic* as noted earlier. Actually there are two distinct kinds of intrinsic material, pure and compensated. In *pure intrinsic* the total number of impurities is very small, much less than the hole and electron concentrations, or symbolically $N_d + N_a \ll n_i$.

In *compensated intrinsic,* significant but essentially equal numbers of donors and acceptors are present so that they effectively cancel one another. The criterion for compensated intrinsic is $|N_d - N_a| \ll n_i$.

Note in all equations involving N_d and/or N_a, we have assumed that all donors give up their fifth electron and that all acceptors acquire an extra electron so all impurities are ionized. We have no analytical basis for knowing whether this is entirely true. We do know that the nondominant impurity (acceptors in n-type material for example) is fully ionized but we cannot be sure about the dominant impurity (donors in n-type material for example). It is shown in Chap. 5 that the dominant impurities are all ionized at normal temperatures.

SUMMARY

- The highest energy band occupied at 0 K contains the valence electrons and is known as the valence band.
- The energy band in which electrons move as essentially free particles is known as the conduction band.
- In metals the valence band is only partially filled at any temperature; hence the valence band is also the conduction band.
- In semiconductors the valence band is completely filled at 0 K. At normal temperatures a few electrons are excited to the next band above where they move as free carriers. This next band is thus the conduction band.
- In insulators the band structure is the same as for semiconductors with one exception: the energy gap between the valence and conduction bands is much larger in the insulator. As a result many fewer electrons are excited to the conduction band and very little conduction takes place.
- When electrons are excited out of the valence band in a semiconductor or insulator, quantum states there are vacated. These vacant quantum states are called holes and are treated like positive charge-carrying particles because the valence electron movement permitted by the vacancies produces current that appears to be carried by the vacancies.
- The excitation of electrons from the valence band to the conduction band of a semiconductor produces hole-electron pairs. The

excitation can be due to heat or light or both. The excitation due to heat is always present (unless $T = 0$ K) and is known as thermal generation.

• In thermal equilibrium the thermal generation process is exactly balanced by recombination, the annihilation of hole-electron pairs when conduction electrons drop back into the valence band. The rate of recombination is proportional to the product of the hole and electron concentrations. The balance between recombination and generation implies an equilibrium value of $p_o n_o$ = constant = n_i^2.

• The concentration of conduction electrons in a semiconductor can be increased by the introduction of donor impurities—elements with five rather than four valence electrons. This resulting semiconductor is known as n-type.

• The concentration of holes in a semiconductor can be increased by the introduction of acceptor impurities—elements with three rather than four valence electrons. The resulting semiconductor is known as p-type.

• When both donor and acceptor impurities are introduced there is an effective cancellation and the net difference increases either the electron concentration or the hole concentration.

• When impurities are introduced to increase one carrier type, the other carrier type actually is decreased in accordance with the carrier product equation (CPE), $p_o n_o = n_i^2$. This must occur in order to bring about a thermal equilibrium balance between thermal generation and recombination.

PROBLEMS

4.1. A sample of germanium at 300 K contains 10^{14} acceptors/cm^3 and 5×10^{13} donors/cm^3. Calculate n_o and p_o. [Ans.: $p_o \simeq 6.0 \times 10^{13}$]

4.2. A sample of silicon at 300 K contains 10^{16} acceptors/cm^3 and no donors. Calculate p_o and n_o. [Ans.: $n_o = 2.25 \times 10^4$]

4.3. How much larger than n_i must N_n be for n_{no} to be within 20% of N_n?

4.4. Suppose $N_p = 10 \, n_i$. Calculate p_{po} and n_{po} approximately and calculate the relative error in the answers. [Ans.: $p_{po} = 10 \, n_i$, $n_{po} = 0.1 \, n_i$, r.e. = 1%]

4.5. Suppose $N_p = n_i$. Calculate p_{po} and n_{po} exactly and approximately. Calculate the relative error both exactly and approximately. [Ans.: $p_{po} = 1.62 \, n_i$, $\simeq n_i$; r.e. = 38%, $\simeq 100\%$]

4.6. A crucible containing 25 cm^3 of pure germanium is heated until molten. A speck of dust containing 0.01 mg phosphorus falls into the crucible. After uniform mixing the material is allowed to solidify to 300 K. Assuming all the phosphorous atoms in the crystal are ionized, what is the concentration of electrons in the sample? Compare with the intrinsic electron concentration at 300 K.

4.7. Consider a silicon sample containing 10^{16} arsenic atoms/cm^3, uniformly distributed.

      a)   Is the material n-type or p-type?

      b)   What is the majority carrier?

      c)   How does the average spacing of the impurity atoms compare with the lattice constant of silicon?

4.8.   Find p_o and n_o at 300 K in silicon containing 2.4×10^{13} atoms of antimony/cm^3. Repeat at 200 K and 400 K.

4.9.   Suppose 4.8×10^{13} atoms/cm^3 of indium in addition to the antimony are added to the silicon of Prob. 4.8. and answer the same questions.

4.10. Based on the information given in this chapter, calculate the donor or acceptor concentration required to increase the electrical conductivity of 300 K germanium by a factor of 100. What impurity percentage is this? There are 4.5×10^{22} germanium atoms/cm^3 and $n_i = p_i = 2.4 \times 10^{13}$/cm^3 at 300 K. [Ans.: approximately 2.4×10^{15}–4.8×10^{15} impurities/cm^3, of the order of $10^{-5}\%$ impureness]

CHAPTER 5

Distribution and Occupation of Quantum States

5.1 INTRODUCTION

In the previous chapter we describe the energy band structures of metals, insulators, and semiconductors with special emphasis on the latter. We also describe from both mechanistic and quantum-state viewpoints how the conduction properties of semiconductors are strongly influenced by the concentrations of certain kinds of impurity atoms, and we show how the equilibrium concentrations p_o and n_o of the two carrier types, holes and electrons, may be calculated in terms of these impurity concentrations and a semiconductor parameter n_i.

As we proceed to discuss semiconductor diodes and transistors, we shall find the ability to determine p_o and n_o very useful and important. However we will also find that additional information about the holes and electrons is needed. Specifically we need to know how these carriers are distributed as functions of energy within the bands. A precise answer to this question is the principal goal of this chapter. It is obtained from knowing (1) how allowed quantum states are distributed in energy, and (2) how electrons distribute themselves within the allowed quantum states.

The distribution of quantum states is specified by the *density of states functions* $S_c(E)$ and $S_v(E)$ for the conduction and valence bands. These functions specify the number of quantum states per unit energy and per unit volume at a given energy in a band. The units of the functions thus are states/(cm$^3 \cdot$ eV).

The distribution of electrons within the quantum states is specified by a probability function $f(E)$ known as the *Fermi function*. It specifies the probability that a quantum state at energy E is occupied by an electron at a particular time, or equivalently, it specifies the relative amount of time that the quantum state is occupied by an electron.

Given these two functions, it is possible to predict the distribution of electrons as a function of energy by simply multiplying together the Fermi function and the appropriate density of states function. Graphs of these products are used (as illustrated in Chap. 7) to predict semiconductor device behavior.

In addition the results of these multiplications can be used to evaluate the equilibrium carrier concentrations n_o and p_o in terms of the parameters making up the Fermi function and the density of states functions. These in turn make possible a theoretical prediction of how the intrinsic concentration, required for use of the carrier product equation, depends upon temperature and upon the fundamental properties of the semiconductor being considered.

Finally, as another result of evaluations of n_o and p_o, it becomes possible to evaluate a parameter known as the Fermi energy which is very important in obtaining the energy band structure of semiconductor diodes and transistors.

5.2 DENSITY OF STATES FUNCTIONS

The density of states functions $S_c(E)$ and $S_v(E)$ describe the distribution of quantum states within the conduction and valence bands by specifying the density (in energy) of states at a given energy. Suppose that in an infinitesimal energy range between E and $E + dE$ there are dQ quantum states per unit volume. The density of states function is then $S(E) = dQ/dE$. Conversely, if the density of states at E is $S_c(E)$ then there are $dQ = S_c(E) \, dE$ quantum states per unit volume between the energy E and the energy $E + dE$.

The determination of $S_c(E)$ thus requires a knowledge of the number of allowed quantum states between E and $E + dE$. The exact determination of this number would require solving the Schrödinger wave equation using the actual periodic three-dimensional lattice potential energy and the mutual potential energies among all the electrons. This would be a hopeless task. Hence we must settle for a useful approximation. In Chap. 4 we indicated that because there are few conduction electrons compared with the number of conduction band states available, the conduction electrons behave more or less as free particles. They are not exactly free, however, because their motion is still subject to various forces arising from the environment in the crystal. In principle then, one must calculate $U(x)$ from the forces and solve Schrödinger's equation to predict the electron motion. If we were to do this (the calculation is far too difficult to carry out here), we would find a rather amazing result: the electron's behavior in a solid is equivalent to that of a particle whose mass m_e^* differs somewhat from the true electron mass m and whose potential energy within the solid is E_c, the lowest allowed energy in the conduction band. Assuming any impurity atoms are uniformly distributed, E_c will be a constant throughout the crystal. There is a rise in the potential energy at the boundaries that prevents the electrons from leaving the solid; we may therefore treat the conduction electrons as particles of mass m_e^* confined in a three-dimensional square well in which their potential energy is constant. Thus, within the solid we have simply

$$E = p^2/2m_e^* + E_c \tag{5.1}$$

where $p^2/2m_e^*$ is the equivalent kinetic energy of the particle with mass m_e^* and potential energy E_c.

The mass m_e^* is called the *effective mass* of the conduction electron. In silicon it is slightly greater than the true electronic mass m_o, while in germanium it is about half as large.

Because the conduction electron behaves as though it has a mass m_e^* and resides in a square well, the three-dimensional square well results from Chap. 3 can be adapted to describe the allowed values of energy here. (We assume the potential energy rises at the boundaries of the solid are large so that the three-dimensional infinite square well results are a good approximation in the present situation.) In that analysis the potential energy is zero inside the well and the allowed energies are given by

$$E = (h^2/8mL^2)(n_x^2 + n_y^2 + n_z^2) \tag{5.2}$$

where m is the electron mass; L is the side dimension of the cubical volume considered, and n_x, n_y, and n_z are positive integers. Adapting this to the present situation we write

$$E = E_c + (h^2/8m_e^*L^2)(n_x^2 + n_y^2 + n_z^2) \tag{5.3}$$

The number of quantum states in the range E to $E + dE$ depends on the number of combinations of n_x, n_y, and n_z leading to energies in this range. More precisely, $S_c(E)\,dE$ is exactly two times this number of combinations, since, by the Pauli exclusion principle, as many as two electrons may have the same set of quantum numbers n_x, n_y, and n_z. (Recall that $m_s = \pm 1/2$.)

The number of combinations of n_x, n_y, and n_z corresponding to a given energy range can be established by considering a rectangular coordinate system with axes n_x, n_y, and n_z. A point in this coordinate system corresponds to each combination of integers. We thus wish to determine the number of points corresponding to a given energy range. Since the integers n_x, n_y, and n_z are positive we deal only with points in the first octant.

What is the relationship between the location of a given point and the energy corresponding to it? The distance from the origin of the integer coordinate system to the point in question is

$$(n_x^2 + n_y^2 + n_z^2)^{1/2} \equiv r \tag{5.4}$$

Combining (5.3) and (5.4) we discover that

$$r = (8m_e^*L^2/h^2)^{1/2}(E - E_c)^{1/2} \tag{5.5}$$

This establishes the relationship between energy and point location.

How do we count points? We can associate a volume of dimensions $\Delta n_x = \Delta n_y = \Delta n_z = 1$ with each point and then calculate volumes in the integer coordinate system by the methods of solid geometry. To be more specific, visualize placing a unit cube around each point. These cubes will fill the coordinate system with no gaps between cubes and no overlap of the cubes. Each point and its cube together occupy a unit volume. Thus the number of points in a given region is equal to the volume of that region.

A constant value of E corresponds to a spherical surface of radius r. The number of points in the range E to $E + dE$ is thus the volume between the spherical shells whose radii are $r(E)$ and $r(E + dE)$, where $r(E)$ is given by (5.5). This volume is simply the surface area of either shell (they differ only infinitesimally) times the volume thickness dr. The area is (in the first octant) $(1/8)4\pi r^2 = \pi r^2/2$. Thus the number of points is $(\pi r^2/2) dr$. Between r and $r + dr$ with two allowed states per point we have $N_s = \pi r^2 dr$ states. The quantity N_s gives the number of quantum states between r and $r + dr$, where r is specified by (5.5).

Using (5.5) to express N_s in terms of energy we have

$$N_s = (\pi/2)(8m_e^*/h^2)^{3/2} L^3(E - E_c)^{1/2} dE \text{ states}$$

Finally dividing by the volume L^3 we obtain

$$N_s/L^3 = (\pi/2)(8m_e^*/h^2)^{3/2}(E - E_c)^{1/2} dE$$
$$= S_c(E) dE (\text{states/unit volume})$$

or

$$S_c(E) = A_c(E - E_c)^{1/2} \text{ states/(unit volume} \cdot \text{unit energy)} \tag{5.6}$$

where

$$A_c \equiv (\pi/2)(8m_e^*/h^2)^{3/2} \tag{5.7}$$

The expression given for $S_c(E)$ in (5.6) is an approximation. The model implicit in (5.1) holds only for energy E fairly close to E_c. Thus for $E \gg E_c$, (5.1)–(5.6) are inaccurate descriptions of the electron behavior and allowed quantum states.

The form of $S_c(E)$ is known from advanced theoretical and experimental studies. It is found to vary with different crystal structures. A representative form of the exact $S_c(E)$ and the approximate curve given by (5.6) are shown in Fig. 5.1. We see that (5.6) agrees very well

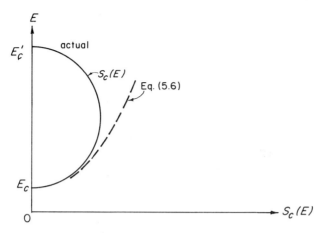

FIG. 5.1 Plots of the actual density of states function $S_c(E)$ and the approximation given by (5.6).

with the actual function near $E = E_c$ but deviates at higher energies. The agreement near $E = E_c$ is a direct consequence of choosing the "right" value for the effective mass m_e^*. That the amount of agreement between (5.6) and the actual function is sufficient to make the equation useful is not immediately apparent. We shall see via the Fermi function that almost all the conduction band electrons are found near E_c so that errors in the approximate $S_c(E)$ for $E \gg E_c$ are inconsequential.

We have argued in Chap. 4 that both conduction electrons and holes may be treated as free particles—the former in the conduction band, the latter in the valence band. This analogy can be used to develop equations corresponding to (5.6) and (5.7) that apply to holes. It is possible in this way to derive a function $S_v(E)$ which is the density of hole quantum states in the valence band. The function $S_v(E)$ has the same form as $S_c(E)$ with m_e^* replaced by m_h^*, the effective mass of holes, and $E - E_c$ replaced by $E_v - E$. This function is shown explicitly in Sec. 5.6.

5.3 FERMI FUNCTION

The Fermi function is described as the probability that an electron state is occupied. We speak of probabilities because the numbers of states and electrons involved are so large it is a practical impossibility to determine the exact condition of each individual electron. All we can obtain (and really need) is a statistical description of the behavior of the electrons as a group. This probability is developed in two ways: a brief derivation based on the rate of electron transfer among energy levels and the other based on the laws of mathematical probability. The first has the virtue of being brief. The second, while mathematically more involved, brings out more fully the probabilistic nature of the situation.

First Derivation
     Consider two electrons that collide elastically with one another (as contrasted to colliding with the lattice). The electrons have energies E_1 and E_2 before the collision and energies E_1' and E_2' after the collision. Since the collision is assumed to be elastic, $E_1 + E_2 = E_1' + E_2'$ or

$$E_1' - E_1 = -(E_2' - E_2) \equiv \Delta E \tag{5.8}$$

Let r represent the average number of such collisions per second. Meanwhile electrons having energies E_1' and E_2' will collide with one another and acquire energies E_1 and E_2 at the average rate of r' such collisions per second. In thermal equilibrium these two collision rates, the one describing transitions $(E_1, E_2) \rightarrow (E_1', E_2')$ and the other describing transitions $(E_1', E_2') \rightarrow (E_1, E_2)$, must be equal. If they are not equal the system has not become completely randomized and it is not in thermal equilibrium.
     Now the occurrence of $(E_1, E_2) \rightarrow (E_1', E_2')$ transitions requires that four things be true: (1) there must be electrons at energy E_1, (2) there must be electrons at energy E_2, (3) there must be empty states at energy E_1', and (4) there must be empty states at energy E_2'. The empty state requirements follow from the Pauli principle—no two electrons may exist in the same quantum state at the same time. The rate r at which these transitions occur depends on the number of available electrons and empty states at the various energies. Specifically r is proportional to the probability that states at E_1 and E_2 are occupied and that states at E_1' and E_2' are empty. These probabilities are respectively $f(E_1)$, $f(E_2)$, $[1 - f(E_1')]$, and $[1 - f(E_2')]$. Letting C be the constant of proportionality we have

$$r = Cf(E_1)f(E_2)[1 - f(E_1')][1 - f(E_2')]$$

Similarly,

$$r' = Cf(E_1')f(E_2')[1 - f(E_1)][1 - f(E_2)]$$

Equating r to r' and dividing by $f(E_1)f(E_2)f(E_1')f(E_2')$ yields

$$[1/f(E_1) - 1][1/f(E_2) - 1] = [1/f(E_1') - 1][1/f(E_2') - 1] \tag{5.9}$$

Noting that $E_1' = E_1 + \Delta E$ and $E_2' = E_2 - \Delta E$ and defining

$$[1/f(E)] - 1 = g(E) \tag{5.10}$$

we have

$$g(E_1)g(E_2) = g(E_1 + \Delta E)g(E_2 - \Delta E) \tag{5.11}$$

Searching for a function $g(E)$ to satisfy this equation we find that $A \exp(\beta E)$ will do nicely.

[*Exercise:* Show that $A \exp(\beta E)$ is indeed a solution.]

Solving (5.10) for $f(E)$ and using $g(E) = A \exp(\beta E)$ we have

$$f(E) = 1/[1 + g(E)] = 1/[1 + A \exp(\beta E)] \qquad (5.12)$$

To determine β consider E large enough that $A \exp(\beta E) \gg 1$. In this case

$$f(E) \simeq (1/A)\exp(-\beta E) \ll 1 \qquad (5.13)$$

When $f(E) \ll 1$, the chance of two electrons trying to occupy the same quantum state is negligible. In other words the electrons are essentially noninteracting and behave like ideal gas molecules. For an ideal gas it is known that

$$f(E) = A' \exp(-E/kT) \qquad (5.14)$$

where k is Boltzmann's constant and T is the absolute temperature. Comparing (5.13) and (5.14), we see that $\beta = 1/kT$.

Let us define a parameter E_f such that $\exp(-E_f/kT) = A$. Then (5.12) becomes

$$f(E) = \{1 + \exp[(E - E_f)/kT]\}^{-1} \qquad (5.15)$$

The function $f(E)$ gives the probability that a quantum state with an energy E is occupied by an electron. It is a quantum-mechanical function in that it describes particles that obey the Pauli principle. It is more general than indicated in the derivation since it applies to all particles governed by the Pauli principle. Such particles carry the group name *fermions*. As noted in Chap. 3 this group includes electrons, protons, and neutrons.

Second Derivation: (may be omitted in introductory studies)

Here we consider the entire system rather than transitions among a few states of the system. Let the energy scale be divided into M narrow intervals and let each interval be characterized by its average energy E_i, a number of quantum states S_i, and the number of electrons N_i in the S_i quantum states. We wish to determine the set N_i, i.e., $N_1, N_2, \ldots,$ N_i, the number of electrons in each interval. Three restrictions are imposed upon the system and this set of numbers:

1. By the Pauli exclusion principle no more than one electron can be in a given quantum state at a given time. A given state is therefore either empty or filled with one electron.
2. The sum of numbers of the set add up to the total number of electrons N_T in the system, expressed by $\sum_{i=1}^{M} N_i = N_T$.

3. The numbers must predict the actual total energy E_T in the system. Thus $\sum_{i=1}^{M} N_i E_i = E_T$.

Even given the above constraints there are many possible sets of numbers N_i. What we seek is the most probable set since that is the one that will, by assumption, be encountered most often in nature. In fact (though we shall not prove it) the most probable distribution is much more likely than all others combined; that is, there is little statistical deviation from the most probable distribution.

To find this distribution for each given interval we seek the probability that a given number of states N_i out of the total S_i are occupied. We then multiply together these probabilities to obtain the compound probability for a particular (unspecified) set of N_i and maximize this compound probability subject to the constraints discussed above.

The probability that N_i of S_i states are filled is proportional to the number of different ways W_i such an event can occur. The more ways there are, the more likely the event. The number of ways W of selecting N filled states out of S available states is $W = S!/N!(S - N)!$. (For simplicity we temporarily omit the subscript i.)

To see that this is correct, consider a simple numerical example. Suppose $S = 4$ and we wish to compute W for the case $N = 2$. The equation predicts $W = 4!/2!2! = 4 \cdot 3 \cdot 2 \cdot 1/(2 \cdot 1)(2 \cdot 1) = 6$. These six different ways may be illustrated as shown in Fig. 5.2, using dots for electrons and squares for states.

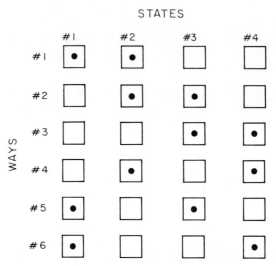

FIG. 5.2   The six ways of filling four states two at a time.

[*Exercise:* Verify that the equation is correct for $S = 4$ and $N = 0$, 1, 3, 4.]

Notice that W is a function of N. We thus more properly should write $W(N) = S!/N!(S - N)!$. The total number T of ways of filling the S states is

$$T = W(0) + W(1) + \cdots + W(S) = \sum_{N=0}^{S} W(N)$$

[*Exercise:* Find T for $S = 4$.]

The probability that N states are occupied thus is

$$P(N) = W(N)/T = S!/N!(S - N)!T = K/N!(S - N)!$$

where $K = S!/T$. Having made the point that W and P do depend on N we shall, for the sake of simplicity, drop the functional notation in the developments below.

[*Exercise:* Find P for $S = 4$ and $N = 0, 1, 2, 3, 4$.]

When all intervals are considered simultaneously, we use subscripts and calculate the compound probability of obtaining a given set of N_i. This is

$$P = P_1 P_2 P_3 \ldots P_M = \prod_{i=1}^{M} P_i = K_T \prod_{i=1}^{M} N_i!(S_i - N_i)!$$

where $K_T = \prod_{i=1}^{M} K_i$.

We now wish to maximize P with respect to N_i. This can be done straightforwardly but the algebra is very complicated. We, therefore, seek to first simplify the problem. If we had a function involving summations rather than multiplications, the required differentiations would be much easier to perform. Suppose we take the logarithm of P to convert the products to sums. Then, since $\ln P$ is a monotonic function, maximum P and maximum $\ln P$ occur simultaneously. This can also be seen as follows. For maximum $\ln P$ we equate the total differential to zero, i.e., $d(\ln P) = 0$. But this is simply $dP/P = 0$. Assuming P finite, $dP/P = 0$ requires $dP = 0$, the condition for a maximum in P.

The maximization problem may now be stated: maximize the function $f = \ln P$ subject to the conditions

$$\phi_a = N_T - \Sigma N_i = 0 \qquad \phi_b = E_T - \Sigma E_i N_i = 0 \tag{5.16}$$

Using the method of Lagrange multipliers we form the function $F = f + \alpha\phi_a + \beta\phi_b$ and require zero partial derivatives of F with respect to α and β and each N_i. Thus the function F is given by

$$F = \ln\left[K_T \middle/ \prod_{i=1}^{M} N_i!(S_i - N_i)!\right] + \alpha\left(N_T - \sum_{i=1}^{M} N_i\right)$$

$$+ \beta\left(E_T - \sum_{i=1}^{M} EN_i\right)$$

$$= \ln K_T - \sum_{i=1}^{M} [\ln N_i! + \ln(S_i - N_i)!] + \alpha N_T - \alpha\sum_{i=1}^{M} N_i$$

$$+ \beta E_T - \beta\sum_{i=1}^{M} E_i N_i \tag{5.17}$$

The first two partial derivatives F_α and F_β are

$$\frac{\partial F}{\partial \alpha} = N_T - \sum_{i=1}^{M} N_i \qquad \frac{\partial F}{\partial \beta} = E_T - \sum_{i=1}^{M} E_i N_i \tag{5.18}$$

Equating these to zero simply confirms that the side conditions will be obeyed in the course of the maximization.

The remaining derivatives $F_{N_1}, F_{N_2}, \ldots, F_{N_i}$ all have the same form, namely,

$$\frac{\partial F}{\partial N_i} = -\frac{\partial}{\partial N_i}\ln N_i! - \frac{\partial}{\partial N_i}\ln(S_i - N_i)! - \alpha - \beta E_i \tag{5.19}$$

Before evaluating the derivatives of the logarithmic terms, we first use Stirling's approximation $\ln Q! \simeq Q \ln Q - Q$ when Q is large. Differentiating with respect to N_i then yields

$$\frac{d(\ln Q!)}{dN_i} = \ln Q \frac{dQ}{dN_i} + Q(1/Q)\frac{dQ}{dN_i} - \frac{dQ}{dN_i} = \ln Q \frac{dQ}{dN_i}$$

Applying this and equating $\partial F/\partial N_i$ to zero we have

$$\frac{\partial F}{\partial N_i} = -\ln N_i - \ln(S_i - N_i)(-1) - \alpha - \beta E_i = 0 \tag{5.20}$$

or, after rearrangement,

$$N_i/S_i = [1 + \exp(\alpha + \beta E_i)]^{-1} \tag{5.21}$$

Now define $\alpha = -\beta E_f$ or equivalently $E_f = -\alpha/\beta$ so that (5.21) may be written as

$$N_i/S_i = \{1 + \exp[(E_i - E_f)\beta]\}^{-1}$$

By the same argument used in the first derivation we can show that $\beta = 1/kT$.

Now N_i/S_i is the fraction of occupied states in the ith interval. At some instant N_i states will be occupied. At another time a different group of N_i states will be occupied. For a period of time a given state will be occupied for a fraction N_i/S_i of that time. Hence the probability of finding a given state occupied is $f(E_i) = N_i/S_i = \{1 + \exp[(E_i - E_f)/kT]\}^{-1}$ or, dropping the subscript i (since this was simply being used as an index in the summations and multiplications),

$$f(E) = \{1 + \exp[(E - E_f)/kT]\}^{-1} \quad \text{for all } E \tag{5.22}$$

Fermi Energy

The Fermi energy, or Fermi level, E_f is a parameter introduced in the course of the derivations. In order to use $f(E)$ one must know E_f. This parameter is not a universal constant nor a quantity given in tables of material constants. It depends on temperature, the type of material, the choice for $E = 0$ on the energy scale, and, especially in semiconductors, the impurities present. It appears in $f(E)$ because of the requirement that $\Sigma N_i = N_T$, i.e., it is the parameter which permits $f(E)$ to predict the proper total number of electrons. We can therefore anticipate that knowledge of the total electron concentration n_o is used in determining E_f. This will be shown in later sections. For the moment let us note that

$$f(E) = 0.5 \quad \text{for } E = E_f \tag{5.23}$$

so that E_f may be thought of as the energy level separating states which are probably occupied, $f(E) > 0.5$, from states which are probably empty, $f(E) < 0.5$.

This is illustrated in Fig. 5.3. For $E > E_f$ the exponential in (5.22) is larger than unity and therefore $f(E) < 0.5$. If E is at least $4\,kT$ units of energy above E_f the exponential is much larger than unity and the Fermi function becomes approximately

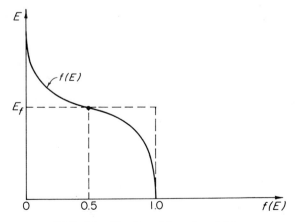

FIG. 5.3   The Fermi function $f(E)$.

$$f(E) \simeq \exp[-(E - E_f)/kT] \quad \text{for } E > E_f + 4\,kT \tag{5.24}$$

When $E < E_f$ the exponential is smaller than unity and $f(E) > 0.5$. If E is at least $4\,kT$ units of energy below E_f the exponential becomes much smaller than unity so that $f(E) \simeq 1.0$, or more accurately,

$$f(E) \simeq 1 - \exp[(E - E_f)/kT] \quad \text{for } E < E_f - 4\,kT \tag{5.25}$$

The derivation of (5.25) is not difficult if we use the approximation that $1/(1 + x) \simeq 1 - x$ when $|x| \ll 1$, letting x be the exponential in (5.22).

5.4   ELECTRON AND HOLE DISTRIBUTIONS

With the density of states functions and the Fermi function available it is a simple matter to determine the distribution of electrons among the various energy levels. If there are $dQ = S(E)\,dE$ quantum states/cm^3 between E and $E + dE$ and if the occupation probability for each state is $f(E)$, then it follows that there are $f(E)S(E)\,dE$ occupied quantum states/cm^3 between E and $E + dE$. Since occupation means the presence of one electron, there are $f(E)S(E)\,dE$ electrons/cm^3 in the energy range E to $E + dE$. A plot of $f(E)S(E)$ therefore shows how electrons are distributed in energy. Figure 5.4 shows this product for both the conduction and the valence bands and the individual functions $f(E)$, $S_c(E)$, and $S_v(E)$.

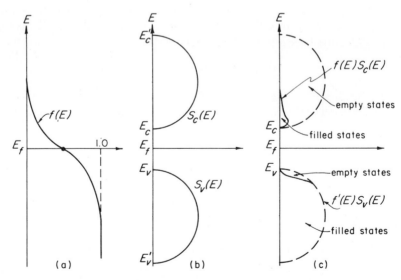

FIG. 5.4   Plots of (a) Fermi function, (b) density of states functions, and (c) products of the Fermi and density of states functions.

Let us now try to see how the functions $f(E)$ and $S(E)$ can be used to find the density of conduction electrons and holes. We know that between E and $E + dE$ there are $f(E)S(E)$ dE electrons/cm^3. If we divide the conduction band (for example) into an infinite number of such infinitesimal intervals and sum the numbers of electrons/cm^3 for all the intervals, the result is the total number of electrons/cm^3 in that band. This is nothing more than the integration of $f(E)S_c(E)$ dE over the range $E = E_c$ to $E = E_c'$, where E_c and E_c' are the edges of the conduction band (see Fig. 5.4b). The area labeled as filled states in Fig. 5.4c is thus equal to the number of conduction electrons/cm^3.

By similar reasoning the integral of $S(E)$ dE over a band is the number of states/cm^3 in that band. Subtraction of the number of electrons/cm^3 in the band from the number of states/cm^3 yields the number of unoccupied states/cm^3. This explains why the areas between the dashed and solid curves in Fig. 5.4c are labeled empty states. The density of empty states in the valence band is just equal to the density of holes.

Two important facts are evident in Fig. 5.4c. We see that most of the conduction electrons are near the bottom of the conduction band and most of the empty valence states are near the top of the valence band. This means nearly all the conduction electrons are near $E = E_c$ so that this is the region where an accurate expression is required for $S_c(E)$. Similarly most of the holes are near $E = E_v$ so that when the properties of holes are considered it is important to describe $S_v(E)$ accurately near E_v, i.e., near the top of the valence band.

The hole distribution can be seen more clearly if a different product of functions is graphed. We know that between E and $E + dE$ there are $S_v(E)$ dE valence states/cm^3 and $f(E)S_v(E)$ dE valence electrons/cm^3. The difference between these quantities is the number of unoccupied states or holes/cm^3. Thus we may say that there are $[1 - f(E)]S_v(E)$ dE holes/cm^3 in the interval. This may also be obtained by another line of reasoning. If $f(E)$ is the probability a state is filled then $1 - f(E)$ is the probability the state is empty. Hence $[1 - f(E)]S_v(E)$ dE is the number of empty states/cm^3. The quantity $1 - f(E)$ thus plays for holes the role $f(E)$ plays for electrons. Let us symbolize $1 - f(E)$ as $f'(E)$ and call it the hole probability. The function $S_v(E)$ may then be regarded as available to either an electron or a hole; $f(E)$ is the probability it is occupied by an electron and $f'(E)$ is the probability it is occupied by a hole. Plotting $f(E)$ only for $E > E_f$ and $f'(E)$ only for $E < E_f$ (to lessen confusion from too many curves) and $S_c(E)$, $S_v(E)$, $f(E)S_c(E)$, and $f'(E)S_v(E)$, we obtain the graphs in Fig. 5.5.

5.5   CALCULATION OF n_o FROM $f(E)S_c(E)$.

In Fig. 5.4c the area inside the $f(E)S_c(E)$ curve represents the number of occupied conduction band states/cm^3 and hence the

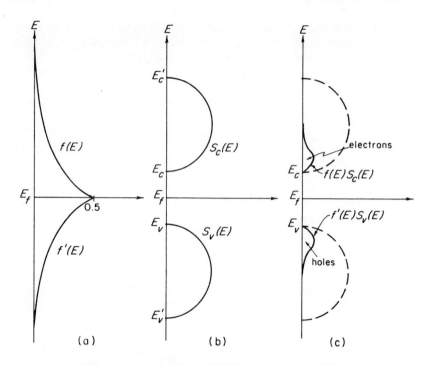

FIG. 5.5   Plots of (a) Fermi function $f(E)$ and hole
probability $f'(E)$, (b) density of states functions $S_c(E)$
and $S_v(E)$, and (c) electron and hole distribution functions $f(E)S_c(E)$ and $f'(E)S_v(E)$.

conduction electron concentration n_o. Let us calculate that area, i.e.,
evaluate the following integral expression.

$$n_o = \int_{E_c}^{E_c'} f(E)S_c(E)\,dE$$

$$= \int_{E_c}^{E_c'} A_c(E - E_c)^{1/2}\,dE\{1 + \exp[(E - E_f)/kT]\}^{-1} \qquad (5.26)$$

Note that in forming the integrand in this equation we have used (5.6)
for $S_c(E)$ and (5.22) for $f(E)$. Examining this equation and reviewing
tables of integrals and standard methods for simplifying integrals reveals a rather formidable task; there is no exact solution available. One
must thus choose one of two kinds of approximation: (1) numerical
integration via digital computation for various combinations of values
of E_c, E_c', and E_f, or (2) analytic approximations permitting an analytic
solution. Both approaches are useful. Here we shall concentrate on the
analytic solution.

Suppose we wish to derive equations applicable to materials which contain normal amounts of impurities, i.e., materials which do not have excessive doping. This means a net impurity concentration smaller than 10^{19} impurities/cm^3 and thus n_o is smaller than 10^{19} electrons/cm^3. The conduction band of a semiconductor has about 10^{23} states/cm^3. This means that very few states (less than 0.01%) are occupied which suggests that the Fermi function $f(E)$ is much smaller than unity throughout the conduction band. If this is true then a simpler form of the Fermi function can be used. If $f(E) \ll 1$, the exponential in (5.22) and (5.26) must be much larger than unity, which immediately leads to (5.24). Note this also implies that E_f is at least $4kT$ below E_c. Using (5.24) means that (5.26) simplifies to

$$n_o = \int_{E_c}^{E_c'} f(E) S_c(E)\, dE$$

$$\simeq \int_{E_c}^{E_c'} \exp\left[-(E - E_f)/kT\right] A_c (E - E_c)^{1/2}\, dE \qquad (5.27)$$

To write (5.27) in a form that might be found in tables, introduce the following change of variable, $(E - E_c)/kT = x$. Then (5.27) becomes

$$n_o = A_c (kT)^{3/2} \exp\left[-(E_c - E_f)/kT\right] \int_0^{x_c'} \sqrt{x}\, e^{-x}\, dx \qquad (5.28)$$

where x_c' is defined as $x_c' = (E_c' - E_c)/kT$.

A search through tables of integrals reveals that the integral in (5.28) is given for the special case where the upper limit is infinite; then the integral has the value $\sqrt{\pi}/2$. But x_c' is not infinite so the integral in (5.28) must be somewhat less than $\sqrt{\pi}/2$. To see how much less consider how the integrand varies with x and what values x_c' takes on. The conduction band width $E_c' - E_c$ is typically 1 or 2 eV. At the highest temperature of interest for semiconductor devices, say 500 K, kT is only about 0.043 eV. Thus x_c' is at least $1/0.043 = 23$.

Consider the integrand in (5.28). This is tabulated in Table 5.1 and plotted in Fig. 5.6. Note how rapidly the integrand decreases with increasing x; recognizing that the desired integral is the area under the curve, nearly the same value will be obtained whether one integrates from zero to 5, 10, 23, or infinity. The answer will be essentially $\sqrt{\pi}/2 = 0.886$. (As confirmation of this the reader is invited to evaluate the integral from zero to five by graphical means in Prob. 5.9.)

The calculation of n_o is now complete. Using the value $\sqrt{\pi}/2$, (5.28) becomes

$$n_o = A_c k^{3/2} (\sqrt{\pi}/2) T^{3/2} \exp\left[-(E_c - E_f)/kT\right] \qquad (5.29)$$

This may be written more compactly by defining $A_c k^{3/2} \sqrt{\pi}/2 = B_c$; then

Table 5.1.   Integrand calculations for the integral in (5.28).

x	$\sqrt{x}$	e^{-x}	$\sqrt{x}\,e^{-x}$
0	0	1.0	0
0.25	0.5	0.78	0.39
0.5	0.7	0.61	0.43
1	1.0	0.37	0.37
2	1.4	0.14	0.20
3	1.7	0.05	0.085
4	2.0	0.018	0.036
5	2.2	0.007	0.015
23	4.8	10^{-10}	4.8×10^{-10}

$$n_o = B_c T^{3/2} \exp[-(E_c - E_f)/kT] \tag{5.30}$$

For further compactness, when T is constant one may define

$$B_c T^{3/2} = N_c \tag{5.31}$$

and thereby obtain

$$n_o = N_c \exp[-(E_c - E_f)/kT] \tag{5.32}$$

Values for N_c at 300 K and for B_c are given in Table 5.2 (p. 113).

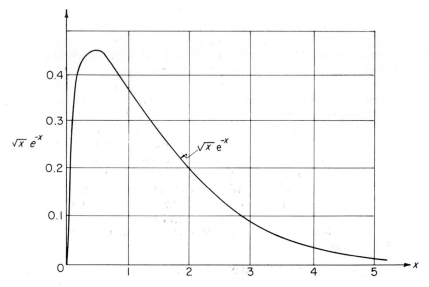

FIG. 5.6   Integrand from (5.28).

Table 5.2. Values for B_c, B_v, N_c (300 K), and N_v (300 K) for silicon and germanium.

	Si	Ge	Unit
B_c	5.6×10^{15}	1.7×10^{15}	$cm^{-3} \cdot K^{-3/2}$
B_v	2.2×10^{15}	1.2×10^{15}	$cm^{-3} \cdot K^{-3/2}$
$N_c(300\ K)$	2.9×10^{19}	8.8×10^{18}	cm^{-3}
$N_v(300\ K)$	1.1×10^{19}	6.2×10^{18}	cm^{-3}

5.6   CALCULATION OF p_o FROM $f'(E)S_v(E)$

The calculation of p_o is the mirror image of that for n_o, as would be expected from the relative shapes of $f(E)S_c(E)$ and $f'(E)S_v(E)$ in Fig. 5.5c. The equation for $S_v(E)$ can be derived by methods similar to those in Sec. 5.2. The result is simply $S_v(E) = A_v(E_v - E)^{1/2}$ where A_v is a constant similar to A_c. This is accurate near $E = E_v$ just as (5.6) is accurate near $E = E_c$. From Fig. 5.5c it is apparent that this is the important energy range.

The hole probability $f'(E)$ is given by

$$f'(E) = 1 - f(E) = 1 - \{1 + \exp[(E - E_f)/kT]\}^{-1}$$

$$f'(E) = \{\exp[(E_f - E)/kT] + 1\}^{-1} \quad \text{for all } E \tag{5.33}$$

$$f'(E) \simeq 1 - \exp[(E_f - E)/kT] \quad \text{for } E > E_f + 4kT \tag{5.34}$$

$$f'(E) = 0.5 \quad \text{for } E = E_f \tag{5.35}$$

$$f'(E) = \exp[-(E_f - E)/kT] \quad \text{for } E < E_f - 4kT \tag{5.36}$$

The calculation of p_o involves evaluating the following integral expression.

$$p_o = \int_{E_v'}^{E_v} f'(E)S_v(E)\, dE \tag{5.37}$$

This evaluation uses (5.36) for $f'(E)$ under the assumption that $f'(E) \ll 1$ throughout the valence band. It also in effect replaces E_v' by negative infinity to obtain a definite integral whose value will again be $\sqrt{\pi}/2$. The result is as follows:

$$p_o = A_v k^{3/2}(\sqrt{\pi}/2)\, T^{3/2} \exp[-(E_f - E_v)/kT] \tag{5.38}$$

$$= B_v T^{3/2} \exp[-(E_f - E_v)/kT] \tag{5.39}$$

$$= N_v \exp[-(E_f - E_v)/kT] \tag{5.40}$$

where $B_v = A_v k^{3/2} \sqrt{\pi}/2$ and $N_v = B_v T^{3/2}$. Table 5.2 gives values for B_c and B_v.

[*Exercise:* Derive (5.39) from (5.37), carefully indicating the reasoning as well as the mathematical steps involved.]

[*Exercise:* Verify the values of N_c and N_v for silicon at 300 K. Would (5.31) and/or (5.39) be correct if n_o and/or p_o were of the order of magnitude of N_c or N_v? Discuss.]

5.7 CARRIER PRODUCT EQUATION REVISITED

In Chap. 4 the carrier product equation (CPE) was developed from consideration of the thermal equilibrium balance between recombination and thermal generation. With the aid of (5.30) and (5.39) we now reaffirm that relationship and in addition find n_i^2 in terms of E_g and T.

If n_o and p_o, given by (5.30) and (5.39), are multiplied together one obtains the following carrier product expression:

$$p_o n_o = B_c B_v T^3 \exp[-(E_c - E_v)/kT] \tag{5.41}$$

Now $E_c - E_v = E_g$, the energy gap. Hence $p_o n_o = B_c B_v T^3 \exp(-E_g/kT)$. At a fixed temperature the right side of this equation is a constant. Thus the form of (4.8) is confirmed, and it is seen that

$$n_i^2 = B_c B_v T^3 \exp(-E_g/kT) \tag{5.42}$$

From (5.42) it is evident that n_i^2 is a strong function of temperature; the temperature dependence is determined by the exponential and T^3 factors. It might appear that the T^3 term would be dominant around room temperature. This is not true. If we wish to find the absolute change in n_i^2 we should simply calculate the differential dn_i^2 for a change, dT. It is more useful, however, to calculate the per unit change (the percent change divided by 100) which is dn_i^2/n_i^2. But this is simply the differential of $\ln n_i^2$. Taking $\ln n_i^2$ and its differential we have, from (5.42),

$$\ln n_i^2 = \ln B_v B_c + 3 \ln T - E_g/kT$$

$$d(\ln n_i^2) = 3\,dT/T + (E_g/kT^2)\,dT = (3 + E_g/kT)(dT/T) \tag{5.43}$$

Using $T = 300$ K and $E_g = 1.1$ eV (appropriate to silicon) in (5.43) it may be verified that the term derived from the exponential is the more significant.

[*Exercise:* Verify this statement.]

[*Exercise:* Find the temperature at which the T^3 term and the exponential term are equally important in determining the change in n_i^2 with temperature for both silicon and germanium.]

Because the exponential term is dominant, a plot of $\ln n_i$ (and therefore n_i^2) vs T^{-1} is approximately a straight line as shown in Fig. 5.7. (The ordinate in Fig. 5.7 is n_i plotted on a logarithmic scale. This

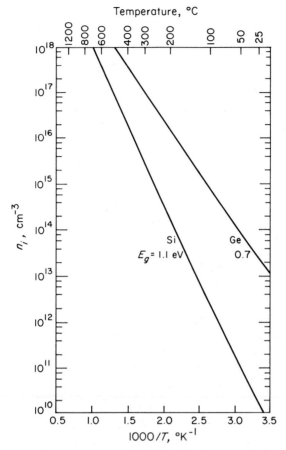

FIG. 5.7 Intrinsic carrier concentration n_i as a function of temperature. (From A. S. Grove, 1969, *Physics and Technology of Semiconductor Devices,* Wiley, New York, p. 91)

Table 5.3. Intrinsic carrier concentration n_i and its square versus temperatures for silicon and germanium.

Density Concentration	300 K	310 K	400 K	Unit
$n_i(\text{Si})$	1.5×10^{10}	3.3×10^{10}	7.9×10^{12}	cm^{-3}
$n_i(\text{Ge})$	2.4×10^{13}	4.1×10^{13}	16×10^{14}	cm^{-3}
$n_i^2(\text{Si})$	2.2×10^{20}	10.9×10^{20}	6.3×10^{25}	cm^{-6}
$n_i^2(\text{Ge})$	5.8×10^{26}	17×10^{26}	27×10^{29}	cm^{-6}

of course yields the same curve as plotting $\ln n_i$ on a linear scale.) Figure 5.7 shows that n_i is in general smaller in silicon than in germanium but on a percentage basis its rate of change is greater in silicon. This may also be seen in Table 5.3.

5.8   CHARGE NEUTRALITY EQUATION

In (5.30) and (5.39), p_o and n_o are expressed in terms of the Fermi level E_f and the temperature T. Usually the temperature is known so we have two equations in three unknowns. The Fermi level E_f may be eliminated by combining the two equations to obtain the CPE, which is one equation in two unknowns. Whether the two equations are combined or not, we therefore require an additional equation in order to be able to determine p_o, n_o, and/or E_f.

If we assume full ionization of all impurities (as in Sec. 4.5) then the required equation is provided by $n_{no} = N_d - N_a + p_{no}$ or $p_{po} = N_a - N_d + n_{po}$ which are both equivalent to

$$p_o + N_d = n_o + N_a \tag{5.44}$$

What about the more general case where full ionization may not be a justifiable assumption? How do we decide whether full ionization may be assumed? At what temperature is essentially full ionization obtained? To answer these questions a more general relationship analogous to (5.44) must be developed. Since it is the ionized impurities (plus hole-electron pair generation) that give rise to holes and electrons, we should expect the general equation to be $p_o + N_d^+ = n_o + N_a^-$, where N_d^+ stands for the concentration of ionized donors and N_a^- for that of ionized acceptors. We shall derive this equation and determine the circumstances under which it may be used.

The space charge density ρ, i.e., the net charge per unit volume, at any point in a semiconductor, can be calculated in terms of four kinds of charges: conduction electrons, holes, ionized donors, and ionized acceptors.

There are n conduction electrons per unit volume, each with a charge $-q$. Hence the electron contribution to the charge per unit volume is $-qn$. Similarly there are p holes per unit volume, each with a charge $+q$. These contribute a component $+qp$. Ionized donor atoms are those from which thermal vibrations have stripped the fifth valence electron leaving a net charge $+q$ per atom. Let N_d^+ be the concentration of ionized donor atoms contributing $+qN_d^+$. Finally, ionized acceptor atoms have acquired an extra valence electron and a corresponding net charge of $-q$ per atom. The density of these atoms is N_a^- and they contribute $-qN_a^-$.

Summing the above components we find the net space charge density is

$$\rho = q(p + N_d^+ - n - N_a^-) \, C/cm^3$$

In thermal equilibrium this is $\rho_o = q(p_o + N_d^+ - n_o - N_a^-)$.

Suppose the semiconductor as a whole is neutral and homogeneous, i.e., the distribution of impurities is uniform. Then the space charge must be zero everywhere. Setting $\rho_o = 0$ immediately leads to

$$p_o + N_d^+ = n_o + N_a^- \tag{5.45}$$

This is precisely the expression expected. Equation (5.45) is known as the charge neutrality equation (CNE) and it applies to homogeneous material in thermal equilibrium.

Note that (5.45) does not explicitly include the Fermi level E_f. It may be introduced by expressing N_d^+ and N_a^- in terms of the Fermi function. The concentration of ionized donors is simply the total donor concentration times the probability $1 - f(E_d)$ of not finding an electron in a donor quantum state (E_d = energy level of the donor states).[1] Thus

$$N_d^+ = N_d[1 - f(E_d)] = N_d\{1 + \exp[(E_f - E_d)/kT]\}^{-1} \tag{5.46}$$

Likewise N_a^- is the total acceptor concentration times the probability $f(E_a)$ of finding an electron in an acceptor quantum state (E_a = energy level of the acceptor states).[1] Thus

$$N_a^- = N_a f(E_a) = N_a\{1 + \exp[(E_a - E_f)/kT]\}^{-1} \tag{5.47}$$

If these two expressions are substituted in (5.45) then the result, (5.30), and (5.39) provide a set of three equations from which n_o, p_o, and E_f may be determined at any temperature.

5.9   FERMI LEVEL CALCULATIONS

The Fermi level E_f is an important parameter in that its location must be known for the CNE to be useful in calculating p_o and n_o. Another extremely important property of E_f which we state here and make use of in Chap. 6 is: for any system in thermal equilibrium the Fermi level is a constant, i.e., independent of time and spatial position. Proof of this statement depends on the theory of thermodynamics and will not be given. Rather, let us consider locating the Fermi level in various circumstances.

---

1. For purposes of discussion we will consider (5.46) and (5.47) as being correct. However, a detailed derivation for N_d^+/N_d, analogous to the second derivation of $N_i/S_i = f(E_i)$ in energy bands, leads to a result differing somewhat from that given in (5.46); likewise (5.47) is not a rigorous expression for N_a^-.

5.9.1 Intrinsic Material

A semiconductor is said to be *intrinsic* if it contains no impurities or if $N_d = N_a$. In fact $|N_d - N_a| \ll n_i$ is sufficient for the material to be described as intrinsic. For this case the CNE reduces to simply $n_o = p_o$. Using (5.30) and (5.39) this becomes

$$B_c T^{3/2} \exp[(E_f - E_c)/kT] = B_v T^{3/2} \exp[(E_v - E_f)/kT]$$

Solving for E_f we find

$$E_f = (E_c + E_v)/2 + (kT/2) \ln (B_v/B_c) \equiv E_i \qquad (5.48)$$

This equation serves to define E_i, the Fermi level in intrinsic material. The first term in the expression for E_i is the energy in the center of the energy gap, which might be expected from the fact that $p_o = n_o$ and $f(E)$ and $f'(E)$ are symmetric around E_f, i.e.,

$$f(E_f + \Delta E) = f'(E_f - \Delta E) \qquad (5.49)$$

[*Exercise:* Verify (5.49).]

The second term in the expression for E_i, (5.48), arises from the fact that $S_c(E)$ and $S_v(E)$ are not quite mirror images of one another since $A_v \neq A_c$. From the data in Table 5.2 we find

$$(kT/2) \ln (B_v/B_c) = -0.467(kT) \quad \text{for silicon}$$
$$= -0.174(kT) \quad \text{for germanium}$$

At a temperature of 300 K, $kT = 0.026$ eV and these terms represent deviations of only -0.0121 eV and 0.00452 eV from the center of the gap. For most purposes we may ignore such deviations and write $E_i = (E_c + E_v)/2 = E_v + E_g/2$.

5.9.2 Extrinsic Material

The net impurity concentration $|N_d - N_a|$ in *extrinsic* material is comparable to or larger than n_i. The Fermi level for such material departs from the intrinsic level E_i by an amount which depends on the ratio n_o/p_o. This may be seen by dividing (5.30) by (5.39) and solving for E_f to obtain

$$E_f = (E_c + E_v)/2 + (kT/2) \ln (B_v/B_c) + (kT/2) \ln (n_o/p_o) \quad (5.50)$$

This may be simplified by recalling (5.48) and writing

$$E_f = E_i + (kT/2) \ln (n_o/p_o) \qquad (5.51)$$

This shows that for $n_o > p_o$ (n-type material) E_f is above the gap center, while for $p_o > n_o$ (p-type material) E_f is below the gap center.

The Fermi level may also be expressed in terms of either n_o or p_o

alone. Solving (5.32) for E_f, one finds the value most useful for n-type,

$$E_f = E_c - kT \ln (N_c/n_o) \tag{5.52}$$

Alternately one may use (5.40) to obtain the value most useful for p-type,

$$E_f = E_v + kT \ln(N_v/p_o) \tag{5.53}$$

Which of the above three equations one should use, or whether any of them is useful, depends upon the situation and what one wants to know. None of the equations is useful if n_o and p_o are unknown.

For n-type materials with n_o known, (5.52) is the logical choice (see Sec. 5.9.3). Similarly for p-type materials with p_o known, (5.53) is the best candidate. When neither n_o nor p_o is known a more difficult problem exists. The solution in this case is discussed in Sec. 5.9.4.

The key point in knowing or not knowing n_o and p_o and thus finding E_f is the extent to which the impurities are ionized. Hence the next three sections deal with (1) finding E_f when the ionization is complete, (2) finding E_f when the degree of ionization is unknown, and (3) determining whether one may safely assume complete ionization.

5.9.3 Ionization Complete, E_f Unknown.

At room temperature and above, impurities are usually completely ionized. In Sec. 5.9.5, for example, we find that 99% of the donors in a particular sample of silicon are ionized at 95 K. When complete ionization exists, n_o and/or p_o can be calculated by use of the CNE and CPE. These results can then be substituted into (5.51), (5.52), or (5.53) as appropriate. In most cases simpler calculations and more accurate results are realized by calculating the majority carrier density and using the appropriate equation.

EXAMPLE

Given a sample of silicon at 300 K with $N_d - N_a = 10^{14}/\text{cm}^3$; find E_f.

At this temperature we may reasonably assume that all impurities are ionized. Thus the majority carrier density is given by $n_o = N_d - N_a + p_o$. At 300 K, $n_i = 1.5 \times 10^{10}/\text{cm}^3$. Since $|N_d - N_a| = 10^{14}/\text{cm}^3 \gg 4n_i$ we may, as noted in Sec. 4.7, neglect p_o in comparison with $N_d - N_a$ and write $n_o \simeq N_d - N_a = 10^{14}/\text{cm}^3$. Noting that $N_c = 2.9 \times 10^{19}/\text{cm}^3$ here (see Table 5.2), we find from (5.52) that E_f is given by

$$E_f = E_c - (0.026 \text{ eV}) \ln(2.9 \times 10^{19}/10^{14}) = E_c - 0.327 \text{ eV}$$

Thus the Fermi level is 0.327 eV below the conduction band. Given this result one may now determine whether $f(E_d) \ll 1$ as a check on the assumption of complete ionization.

If in the above example $f(E_d)$ were not small compared with unity, it would be necessary to abandon the assumption of complete ionization and proceed with a more general analysis.

5.9.4 Ionization Unknown, E_f Unknown

The Fermi level is involved in determining the electron concentration, the hole concentration, and the ionized impurity concentrations. We have seen that these four quantities are related to one another by the charge neutrality equation (CNE). Writing the CNE in both its compact and detailed forms we have (5.45),

$$p_o + N_d^+ = n_o + N_a^-$$

which becomes, using (5.39), (5.46), (5.30), and (5.47)

$$B_v T^{3/2} \ \exp[(E_v - E_f)/kT] + N_d\{1 + \exp[(E_f - E_d)/kT]\}^{-1}$$
$$= B_c T^{3/2} \exp[(E_f - E_c)/kT] + N_a\{1 + \exp[(E_a - E_f)/kT]\}^{-1} \quad (5.54)$$

Specifying the semiconductor and impurities under consideration fixes most of the parameters in (5.54), namely B_v, E_v, N_d, B_c, E_c, N_a, and E_a. Only the variables E_f and T remain, so this equation implicitly gives either as a function of the other. The problem is to find an explicit answer from this implicit general relationship. A general explicit relationship could be derived for E_f by defining a variable $Z = \exp(E_f/kT)$ and rearranging (5.54) into a quartic algebraic equation for which general solutions do exist. However the result would be so complicated that little if any physical insight would be available.

A better approach is to use certain known facts about the terms in (5.54) in any specific case and simplify the equation as much as possible. For example, we have seen in Secs. 4.5 and 4.7 that the non-dominant impurity type is fully ionized at any temperature. Thus either the N_d^+ or N_a^- term in (5.45) and (5.54) may be stated as N_d or N_a. In addition, in the temperature range where there is appreciable ionization but some question about the precise degree of ionization of the dominant impurity type, it is almost always true that the minority carrier density is negligible. In that case (5.45) can be simplified to

$$p_o = N_a^- - N_d \quad \text{p-type material} \quad\quad\quad\quad (5.55)$$

$$n_o = N_d^+ - N_a \quad \text{n-type material} \quad\quad\quad\quad (5.56)$$

The corresponding versions of (5.54) are considerably simplified. In fact it has been reduced to a quadratic equation in $Z = \exp(E_f/kT)$ and finding the solution is not difficult.

EXAMPLE

Given silicon with $N_d = 2 \times 10^{14}$ donors/cm^3 and $N_a = 10^{14}$ acceptors/cm^3, find E_f as a function of T over the range 100–300 K.

In this case (5.56) applies. Writing the corresponding form of (5.54) we have

$$B_c T^{3/2} \exp[(E_f - E_c)/kT] = N_d\{1 + \exp[(E_f - E_d)/kT]\}^{-1} - N_a$$

Since we are free to choose the origin on the energy scale, let us select $E_c = 0$. Defining $\exp(E_f/kT) = Z$ our equation becomes

$$B_c T^{3/2} Z = N_d[1 + Z\exp(-E_d/kT)]^{-1} - N_a$$

Rearranging algebraically this in turn becomes

$$Z^2 + Z[B_c T^{3/2} + N_a \exp(-E_d/kT)][B_c T^{3/2} \exp(-E_d/kT)]^{-1}$$
$$+ N_a - N_d = 0$$

The quadratic formula may be applied to obtain an expression for Z. Using this and the relationship $E_f = kT \ln Z$ gives E_f as a function of T. This expression may then be evaluated through a simple digital computer program. Note that resulting values of E_f are specified relative to $E_c = 0$.

5.9.5 Ionization Specified, T Unknown

When full impurity ionization cannot be assumed the determination of E_f involves considerable effort. It would therefore be useful to know at what temperature essentially full ionization is attained. Then for all higher temperatures full ionization can be assumed.

EXAMPLE

Given silicon with $N_d = 2 \times 10^{14}$ donors/cm³, $N_a = 10^{14}$ acceptors/cm³, and $E_c - E_d = 0.05$ eV, find the temperature at which essentially full ionization occurs. (Suppose that 99% is selected as the criterion for "essentially full ionization.")

The pertinent equation is again (5.56) with $N_d^+ = 0.99\,N_d$. Writing this equation with (5.30) used to substitute for n_o we obtain

$$B_c T^{3/2} \exp[(E_f - E_c)/kT] = 0.99\,N_d - N_a$$

To solve for T we need E_f. The value of E_f is implicit in the 99% ionization condition.

For 99% ionization only 1% of the donors can be occupied by electrons. Thus $f(E_d) = 0.01$ and hence, from (5.22),

$$1/100 = \{1 + \exp[(E_d - E_f)/kT]\}^{-1}$$
$$99 = \exp[(E_d - E_f)/kT]$$
$$E_f = E_d - kT \ln 99$$

Using this expression for E_f and again arbitrarily setting $E_c = 0$ we can write

$$B_c T^{3/2} \exp\left[(E_d - kT \ln 99)/kT\right] = 0.99\, N_d - N_a$$

This is a transcendental equation which cannot be solved analytically for T. Iterative numerical techniques are required. One such technique is the Newton-Raphson method available in digital computer libraries. An even simpler method of solving many problems involving exponentials or logarithms follows.

Solve for T in the exponential term of the equation in terms of T in the other terms in the equation. Guess an initial value for T and substitute for T in the other terms. The equation then yields a new value of T which is likewise substituted, yielding a new (and better, we hope) value. This procedure is continued until it converges to a repeating answer.

Implementing this method we proceed as follows. Solving for T in the exponent of the equation above yields

$$T = \frac{(2/3)(-E_d/k)}{\ln T - (2/3)\left[\ln 99 + \ln(0.99\, N_d - N_a) - \ln B_c\right]}$$

Inserting values for E_d, k, N_d, and B_c and adding iteration subscripts to the two Ts we have $T_{n+1} = 397/(\ln T_n - 0.37)$. As an initial guess let us try $T_n = 300$ K. Calculating T_{n+1} and continuing the iteration we obtain the following results.

T_n(K)	$\ln T_n$	T_{n+1}(K)
300	5.71	74.4
74.4	4.31	101
101	4.62	93.4
93.4	4.53	95.5
95.5	4.56	94.8
94.8	4.55	94.8

We thus find that at $T = 94.8$ K, 99% of the donors are ionized.

[*Exercise:* Repeat for $E_c - E_d = 0.1$ eV. (The result for $E_c - E_d = 0.1$ eV is somewhat higher, about 170 K.)]

These results are representative of all practical cases. Full ionization is attained somewhere between roughly 100–200 K. Since 200 K is $-73°$C, full ionization may be assumed in all practical cases.

5.10   TEMPERATURE EFFECTS

In previous sections some consideration has been given to the effect of temperature upon n_i^2 and E_f. The discussion of n_i^2 was fairly complete, and the only remaining features we shall consider are presented in Prob. 5.13. We have discussed means for calculating the

Fermi level E_f at any temperature, but we have not looked at the overall results. These will be presented and discussed in this section. We also consider how the carrier concentrations n_o and p_o vary with temperature.

5.10.1 Temperature Dependence of n_o and p_o

Holes and conduction electrons result from impurity ionization and hole-electron pair production. The effects of temperature on these processes dictate temperature dependences of n_o and p_o. Let us consider n-type material, i.e., let N_d be greater than N_a. At $T = 0$ K all acceptors and N_a donors are ionized. There is no hole-electron pair production so $p_o = n_o = 0$.

As T is increased the major change is due to increased donor ionization so that $N_d^+ > N_a$. In that case $n_o = N_d^+ - N_a$ since pair production will be very small. The small number produced leads to $p_o = n_i^2 / (N_d^+ - N_a)$. At some temperature, in the neighborhood of $T = 100$ K perhaps, donor ionization becomes essentially complete and n_o is constant since p_o is still negligible.

As temperature is increased further p_o can no longer be neglected and we must use the CNE and CPE simultaneously. Defining $N_d - N_a = N$, the CNE can be written as $n_o = N + p_o$. Eliminating p_o by use of the CPE, we have $n_o^2 - N n_o - n_i^2 = 0$, the solution to which is

$$n_o = N/2 + [(N/2)^2 + n_i^2]^{1/2} \tag{5.57}$$

Since the temperature dependence of n_i^2 is known, (5.57) permits calculation of n_o for all temperatures above the temperature at which 100% ionization occurs. Then, p_o is easily found from the CPE, i.e., $p_o = n_i^2 / n_o$. At high temperatures n_i^2 will be large compared to $N^2/4$. In that case one finds $n_o = p_o = n_i$, i.e., the material has become in-

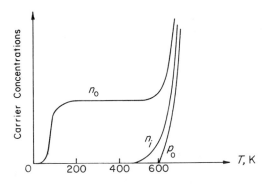

FIG. 5.8   Typical temperature dependence of n_o and p_o in n-type material; n_i is also shown for comparison purposes.

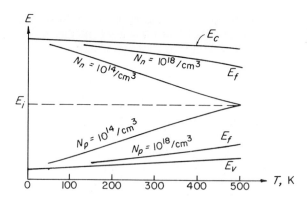

FIG. 5.9   Temperature dependences of E_f, E_c, and E_v in silicon material containing various impurity concentrations.

trinsic. Plotting the relationships discussed above we have the graph of Fig. 5.8.

5.10.2   Temperature Dependence of E_f.

The temperature dependence of E_f may be determined by two means. If n_o or p_o or both are known the equations of Sec. 5.9.2 may be used. From (5.51), for example, we see that as the temperature moves into the high range in Fig. 5.8, the Fermi level approaches the intrinsic level E_i, the center of the energy gap. This is true for both n-type and p-type materials.

When n_o and p_o are not known, (5.54) must be solved at each temperature of interest. The results for the example in Sec. 5.9.4 and for several similar cases are given in Fig. 5.9. Note also an additional effect illustrated in Fig. 5.9. The energy gap E_g is a function of temperature; specifically, there is a significant decrease in E_g as the temperature increases. We will note this again in Chap. 7 in connection with the temperature dependence of Zener breakdown.

SUMMARY

- The distributions of quantum states in the conduction and valence bands are characterized by density of states functions $S_c(E) \simeq A_c(E - E_c)^{1/2}$ and $S_v(E) \simeq A_v(E_v - E)^{1/2}$. In these functions $S(E)dE$ is the number of quantum states per unit volume in the energy range E to $E + dE$.

- The occupation of quantum states is characterized by the Fermi function $f(E) = \{1 + \exp[(E - E_f)/kT]\}^{-1}$ and its complement $f'(E) = 1 - f(E)$. The Fermi function $f(E)$ is the probability that a quantum state is occupied by an electron; $f'(E)$ is the probability that the quantum state is empty, i.e., that it is occupied by a hole. The parameter E_f is the Fermi energy, a constant for a system in thermal equilibrium.

• The distribution of electrons in the conduction band is given by the product $f(E)S_c(E)$. This product multiplied by dE is the number of electrons per unit volume having energies in the energy range E to $E + dE$.

• The distribution of holes in the valence band is given by the product $f'(E)S_v(E)$. This product multiplied by dE is the number of holes per unit volume having energies between E and $E + dE$.

• The thermal equilibrium electron concentration n_o is given by the integral of the product $f(E)S_c(E)dE$ over the conduction band. The resulting expression relates n_o to $E_c - E_f$, the separation between the Fermi energy and the bottom of the conduction band.

• The thermal equilibrium hole concentration p_o is given by the integral of the product $f'(E)S_v(E)dE$ over the valence band. The resulting expression relates n_o to $E_f - E_v$, the separation between the Fermi energy and the top of the valence band.

• Calculations of n_o and p_o in terms of the impurity concentrations involves use of the carrier product equation (CPE), $p_o n_o = n_i^2$, and a relationship known as the charge neutrality equation (CNE), $p_o + N_d^+ = n_o + N_a^-$, where N_d^+ and N_a^- are the concentrations of ionized impurities. At normal temperatures all impurities are ionized so that the CNE becomes $p_o + N_d = n_o + N_a$.

PROBLEMS

5.1. Calculate the number of quantum states per unit volume between $E = E_c$ and $E = E_c + 100(h^2/8m_e^* L^2)$. For convenience choose $E_c = 0$, abbreviate $h^2/8m_e^* L^2$ as E_o, and express A_c in terms of E_o and L. [Ans.: $1000\pi/3L^3$]

5.2. a) There are 10^{16} quantum states/cm^3 at $E = E_f$. Calculate the number of electrons/cm^3 to be found at this energy level. [Ans.: $5 \times 10^{15}/$cm^3]

   b) There are 10^{19} quantum states/cm^3 at $E = E_f + 15kT$. Calculate the number of electrons to be found at this energy level. [Ans.: $3.01 \times 10^{12}/$cm^3]

   c) There are equal numbers of quantum states at $E = E_f + 15kT$ and $E = E_f - 15kT$. Calculate the ratio of the numbers of electrons to be found at the two energy levels. [Ans.: 3.01×10^{-7}]

5.3. When donor quantum states are included in a rigorous analysis of the population of quantum states in a semiconductor, the compound probability P is found to be

$$P = K_T' 2^{N_d^x}/N_d^x!(N_d - N_d^x)! \, \Pi_{i=1}^{M} N_i!(S_i - N_i)!$$

where N_d is the total donor concentration and N_d^x is the neutral donor concentration. The side conditions become $N_T = N_d^x + \sum_{i=1}^{M} N_i$ and

$E_T = N_d^x E_d + \sum_{i=1}^{M} N_i E_i$ where E_d is the energy level of the donor quantum states. Maximize P and thereby derive expressions for N_i/S_i and N_d^x/N_d.

5.4. Develop an inequality for the Fermi level such that the approximation to the Fermi function in (5.27) is in error by at most 3% and the resulting value for n_o can be considered accurate within 3%.

    a) Form the expression for the relative error in $f(E)$ by writing r.e. = |exact − approximate|/exact. [Note: To simplify the algebra it may be convenient to temporarily define $\exp(E - E_f)/kT = e^x$.]

    b) Recognizing that r.e. contains the variable E, select from the range of integration in (5.27) the energy that gives the greatest r.e.

    c) Set this greatest r.e. ≤ 0.03 and solve for E_f. Your answer will be in terms of kT and the energy selected above. [Ans.: $E_f \leq E_c - 3.5\,kT$]

    d) Evaluate kT in eV at 300 K and use this in the above result. [Ans.: $kT = 0.026\,\text{eV}, E_f \leq E_c - 0.091\,\text{eV}$]

5.5. In Prob. 5.4c it was found that the Fermi level must be at least 3.5 kT below E_c if calculations that eventually lead to n_o are to be accurate within 3%. Translate this condition into an inequality relating n_o and N_c by use of (5.32). [Ans.: $n_o \leq 0.03\,N_c$]

5.6. Prove that the CPE is in serious error when $p_o = N_v$ or $n_o = N_c$.

5.7. Calculate n_o and p_o for intrinsic silicon at 350 K, given B_c and B_v from Table 5.2 and $E_g = 1.1$ eV.

5.8. The quantity kT arises often in semiconductor work and it would be efficient to calculate its value for one important temperature and then use temperature ratios when kT at some other temperature is required.

    a) Given that $k = 1.38 \times 10^{-23}$ J/deg = 8.62×10^{-5} eV/deg, calculate kT in electron volts for $T = 300$ K. Learn this value. [Ans.: $kT = 0.026$ eV].

    b) Given that $kT = 0.026$ eV at 300 K, calculate kT at $T = 350$ K and 400 K. [Ans.: $0.026 \times 3.5/3, 0.026 \times 4/3$]

5.9. Graphically estimate the integral of $\sqrt{x}e^{-x}$ from $x = 0$ to $x = 5$ by counting squares under the curve in Fig. 5.6. Compare with $\sqrt{\pi}/2$ and comment on the validity of approximating the integral from 0 to x_c' by the integral from 0 to ∞.

5.10. A sample of silicon at 300 K contains 10^{16} donors/cm^3 and 4×10^{15} acceptors/cm^3. Assuming 100% ionization of the impurities calculate p_o, n_o, and E_f. Express E_f relative to E_i, to E_c, and to E_v. [Ans.: $E_f = E_c - 0.22$ eV]

5.11. A sample of silicon contains 10^{16} donors/cm^3 and 4×10^{15} acceptors/cm^3. The temperature is 100 K and the number of donors ionized is unknown. Assuming the minority carrier concentration is ignorable, calculate the Fermi level. The donor states are 0.1 eV below E_c. [Ans.: $E_f = E_c - 0.079$ eV]

5.12. A sample of silicon has 4×10^{16} acceptors/cm^3 and 10^{16} donors/cm^3. The acceptor levels are 0.1 eV above the valence band.

    a) Calculate the temperature at which 50% of the acceptors are ionized.

    b) Calculate the temperature at which 95% of the acceptors are ionized.

5.13. Equation (5.42) is a valid but somewhat inconvenient expression for n_i^2. It is difficult to use when solving for T with n_i^2 known because T appears both as T^3 and in the exponential. We need an expression with T in only one place.

a) Show that the following expression is equivalent to (5.42): $n_i^2 = B_c B_v \exp[3 \ln T - (E_g/k)T^{-1}]$

b) In the above expression, T still appears in two separate places. Since the logarithmic term varies slowly it might be reasonable over some reasonable basis the values of A and α which provide the "best pression above as $3 \ln T - (E_g/k)T^{-1} \simeq A - \alpha/T$. Determine on some reasonable basis the values of A and α which provide the "best fit" between the two sides of this equation for the temperature range 250–500 K.

c) To the extent that the above approximation is accurate n_i^2 can now be written as $n_i^2 = K \exp(-\alpha/T)$ where K is a constant. Prove this by finding the expression for K in terms of B_c, B_v, A, etc.

d) Using this approximation for n_i^2, evaluate K and α for silicon and compare the exact and approximate values of n_i^2 at the following temperatures: 250, 300, 400, 500 K. Is the accuracy sufficient to justify using this approximation? [Ans.: sometimes yes, sometimes no]

e) Solving for T, the above is rewritten as $T = \alpha[\ln(K/n_i^2)]^{-1}$. Verify this expression.

f) Using the exact values of n_i^2 calculated in d, use the expression in e to calculate the approximate values of T. Compare these with the exact values; 250, 300, 400, 500 K. Is the accuracy sufficient to justify using the approximate equation for temperature calculations?

5.14. Determine the temperature at which hole-electron pair production accounts for 25% of the majority carrier concentration of a sample of silicon for which $N_d = 10^{14}/cm^3$ and $N_a = 0$. Assume that n_i^2 may be approximated as $n_i^2 = Ke^{-\alpha/T}$ where $\alpha = 1.4 \times 10^4$ K and $K = 4.5 \times 10^{40}$ cm^{-6}. [Ans.: 468 K]

C H A P T E R $\mathbf{6}$

Carrier Motion
in Solids

THUS FAR we have examined largely in a qualitative way the origin of current carriers in solid materials. We have seen how to calculate the density of conduction electrons and holes in a semiconductor. Further, the effect of the principal factors that determine carrier concentrations—the energy gap, impurity concentrations, and temperature—have been studied.

The conductive properties of semiconductors are of great interest to us since the important properties of semiconductor devices are framed in terms of conductive properties. We will thus look at the mechanisms responsible for determining the current-carrying nature of a solid. We will first discuss the types of current which flow in a solid and then examine the factors that influence these currents.

6.1 CURRENT FLOW IN A SOLID

Electric current arises from the flow of charges. Two basic mechanisms can lead to charge flow. The first of these is a potential gradient which leads to *conduction current* described by Ohm's law. The second current-producing mechanism is the existence of a non-uniform concentration of charges, or concentration gradient, which leads to *diffusion current*.

6.2 CONDUCTION CURRENT

It is a familiar fact that a potential difference maintained across a substance causes an electric current to flow. The magnitude of the current is determined by the magnitude of the potential difference and the properties of the material involved. For a large number of cases the potential difference V and the electric current I are linearly related and the constant of proportionality is the resistance R of the material. This is just a statement of Ohm's law.

$$I = V/R = (1/R)V \tag{6.1}$$

The current arising from a potential difference (or equivalently, an electric field) is termed a *conduction current* or *drift current*. It results from electrical forces producing directed motion of electric charges, thus yielding a current.

Equation (6.1) is not the most useful form of Ohm's law in studying material properties since the terms of the equation depend on physical dimensions of the sample and do not include explicit parameters of the conducting medium. We would prefer an equation which, to the largest extent possible, involves only the unique properties of the material. This can be obtained in the following way. Let us consider an infinitesimal volume within the material having a cross-sectional area A perpendicular to the direction of current flow and length dx. The region is sketched in Fig. 6.1.

It is found experimentally that the resistance R of a conducting body is proportional to the length of that body and inversely proportional to the cross-sectional area, the constant of proportionality being called the resistivity ρ.[1] Applying this to Fig. 6.1 we have

$$R = \rho(dx/A) \tag{6.2}$$

From (6.1) and (6.2) we obtain

$$I = (A/\rho\,dx)\,dV \tag{6.3}$$

This may be rewritten in terms of current density J and electric field

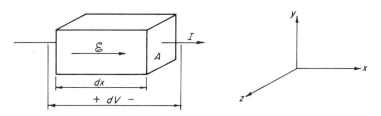

FIG. 6.1   Current-carrying volume $A \times dx$ and its rectangular coordinate system.

---

1. The Greek letter rho ρ is commonly used for electrical resistivity and also for electrical space charge density. Since the latter occurs more frequently in this text we shall, upon completing this section, use ρ only for the space charge density. Developments involving the conducting properties of materials will be phrased in terms of the conductivity σ.

intensity $\mathcal{E}$ by noting that $J = I/A$ and $\mathcal{E} = dV/dx$.[2] Using these, (6.3) becomes $J = (1/\rho)\,\mathcal{E}$ or

$$J = \sigma\mathcal{E} \tag{6.4}$$

where $\sigma = 1/\rho$ = electrical conductivity. This equation is sometimes called the microscopic form of Ohm's law. It is composed of terms independent of the extent of the sample and focuses upon the properties of the conducting medium through the parameter σ.

We wish to examine σ carefully. It is through this term the properties of the conducting material enter Ohm's law. For a given field strength it is the conductivity σ that determines the magnitude of the resulting current density J. From (6.4) we see that it is possible to define σ by the relation

$$\sigma = J/\mathcal{E} \tag{6.5}$$

We cannot infer from (6.5) what determines σ. There is no indication, for example, why the conductivity of a metal is so much larger than that of an insulator.

To gain more insight into the nature of σ, let us calculate the current density J by a different method. Suppose the volume illustrated in Fig. 6.1 contains only holes (no mobile electrons) and their density is p holes per unit volume. Since the current is presumed to flow in the x-direction the holes must have a net velocity in that direction. Denote by v_h the average hole velocity due to the electric field (v_h is commonly called the *hole drift velocity*).

The basic question we wish to answer is, how much charge ΔQ passes through a given cross section of the material in time Δt? To determine this, consider Fig. 6.2a showing a front view of the portion of the conducting material. We designate the location of the cross section of interest as $x = 0$. The cross section with area A is chosen perpendicular to the current flow.

Suppose now (if we may indulge in a bit of fantasy) that all holes

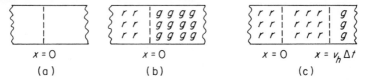

FIG. 6.2   (a) Portion of the sample of Fig. 6.1, (b) arrangement of labeled holes at $t = 0$, and (c) arrangement of labeled holes at $t = \Delta t$.

---

2. Note that in Fig. 6.1 the quantity dV is the drop in potential as one advances a distance dx in the $+x$ direction. This explains why $\mathcal{E} = +dV/dx$ rather than $-dV/dx$; dV/dx is not the potential gradient but instead is its negative.

to the left of $x = 0$ at $t = 0$ are painted red and all those to the right are painted green. Marking red holes r and green holes g, the situation at $t = 0$ is shown in Fig. 6.2b. Given this initial condition, what is the situation at $t = \Delta t$? The velocity of each hole consists of the average drift velocity v_h and a thermal velocity v_t which is random in both magnitude and direction. The average value of the random velocity is zero so its only effect is to mix the red and green holes and thus blur the line dividing them. Ignoring the mixing effects, all holes and the dividing plane between red and green holes have moved to the right a distance $v_h \Delta t$ (see in Fig. 6.2c).

It is now easy to calculate how much charge has passed $x = 0$ in time Δt. The holes between $x = 0$ and $x = v_h \Delta t$ have carried the charge. Since there are p holes per unit volume and the holes of interest occupy a volume $A v_h \Delta t$, the total number of holes passing $x = 0$ in time Δt is $p A v_h \Delta t$. Multiplying this by the charge per hole $+q$ gives the corresponding charge ΔQ to be $\Delta Q = q p A v_h \Delta t$, from which we recognize the hole current and current density to be

$$I_h = \Delta Q / \Delta t = q p A v_h \tag{6.6}$$

$$J_h = I/A = q p v_h \tag{6.7}$$

Now (6.4) and (6.7) both give the current density. Equating them and solving for the conductivity gives

$$\sigma_h = q p (v_h / \mathcal{E}) \tag{6.8}$$

The subscript h has been added to σ because this is the conductivity arising from the presence of holes. Obviously, electrons also contribute to the conductivity when they are present.

We have obtained in (6.8) an expression for the conductivity in terms of the material parameters. Let us examine their significance. It is clear that the conductivity of a material should increase as the density p of mobile carriers increases so it is reasonable that σ should be proportional to the hole density p. Further, if the charge q associated with each carrier is increased, the current for a given carrier flow increases and hence the conductivity increases. Finally, consider $v_h / \mathcal{E}$. Recalling that v_h is the hole drift velocity (the hole velocity increment due to the electric field), we see that $v_h / \mathcal{E}$ measures the ease with which a carrier moves through a material while under the influence of an electric field. We shall call $v_h / \mathcal{E}$ the hole *mobility* μ_h. Thus

$$\mu_h = v_h / \mathcal{E} \tag{6.9}$$

There is similarly an electron mobility μ_e. In the next section we will discuss the factors which determine the magnitude of these mobilities.

We may now rewrite (6.8) in terms of the mobility as

$$\sigma_h = q \mu_h p \tag{6.10}$$

Recall that (6.10) was developed for the hypothetical situation in which only holes are available for carrying current. Actually there are always both holes and electrons present and the currents they carry are additive. To see this, again let there be an electric field directed from left to right in a semiconductor containing p holes/cm^3 and n electrons/cm^3 with carrier mobilities μ_h and μ_e. The electric field moves the holes from left to right producing a positive conventional current density given by (6.7) as

$$J_h = qpv_h = qp\mu_h \, \mathcal{E} = \sigma_h \, \mathcal{E} \tag{6.11}$$

Meanwhile the electric field moves the electrons from right to left producing an electron velocity $v_e = -\mu_e \mathcal{E}$. This flow of electrons from right to left constitutes a conventional current density from left to right,

$$J_e = (-q)nv_e = qn\mu_e \, \mathcal{E} = \sigma_e \, \mathcal{E} \tag{6.12}$$

Since both current densities have the same direction the total conduction current density is given by the sum of J_e and J_h,

$$J = q(p\mu_h + n\mu_e)\mathcal{E} \tag{6.13}$$

which may be rewritten $J = (\sigma_h + \sigma_e)\,\mathcal{E} = \sigma\,\mathcal{E}$ where $\sigma_h = qp\mu_h$ is the hole conductivity, $\sigma_e = qn\mu_e$ is the electron conductivity, and $\sigma = \sigma_h + \sigma_e$ is the total conductivity.

The equations developed above adequately characterize the conduction currents. Unfortunately they do not explain why things behave as they do, e.g., why application of an electric field results in a net drift velocity given by the product of a constant (the mobility) and the intensity of the electric field. Physical insight into the mechanisms involved is important in understanding the nature of conduction and the properties of semiconductor devices. We need therefore to take a closer look at carrier mobilities.

6.2.1   Carrier Mobility

Consider the behavior of a semiconductor in thermal equilibrium. Such a material contains both holes and conduction electrons. Each carrier type possesses an average thermal (kinetic) energy proportional to the temperature and thus a thermal velocity which is quite large, approximately 10^7 cm/s at room temperature.

Even though carrier velocities can be quite high, in thermal equilibrium the carriers as a whole suffer no net displacement. This must be true because in equilibrium no current can flow and a net displacement of the (charged) carriers would constitute a current.

Let us consider the behavior of a conduction electron with average thermal velocity v_t. If we visualize the carriers and lattice atoms or molecules of the crystal in terms of a billiard ball model, we see that

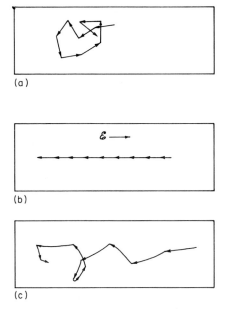

FIG. 6.3   Effect of electric field in superimposing
drift on random motion: (a) random motion of electron in a crystal (for simplicity, equal path lengths between collisions are assumed), (b) component of electron motion added by electric field $\mathcal{E}$, and (c) combination of (a) and (b) representing the superposition of
thermal and electric field effects.

as a conduction electron moves it collides with lattice atoms or other
carriers and in so doing exchanges energy with whatever entity shares
the collision. The electron suffers frequent collisions and after each
it starts off in a new random direction with no memory of its previous
state. The average time between collisions is the *mean free time* T_e and
the average distance traveled between collisions is the *mean free path*
$\mathcal{L}_e$. These are related to the thermal velocity by $\mathcal{L}_e = v_t T_e$.

This situation is illustrated in Fig. 6.3a. As shown, an electron (or
a hole) may possess a large thermal velocity, but in equilibrium it will
suffer no net displacement because of the randomness of the thermal
velocity.

Suppose that an electric field is applied to the sample. The electric field adds a directed nonrandom component to the carrier velocity.
Superimposed upon the random thermal velocity is a velocity component parallel to the field for holes and antiparallel for electrons.
This directed component leads to a net displacement of the carriers

and hence the flow of an electric current. The average net velocity in the direction of the field is termed the *drift velocity* v_d.[3]

These considerations are illustrated in Fig. 6.3. In (b) are shown the equal velocity increments per unit time for an electron, and (c) shows the motion of an electron under superposition of thermal and field effects.

The drift velocity is the ratio of the net displacement s and the time t over which it took place; $v_d = s/t$. It seems that v_d should be a steadily increasing function of time. To see why this might be true consider the behavior of a conduction electron in a material with a constant electric field $\mathcal{E}$. The force on the electron has the constant value $-q\mathcal{E}$. From Newton's third law we would conclude that a constant force leads to a constant acceleration which implies an ever-increasing velocity. The flaw in this reasoning stems from not taking into account the collisions the electron suffers. As it moves through the lattice it collides principally with the lattice atoms, giving up energy to the lattice. The frequency of these collisions increases as the electron velocity increases and thus the rate of energy loss to the lattice also increases. When the rate of energy loss just equals the rate at which energy is acquired from the electric field, the magnitude of the electron velocity will be constant.

This situation is similar to that of a particle moving through a viscous medium under the action of a constant force. Consider a body freely falling through the earth's atmosphere. Two forces act on the body: (1) the (nearly) constant gravitational force and (2) the resistive force of the atmosphere, the latter being proportional to the body's velocity. When the force due to the wind resistance just equals the gravitational force, then acceleration is zero and the velocity of the body reaches its constant terminal value.

This terminal velocity of a hole or an electron in a crystal is the drift velocity v_d and the mobility is the ratio of v_d to the electric field which causes it. Clearly the mobility measures the ease with which a carrier moves through the material. The larger the drift velocity v_d (for a given electric field) the larger the mobility. The magnitude of v_d is determined by the nature of the collision processes of a carrier within a crystal. Two such processes are of particular importance: (1) collisions of the carriers with lattice atoms and (2) collisions of the carriers with ionized impurity atoms. We will examine each process and its effect upon mobility.

6.2.2   Lattice Scattering

The effect of collisions upon a carrier is to divert its motion. Such a process is appropriately termed *scattering*.

---

3. The symbol v_d is used instead of v_h or v_e to indicate drift velocity in general without specifying whether holes or electrons are being considered.

Before considering scattering mechanisms, let us state a fact concerning the motion of carriers within a crystal. A crystal is an arrangement of atoms in a periodic structure. The potential energy of an electron in such a material has the same periodicity. This periodicity gives rise to the energy band structure. In effect the energy band structure specifies a set of electron wavelengths that can exist without attenuation within the crystal. So long as the crystal remains perfectly periodic these allowed wavelengths can propagate through the crystal without attenuation and thus an ideal crystal has zero electrical resistance for those electrons with allowed energies. This situation is analogous to the lossless transmission of any frequency within the band pass of an ideal transmission line.

Any deviation from perfect periodicity results in scattering and hence a nonzero resistance. The most important source of scattering is the temperature. The lattice atoms vibrate about their equilibrium positions with amplitudes directly proportional to the temperature. This thermal vibration degrades the periodic structure of the crystal and therefore makes the motion of the electron through the crystal more difficult.

To visualize this scattering process, again treat the collisions of a conduction electron and the lattice atoms as a billiard ball problem. (This is a gross oversimplification but a convenient model.) The effective size of the atom is the volume it sweeps through as it vibrates. Since both the lattice atom size and the electron velocity increase as the temperature increases, the frequency of such collisions increases. Thus lattice scattering is an increasing function of temperature leading to a decrease in the mobility, which is found to be proportional to $T^{-3/2}$.

Lattice scattering is the dominant mechanism in determining carrier mobility in semiconductors. It is not, however, the only one. Scattering by ionized impurities is also important.

6.2.3 Ionized Impurity Scattering

The presence of impurities in the crystal also disturbs the periodicity of the crystalline potential with a consequent reduction in carrier mobility. Impurities can exist in either the neutral or ionized state and in either case they introduce scattering. Since normally all impurities commonly used in germanium and silicon are ionized we will consider only that case.

In ionized impurity scattering the interaction between the carrier and the scattering center is the coulomb force between two charged particles. For example, the scattering of an electron by an ionized donor is illustrated in Fig. 6.4.

The scattering due to ionized impurities increases as impurity density increases. Impurity scattering is also temperature dependent but in an opposite sense to that of lattice scattering. The effect of the coulomb force in diverting a carrier depends on how long the carrier is

FIG. 6.4   Scattering of an electron by an ionized
donor.

in the vicinity of the scattering center. As the temperature increases the
velocity of the carriers increases, reducing the interaction time and
hence the scattering. The result is that the ionized impurity component
of mobility is an increasing function of temperature proportional to approximately $T^{3/2}$.

While lattice scattering may be the more important in determining
the mobility, ionized impurity scattering is of more interest technologically since we have no control over interactions of the carriers with
the lattice but we must control the impurity concentration to make
useful semiconductor devices. Later we will show how the device characteristics depend upon the carrier mobilities. Accepting for the moment the fact that they do, we need to know how the mobilities vary
with impurity concentration and temperature.

6.2.4   Composite Effect of Lattice and Ionized Impurity Scattering

Shown in Fig. 6.5 is hole mobility–temperature data for samples of
p-type silicon doped with various impurity concentrations. Note that
the mobility decreases as the impurity concentration increases. In the
most heavily doped sample the peak value of the curve corresponds
approximately to the temperature at which lattice and ionized impurity
scattering are equal.

More complete data are shown in Fig. 6.6. Here we see the dependence of mobility on impurity concentration. The normal range of
impurity concentrations in silicon devices is 10^{15}–10^{19}/cm^3. The resulting ratio of maximum mobility to minimum mobility is approximately
14:1. It should be emphasized that the total ionized impurity concentration determines mobility while the net concentration determines carrier
densities. An ionized impurity atom represents a scattering center regardless of its effect on carrier concentrations.

Numerical values for the mobilities of holes and electrons in intrinsic germanium and silicon are shown in Table 6.1 at the end of the
chapter.

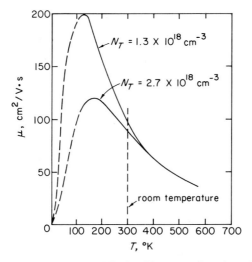

FIG. 6.5   Hole mobility in silicon as a function of temperature. (From A. S. Grove, 1969, *Physics and Technology of Semiconductor Devices,* Wiley, New York, p. 110)

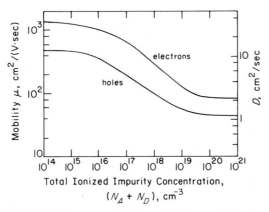

FIG. 6.6   Electron and hole mobilities and diffusion constants as a function of the total ionized impurity concentration in silicon. [Adapted from S. M. Sze, and J. C. Irvin, Resistivity, Mobility and Impurity Levels in GaAs, Ge and Si at 300 K, *Solid-State Electronics* 11(1968):599]

6.2.5   Semiconductor Conductivity

We have found, referring to (6.13), that the conductivity of a semi-conductor is

$$\sigma = q(\mu_e n + \mu_h p) \tag{6.14}$$

where n and p are the carrier concentrations and μ_e and μ_h are their mobilities. Combining the dependence of each of these quantities on temperature we can plot $\ln \sigma$ vs T for an extrinsic semiconductor (see Fig. 6.7). In region A the increase in carrier concentration due to im-purity ionization causes σ to increase. In B all impurities are ionized but the temperature is too low to give appreciable intrinsic generation. Thus the decrease of mobility with increasing temperature causes σ to decrease. In C there is enough intrinsic generation so that the increase in carrier concentration overrides the decrease in mobility and σ in-creases again.

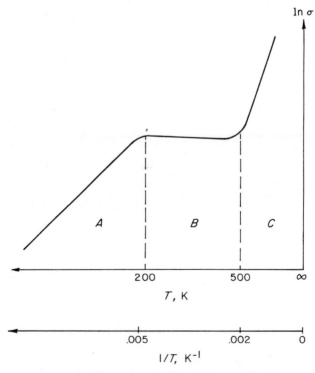

FIG. 6.7   Conductivity versus temperature of a doped semiconductor crystal.

6.3 DIFFUSION OF HOLES AND ELECTRONS

We have assumed that the random motions of holes and electrons average to zero. If the holes and electrons are uniformly distributed, this is correct. When the concentrations are not uniform, the random motion tends to reduce the nonuniformity and results in a net particle motion referred to as *diffusion*. It is not the result of electrostatic forces and it is not a domino effect in which forces are transmitted down a chain of particles. Instead it is particle motion resulting from the fact that random thermal motion leads to a net flow away from regions of higher particle concentration toward regions of lower particle concentration.

Diffusion phenomena are common in everyday life. For example, if a temperature difference is maintained between the ends of a metal rod, we know heat energy will flow away from the region of higher temperature. This flow of energy is due to the diffusion of electrons with large thermal energy from the hotter end of the bar where they are relatively abundant to the colder end where they are relatively scarce. As a second example, consider perfume molecules sprayed in one corner of a still room. In time the odor of the perfume permeates the entire room. No air currents are necessary to cause this. The random thermal motion of the perfume molecules ensures that more such molecules will move out of than into regions of high concentration. Thus the random thermal motion will tend to cause the perfume molecules to become uniformly distributed. When this is attained, no further net motion can take place.

Let us develop a mathematical expression to describe diffusive flow. To have a concrete example, we will look at the diffusion of electrons. For simplicity consider a one-dimensional problem; that is, we assume no variation in concentration in the other two dimensions. Suppose, therefore, a large number of free electrons are constrained to the region between $-x_1$ and $+x_1$, while the regions $|x| > x_1$ are free of electrons. Figuratively, the electrons are in a box extending from $-x_1$ to $+x_1$. These electrons are presumed to be in random thermal motion and uniformly distributed. The system described is illustrated in Fig. 6.8 with the electron concentration denoted by n.

At $t = 0$ let the two opposite ends of the box be removed and consider the electron motions at $t = 0^+$. A number of electrons cross $+x_1$ from left to right and a number cross $-x_1$ from right to left. On the other hand, no electrons can cross $+x_1$ from right to left or $-x_1$ from left to right. Thus at this instant the random motion causes a net transport of electrons from the region of high concentration to the regions of low concentration. For $t > 0^+$ there are electrons crossing $+x_1$ and $-x_1$ in both directions. However if the number of particles just to the left of x_1 is greater than the number just to the right, the net particle flow at x_1 will be to the right. The flow, large at $t = 0^+$, decreases as time increases and the particles spread farther until ultimately the elec-

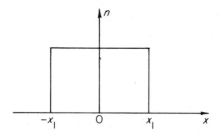

FIG. 6.8   Initial distribution of electrons "in a box."

trons distribute themselves uniformly throughout space. Figure 6.9 is
a sketch of n vs x for several values of t.

To describe diffusion quantitatively we need a quantity to measure flow. As in the case of conduction we would like for this quantity
to be independent of the sample dimensions. Hence we seek a quantity
analogous to the current density J which measures current on a per
unit area basis. In contrast to the conduction case the diffusion phenomenon does not necessarily involve charge motion per se but rather
involves particle motion. The *particle flux density* F (in our example,
the electron flux density) has the required features. The units of F are
particles per second per unit area. It describes the rate at which particles flow through a unit area, i.e., it is the number of particles crossing
a given boundary per second per unit cross-sectional area. Since the
particle flow can vary with respect to both time and space, F is in general a function of t, x, y, and z. Also since flow has direction, F is a
vector. In this text we shall usually consider one-dimensional problems
so F will normally depend only on t and x.

The electron flux density F_e will be different from zero only where
electron concentration n is nonuniform, i.e., where n varies with dis-

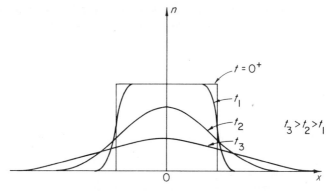

FIG. 6.9   Effect of diffusion on electron concentration n. Parameters t are values of time.

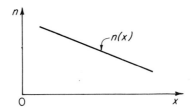

FIG. 6.10   Example in which $n(x)$ decreases with increasing x, giving $F_e(x) > 0$.

tance. (We are assuming zero conduction current for the present.) The more rapidly n varies the larger F_e will be. It seems reasonable that (in one dimension) F_e will be proportional to the magnitude of the slope of n. We must assign a proper direction to the vector F. If n decreases with increasing x as in Fig. 6.10, the slope of n is negative while F_e represents a flow in the positive x-direction. Thus a negative slope of n implies a positive value for F_e and vice versa. Moreover the steeper the slope the greater the particle flow. It thus appears reasonable to write the following proportionality between F_e and dn/dx,

$$F_e \propto -\frac{dn}{dx} \qquad (6.15)$$

The quantity F_e is not determined by dn/dx alone; the properties of the particles flowing (electrons, in our example) and the medium in which they flow also affect F_e. All these factors are incorporated in a quantity D_e, the *diffusion constant* of the electrons in the particular medium being considered. The result is

$$F_e = D_e\left(-\frac{dn}{dx}\right) = -D_e\frac{dn}{dx} \qquad (6.16)$$

This relation is based on the assumption that n is a function only of x. In the more general case, n depends upon all three spatial variables; then

$$F_e = -D_e\nabla n \qquad (6.17)$$

where ∇ is the vector gradient operator. These two equations, often referred to as Fick's law of diffusion, describe a wide variety of diffusion processes.

Note that D depends not only on the type of particle diffusing but also on the medium in which the flow takes place. For example, D_e in silicon is quite different from D_e in germanium.

To describe the diffusion of holes we will have, corresponding to (6.16) and (6.17),

$$F_h = -D_h\frac{dp}{dx} \qquad (6.18)$$

$$F_h = -D_h \nabla p \tag{6.19}$$

Equations (6.16)–(6.19) are stated without derivation. Can we show in a somewhat quantitative manner that they are reasonable?

Consider the motion of electrons whose concentration is n. Exact analysis of the random motion of electrons (or any particle) is complicated. In order to derive the general form of the diffusion law without obscuring the basic principles involved, we shall simplify the situation by pretending that the following conditions hold:

1. The electron motion is random but only in the $\pm x$-direction.
2. All electrons travel the same distance $\mathcal{L}_e$ between collisions.
3. The magnitude of the random thermal velocity is the same for all electrons.

Pretensions (2) and (3) are not realistic except on the average; then all electrons do travel a distance $\mathcal{L}_e$ between collisions (since $\mathcal{L}_e$ is the mean free path) and all have the same thermal velocity v_t. At any instant however different electrons have different free path lengths and velocities.

In general the electron concentration will have a nonconstant slope; that is, a plot of n vs x will probably show some curvature rather than being a straight line. Let n vary with x as in Fig. 6.11 and evaluate the electron flow through an area A (perpendicular to the x-axis) located at $x = 0$. How many electrons pass $x = 0$ (and in which direction) during a particular time interval? Let us select the mean free time T_e as the time interval; here $T_e = \mathcal{L}_e/v_t$. This selection means that if we pretend (again for simplicity) that all electrons suffer a collision at the beginning of the interval, there will be no collisions during the interval to change the motion of any electron. Which electrons and

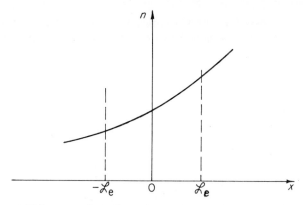

FIG. 6.11   One-dimensional electron distribution used in deriving the diffusion law.

how many will pass $x = 0$ during the interval? Clearly any electron farther away than $\mathcal{L}_e$ cannot reach $x = 0$ during the interval. Conversely any electron initially within the range $-\mathcal{L}_e < x < +\mathcal{L}_e$ can reach $x = 0$ during the interval and will if its initial motion is directed toward $x = 0$.

In the region $-\mathcal{L}_e < x < 0$ there are

$$N_1 = \int_{-\mathcal{L}_e}^{0} n(x)A \, dx \tag{6.20}$$

electrons, half of which will be moving toward $x = 0$. Likewise in the region $0 < x < + \mathcal{L}_e$ there are

$$N_2 = \int_{0}^{+\mathcal{L}_e} n(x)A \, dx \tag{6.21}$$

electrons and half of these are moving toward $x = 0$. The factor of one-half results from the random electron motion making positive and negative velocities equally likely. The quantity $n(x)$ in the integrals in (6.20) and (6.21) is the number of electrons per unit volume as a function of x. The volume between x and $x + dx$ is simply $A \, dx$. The product $n(x)A \, dx$ thus is the number of electrons between x and $x + dx$ and the integrals of this quantity yield the total number of electrons in the two regions.

The net electron flow in the $+x$ direction during the time interval T_e results from $N_1/2$ electrons crossing $x = 0$ from left to right and $N_2/2$ electrons crossing from right to left giving a net number $(N_1 - N_2)/2$. To obtain the electron flux density we simply divide this number by the area A and the time interval T_e to obtain

$$F_e(0) = \frac{(N_1 - N_2)/2}{A \, T_e} = \frac{1}{2 \, T_e} \left[\int_{-\mathcal{L}_e}^{0} n(x) \, dx - \int_{0}^{+\mathcal{L}_e} n(x) \, dx \right] \tag{6.22}$$

We must evaluate the integrals. We do not have an equation describing $n(x)$, but we can approximate $F_e(0)$ by expanding $n(x)$ in a Maclaurin's power series to obtain

$$n(x) = n(0) + \left(\frac{dn}{dx}\right)_0 x + \dots \tag{6.23}$$

Because the mean free path $\mathcal{L}_e$ is very short, the values of x for which the series is to be used ($|x| \leq \mathcal{L}_e$) are very small. Consequently the higher order terms succeeding $(dn/dx)x$ in the series may be ignored.[4]

---

4. It is possible that $n(x)$ might vary so rapidly with x that d^2n/dx^2, etc., would be large enough to make the higher order terms important. In such cases the results developed here would not apply. The cases we shall deal with do not feature such abrupt variations.

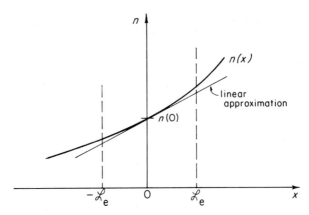

FIG. 6.12   One-dimensional electron distribution used in deriving (6.24).

In effect we are treating $n(x)$ as a linear function passing through the point $n(0)$ with slope $(dn/dx)_0$. This is shown graphically in Fig. 6.12.

The integrals in (6.22) may now be evaluated analytically using (6.23) or graphically using Fig. 6.12. In either case the evaluations are straightforward. Performing them and substituting into (6.22) yields $F_e(0) = (-\mathcal{L}_e^2/2\,T_e)\,(dn/dx)_0$. Since calling the boundary location $x = 0$ is arbitrary, this result immediately generalizes to apply at any point of interest.

$$F_e(x) = -D_e \frac{dn}{dx} \tag{6.24}$$

where $D_e = \mathcal{L}_e^2/2\,T_e$. The form of the diffusion law has thus been verified, and the relation of the diffusion constant to the properties of the electron in the semiconductor has been found.[5]

Recall that several simplifications were made in the derivation of $F_e(0)$. In a detailed analysis of the diffusion process, the diffusion constant D_e calculated above is found to be half its proper size. The reason is in our pretense that all electrons have the same thermal velocity and mean free path; actually there are statistical distributions of both. However, our results show the proper general dependence on $\mathcal{L}_e$ and T_e. The logic in the derivation is accurate. The arithmetic is highly oversimplified and results in the incorrect numerical multiplier.

---

5. The equation for D_e is not really correct. See (6.25) and (6.26) and the discussion therewith.

The expressions for $F_e(0)$ and D_e thus should be amended as

$$F_e(0) = -\frac{\mathcal{L}_e^2}{T_e}\left(\frac{dn}{dx}\right)_0 \tag{6.25}$$

$$D_e = \mathcal{L}_e^2/T_e \tag{6.26}$$

Equation (6.24) is then valid using this value of D_e.

The specific example discussed involves electron motion. A similar description can be given for holes. In that case we would have

$$F_h(x) = -D_h\frac{dp}{dx} \tag{6.27}$$

$$D_h = \mathcal{L}_h^2/T_h \tag{6.28}$$

where the terms have definitions analogous to those for electrons.

In Table 6.1 (p. 163) values are given for D_e and D_h in several semi-conducting materials. The range of values of D in pure samples of silicon and germanium at normal temperatures is 10–100 cm^2/s.

6.4   CONDUCTION AND DIFFUSION

In Secs. 6.2 and 6.3 conduction and diffusion processes are discussed separately. In this section we consider them simultaneously, indicating how they combine. We then derive a relationship between the parameters μ and D.

6.4.1   Total Particle Flux Densities and Currents

The total transport of holes or electrons due to simultaneous conduction and diffusion is simply the superposition of the two effects with both effects expressed on the same basis, i.e., as current densities or as particle flux densities. The relationship between these two densities is simple: since F is the rate at which particles pass through a unit area and J is the rate at which charge passes through a unit area, multiplication of F by the charge carried by each particle yields the current density J. Thus $J = \pm qF$ where the plus sign applies to holes and the minus sign to electrons.

Calculating the conduction particle flux densities and adding those due to diffusion we have

$$F_h = p\mu_h\mathcal{E} - D_h\frac{dp}{dx} \tag{6.29a}$$

$$F_e = -n\mu_e\mathcal{E} - D_e\frac{dn}{dx} \tag{6.29b}$$

To obtain the corresponding electrical current densities multiply by $+q$ and $-q$, respectively, to obtain

$$J_h = qp\mu_h \, \mathcal{E} - q\,D_h\,\frac{dp}{dx} \tag{6.30a}$$

$$J_e = qn\mu_e \, \mathcal{E} + q\,D_e\,\frac{dn}{dx} \tag{6.30b}$$

6.4.2 Thermal Equilibrium in a Nonuniformly Doped Semiconductor and the Einstein Relation

We have seen that the random motions of holes and electrons are involved in both conduction and diffusion currents. Scattering determines the mobility and also randomizes the effects of thermal velocity so the diffusion law applies. We thus might expect to find a relationship between the mobility μ and the diffusion constant D. To find such a relationship we should look for a situation in which both potential and concentration gradients exist simultaneously.

A circumstance which fulfills the above requirements is a semiconductor sample with a nonuniform concentration of impurities. To be specific, consider a sample of n-type material in thermal equilibrium in which the donor concentration varies as shown in Fig. 6.13a.

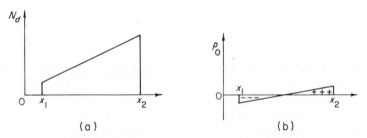

FIG. 6.13   (a) Donor distribution used in discussing the Einstein relation (6.44), and (b) corresponding space charge density ρ_o.

To understand the thermal equilibrium situation, let us perform the following hypothetical experiment. We shall suppose that at $t = 0$ all donors N_d are added to a piece of pure semiconductor and at the same instant each donor ionizes, giving up its extra electron to the conduction band. (This experiment is highly impractical, but it does not violate seriously any physical principle and illustrates the point to be made.) This means that at $t = 0$ the electron concentration $n(x) = N_d$ shown in Fig. 6.13a. Thus $n(x)$ has a gradient equal to dN_d/dx which immediately causes a diffusion of electrons described by the electron flux density,

$$F_1(x) = -D_e \frac{dn(x)}{dx}$$

Since the gradient in n, the slope in Fig. 6.13a, is positive the flux density is negative, i.e., the electron flow is directed to the left. As the electrons diffuse to the left, away from the donors that produced them, a charge unbalance arises and the charge neutrality equation is not exactly satisfied. At the left n is slightly greater than N_d while on the right it is slightly less and there is thus a net space charge density ρ_o equal to $q(N_d - n)$.[6] If ρ_o is sketched the graph of Fig. 6.13b is obtained.

This charge distribution creates an electric field in the x-direction causing a conduction flow of electrons to the right. The conduction flux density is given by

$$F_2(x) = -n(x)\mu_e \mathcal{E} \tag{6.31}$$

Continuing diffusion flow leads to a greater space charge and larger values of $\mathcal{E}$. This process cannot continue indefinitely. What determines the equilibrium value $\mathcal{E}_o$?

In thermal equilibrium there must be no net current. Hence in equilibrium the electron concentration in this n-type sample must vary in such a way that the diffusion set up by the nonuniformity of N_d is just balanced by the conduction flow due to $\mathcal{E}$. This means that when $n(x) = n_o(x)$, the net flux density $F_1 + F_2$ equals zero, and $\mathcal{E} = \mathcal{E}_o$. Thus $-D_e[dn_o(x)/dx] - n_o(x)\mu_e\mathcal{E}_o = 0$, from which we have

$$\frac{\mu_e}{D_e} = -\frac{1}{n_o\mathcal{E}_o}\frac{dn_o}{dx} \tag{6.32}$$

For simplicity we have dropped the (x) notation on n_o. To evaluate the factors $1/n_o$ and dn_o/dx, use (5.32), $n_o = N_c \exp[(E_f - E_c)/kT]$. The only variable on the right side of this equation is E_c. The Fermi level E_f and the temperature T are constant throughout any system in thermal equilibrium and N_c is a constant depending only on temperature and the basic material being considered. Then

$$\frac{dn_o}{dx} = -\frac{1}{kT}\frac{dE_c}{dx}N_c \exp\frac{E_f - E_c}{kT} = -\frac{1}{kT}\frac{dE_c}{dx}n_o \tag{6.33}$$

What now can be said about dE_c/dx? Recall that E_c is the potential energy for the conduction electrons. The gradient of E_c is thus the nega-

---

6. The exact expression for ρ is $q(p + N_d - n)$. For the present discussion p can be disregarded, although for quantitative calculations of ρ it may be important.

tive of the force $-q\mathcal{E}_o$ being applied to the conduction electrons. Thus

$$\frac{dE_c}{dx} = -(-q\mathcal{E}_o) = +q\mathcal{E}_o \tag{6.34}$$

Using this and (6.33) in (6.32), we have

$$\mu_e/D_e = -(1/n_o\mathcal{E}_o)(-1/kT)q\mathcal{E}_o n_o \tag{6.35}$$

Simplifying and rearranging (6.35) leads to

$$D_e/\mu_e = kT/q \tag{6.36a}$$

This is the relation between μ and D whose existence was expected. We could equally well have carried out the development in terms of μ_h and D_h, in which case we would have obtained

$$D_h/\mu_h = kT/q \tag{6.36b}$$

Equations (6.36) are special cases of the general *Einstein relation*

$$D/\mu = kT/q \tag{6.36c}$$

which applies to a class of particles broader than simply holes and electrons. This relation is extremely useful and should be memorized. (The following rhyme may be helpful: "*Dee* over *mu* is *Kay tee* over *que.*")

If the impurity concentration in a semiconductor becomes too large then (6.36a) and (6.36b) are not precisely true. The onset of failure of these relations is found experimentally to be around $N = 10^{19}/cm^3$. Thus the Einstein relations are valid in about the same range of N as (5.32) and (5.40) developed for n_o and p_o. In fact the derivation predicts this since (5.32) is used in obtaining (6.36a).

In developing the Einstein relation we have obtained a fringe benefit. We have found the relationship between the form of the energy band diagram and the electric field. From (6.34) we see that wherever an electric field exists, E_c must be a function of x (in one dimension) such that the slope of E_c is proportional to $\mathcal{E}$. The slope of E_v must be the same as that of E_c because the magnitude of the energy gap E_g is not affected by an electric field. The band diagram appropriate to a constant value of $\mathcal{E}$ is shown in Fig. 6.14. The allowed energy levels within the conduction and valence bands are sketched in this figure. The conduction band levels are shown only in regions where $E \geq E_c$ because the probability of finding a conduction electron in a location where its total energy E is less than its potential energy E_c is just about zero. Classically this probability is exactly zero since (total energy) < (potential energy) implies negative kinetic energy. For a similar reason the allowed levels in the valence band are shown only where $E < E_v$. The potential energy for holes is $-E_v$ and the kinetic energy for holes is $E_v - E$. Thus one finds holes only where $E < E_v$ and the valence electron energy levels are considered to exist only for this condition.

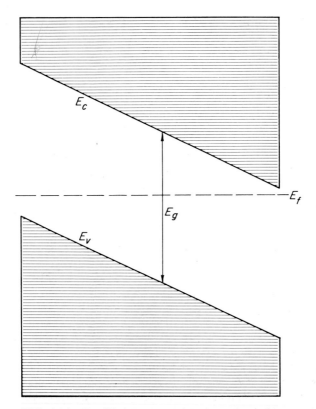

FIG. 6.14 Equilibrium energy band structure of a
semiconductor with nonuniform impurity distribution.

In quantum mechanics a quantum state is defined at all values of x
if it is defined at any value. The wave function simply decays to minute
proportions outside those regions where the classical kinetic energy is
positive. The fact that the wave function is not identically zero in these
regions is important in the discussions of Zener breakdown, the backward diode, and the tunnel diode in Chap. 7.

In Fig. 6.13 we show the thermal equilibrium space charge distribution appropriate to a particular impurity distribution and in (6.31)–
(6.35) we consider the resulting electric field of intensity $\mathcal{E}_o$ and its effects. What is the value of this field? If (6.32) is solved for $\mathcal{E}_o$ and (6.36a)
(the Einstein relation for electrons) is used we obtain

$$\mathcal{E}_o = -\frac{kT}{q}\frac{1}{n_o}\frac{dn_o}{dx} \qquad (6.37a)$$

This expresses the built-in field intensity in terms of the majority carrier concentration and shows explicitly what we also can infer from physical reasoning: in equilibrium a nonzero built-in field exists only if there is a nonuniform carrier concentration, i.e., if $dn_o/dx \neq 0$, which in turn results from a nonuniform impurity distribution.

This field may also be expressed in terms of the net donor concentration $N = N_d - N_a$. If $N \gg n_i$, $n_o \simeq N$ and the result is

$$\mathcal{E}_o = -\frac{kT}{q}\frac{1}{N}\frac{dN}{dx} \tag{6.37b}$$

[*Exercise:* Show that in nonuniformly doped p-type material the equations analogous to (6.37) are

$$\mathcal{E}_o = +\frac{kT}{q}\frac{1}{p_o}\frac{dp_o}{dx} \qquad \mathcal{E}_o = +\frac{kT}{q}\frac{1}{N}\frac{dN}{dx}$$

6.5   CONTINUITY PRINCIPLE AND EQUATIONS

To evaluate the conduction or diffusion current in a semiconductor, the distributions of holes and electrons must be known. The conduction current densities are proportional to the carrier concentrations while the diffusion current densities are proportional to the gradients of the concentrations as shown in (6.30). Furthermore n and p must be known as functions of time as well as the spatial variables, since we must allow for the possibility of time-varying currents.

We now develop the *continuity equations* which are differential equations whose solutions give the distributions of $n(x, y, z, t)$ or $p(x, y, z, t)$. The continuity equations are essentially bookkeeping statements relating the presence, coming, going, creation, and destruction of holes or electrons.

The *continuity principle* upon which the continuity equations are based is: any change in the number of objects in a particular region of space may be accounted for in terms of (1) flow of objects into the region, (2) flow of objects out of the region, (3) creation of additional objects within the region, and (4) destruction of objects within the region; and further, the rate of change of the number of objects is given by an algebraic summation of the rates at which the four processes occur.

Let us apply this to the number of holes in a region of volume ΔV in a semiconductor. Let the region dimensions be Δx, Δy, and Δz. Noting that the creation and destruction processes for holes are generation and recombination, respectively, we may write (net time rate of increase of holes in ΔV) = (time rate of hole flow into ΔV) − (time rate of hole flow out of ΔV) + (time rate of hole generation in ΔV) − (time rate of hole recombination in ΔV).

To translate this into a symbolic equation we proceed as follows. The number of holes in ΔV is $p(x, y, z, t)\, \Delta x\, \Delta y\, \Delta z$, that is, the con-

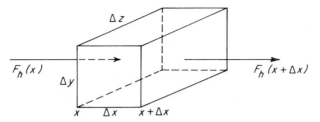

FIG. 6.15   Carrier flow situation used in developing the continuity equation.

centration p times the volume $\Delta V = \Delta x \, \Delta y \, \Delta z$; and the rate of change of the number is simply the time derivative of this product. Since G and R are the per unit volume generation and recombination rates, the total rates are $G \, \Delta x \, \Delta y \, \Delta z$ and $R \, \Delta x \, \Delta y \, \Delta z$, respectively. The flow rates are expressible in terms of the particle flux density for holes; for simplicity consider hole flow to be in the x-direction only as shown in Fig. 6.15. Since F_h is the flow per unit area, the total flow into the volume is $F_h(x) \, \Delta y \, \Delta z$ and the total flow out is $F_h(x + \Delta x) \Delta y \, \Delta z$. The word equation now becomes

$$\frac{\partial}{\partial t}[p(x, y, z, t) \, \Delta x \, \Delta y \, \Delta z] = [F_h(x, t) \, \Delta y \, \Delta z]$$

$$- [F_h(x + \Delta x, t) \, \Delta y \, \Delta z] + [G \, \Delta x \, \Delta y \, \Delta z] - [R \, \Delta x \, \Delta y \, \Delta z] \qquad (6.38)$$

To get a differential equation for p, let the volume ΔV shrink to infinitesimal size by dividing (6.38) by $\Delta x \, \Delta y \, \Delta z$ and letting Δx, Δy, and Δz approach zero; then

$$\frac{\partial p}{\partial t} = \lim_{\Delta x \to 0} \frac{F_h(x, t) - F_h(x + \Delta x, t)}{\Delta x} + G - R$$

By the definition of a partial derivative the first term on the right side is $-\partial F_h / \partial x$. Hence we have the general equation

$$\frac{\partial p}{\partial t} = -\frac{\partial F_h}{\partial x} + G - R \qquad (6.39a)$$

which is the one-dimensional continuity equation for holes.

The continuity equation for electrons is developed by logic identical to that above and is identical in form with (6.39a),

$$\frac{\partial n}{\partial t} = -\frac{\partial F_e}{\partial x} + G - R \qquad (6.39b)$$

Equations (6.39) must be more specific to be really useful. Let us examine the various terms in some detail. The rate of recombination R is proportional to the electron and hole densities. As in (4.5) we write

$R = rpn$ for the number of recombinations per unit volume per second. The generation rate G can be broken into the sum of two terms G_t and G_x, the thermal generation rate and the excess generation rate, respectively. In thermal equilibrium the excess generation rate G_x is zero by definition and the rates of generation and recombination are equal. Hence, in (4.6), we can write $G_t = rp_o n_o$ for the equilibrium number of generations per unit volume per second. This is a constant for any specified temperature since G_t depends basically upon the energy gap and the thermal energy of the valence electrons. Using these expressions for R and G_t we may thus rewrite (6.39) as

$$\frac{\partial p}{\partial t} = -\frac{\partial F_h}{\partial x} - r(pn - p_o n_o) + G_x \qquad (6.40a)$$

$$\frac{\partial n}{\partial t} = -\frac{\partial F_e}{\partial x} - r(pn - p_o n_o) + G_x \qquad (6.40b)$$

[Note: In the majority of problems where these equations are used $R > G_t$. The positive difference $R - G_t$ is generally referred to as the net rate of recombination. In (6.40) this net rate appears as $r(pn - p_o n_o)$.]

Because of the product pn, these equations are nonlinear differential equations that must be solved by computer methods unless some approximations can be found which make an analytical solution possible. Besides pn, another nonlinearity is hidden in (6.40). The flux density terms, if written more explicitly using (6.29), contain the terms $p\mathcal{E}$ and $n\mathcal{E}$, respectively, where $\mathcal{E}$ is the electric field intensity. This intensity depends upon the space charge density ρ which in turn depends upon p and n. Thus $\partial F_h/\partial x$ and $\partial F_e/\partial x$ contain nonlinear terms that can be even more troublesome than the pn terms.

Let us consider the term $pn - p_o n_o$ to see if useful and justifiable approximations can be found to eliminate the nonlinearity. As an aid let us define excess carrier concentrations Δp and Δn as follows:

$$\Delta p = p - p_o \qquad \Delta n = n - n_o \qquad (6.41)$$

These excesses measure the extent of departure from thermal equilibrium since they are zero when thermal equilibrium exists. Using Δp and Δn, the term $r(pn - p_o n_o)$ can be rewritten as

$$r(pn - p_o n_o) = r(p_o n_o + p_o \Delta n + n_o \Delta p + \Delta p \Delta n - p_o n_o)$$
$$= r(p_o \Delta n + n_o \Delta p) + r \Delta p \Delta n \qquad (6.42)$$

In the first term on the right side the variations of n and p appear as a linear sum. However the second term is nonlinear in these variations. Evidently elimination of the nonlinearity in the differential equation implies being able to neglect the second term with respect to the first. The legitimacy of this depends on the size of the excess concentrations Δp and Δn. In all practical cases these excesses are equal for two reasons. Any process creating excess holes or electrons creates hole-electron pairs, thus ensuring $\Delta n = \Delta p$. Second, suppose by some means a localized region of space charge is formed in a semiconductor. In material with a substantial number of mobile carriers the movement of these carriers keeps the space charge density ρ extremely small. If an excess hole concentration Δp is created the excess positive charge $q \Delta p$ attracts a corresponding negative electron charge $-q \Delta n$. If these charges are not equal then the difference attracts or repels charges until equality comes about. Thus $\Delta p = \Delta n$.

Another simplification can be applied to (6.42). In virtually all practical circumstances, the majority carrier concentration in a semiconductor is much larger than the minority carrier concentration. Thus either $n_o \gg p_o$ or $p_o \gg n_o$. To be specific consider n-type material. Unless the material is close to being intrinsic we will have $n_o \gg p_o$ and hence $n_o \Delta p \gg p_o \Delta n$ and (6.42) becomes

$$r(pn - p_o n_o) = rn_o \, \Delta p + r \, \Delta p \, \Delta n \quad \text{n-type material}$$

Similarly, in p-type material

$$r(pn - p_o n_o) = rp_o \, \Delta n + r \, \Delta p \, \Delta n \quad \text{p-type material}$$

The required condition for linearizing the differential equations is now clear: the excess concentration $\Delta p = \Delta n$ must be small in comparison with the majority carrier concentration. If this is satisfied then we have

$$r(pn - p_o n_o) = rn_o \Delta p \quad \text{n-type material} \tag{6.43a}$$

$$r(pn - p_o n_o) = rp_o \Delta n \quad \text{p-type material} \tag{6.43b}$$

Creation of excess carriers is sometimes called *injection* of carriers. The linearizing requirement stated above, $\Delta p = \Delta n \ll$ (majority concentration), is referred to as the condition of low level injection.

It appears from (6.43) that the net recombination rate in either n-type or p-type material is controlled essentially by the majority equilibrium concentration and the minority excess concentration. It seems a bit peculiar that the majority excess concentration is not involved since holes and electrons must recombine at equal rates. Why does only the minority excess concentration appear? Consider the three right-hand terms of (6.42) again: $rp_o \, \Delta n$, $rn_o \, \Delta p$, and $r \, \Delta p \, \Delta n$. These three terms represent the rates at which (1) excess electrons recombine with equilibrium holes, (2) excess holes recombine with equilibrium electrons, and (3) excess holes and electrons recombine with each other, respectively. In n-type material, n_o is large and p_o is small so the second term is large while the first term is small; this means that there is much recombination of minority excess carriers with majority equilibrium carriers and little recombination of majority excess carriers with minority equilibrium carriers. The third term may be larger than the first but will be much smaller than the second if the low level injection condition is fulfilled; thus the dominant net recombination process is minority excess carriers with majority equilibrium carriers. This can also be seen another way. Each minority excess carrier "sees" many majority carriers (most of which are equilibrium carriers) and thus has a high probability of recombining. By contrast each majority excess carrier "sees" only a few minority carriers and thus has a small probability of recombining. Since the number of minority and majority excess carriers are equal and the minorities have a much higher recombination probability, it is clear that the dominant net recombination process is minority excess carriers with majority equilibrium carriers.

Note another aspect of (6.43a) specifically. The left side of this equation is the recombination rate in number of excess carriers/ ($cm^3 \cdot$ sec) in n-type material. From the right side we see that this rate is proportional to the excess hole concentration Δp. The constant of proportionality between Δp and the recombination rate is rn_o. Since the units of Δp are number/cm^3 it follows that rn_o must have the units of sec^{-1} or $1/rn_o$ must have the units of seconds. The quantity $1/rn_o$ is called the *hole lifetime* τ_h. Thus for a given excess carrier concentration Δp, the quantity τ_h specifies the rate at which these carriers recombine. Whatever physical mechanisms govern the recombination process are somehow summarized within τ_h. Similarly in (6.43b), $1/rp_o$ is the *electron lifetime* τ_e. Both quantities τ_e and τ_h are discussed more completely in Sec. 6.6.1 where the reference to these quantities as lifetimes is justified.

Taken together, τ_e and τ_h are referred to as the lifetimes in p-type and n-type materials, respectively. These carrier lifetimes τ_e and τ_h must not be confused with the carrier mean free times T_e and T_h which are orders of magnitude smaller and have entirely different meanings. In terms of τ_h and τ_e, (6.43) are

$$r(pn - p_o n_o) = \Delta p/\tau_h \quad \text{n-type material} \tag{6.44a}$$

$$r(pn - p_o n_o) = \Delta n/\tau_e \quad \text{p-type material} \tag{6.44b}$$

Consider now the flux density terms in (6.40). We have noted that the variation in conduction flux densities introduces nonlinearities because of the terms $p\mathcal{E}$ and $n\mathcal{E}$. Can we ever justify neglecting the conduction flux densities and if so, when? Consider the magnitudes of the various flux density components. Majority conduction flow is always much larger than that of the minority carriers since the majority carrier concentration is much larger than the minority carrier concentration. Thus, since the carriers have comparable mobilities and see the same electric field, the minority conduction flow is nearly always negligible. This in turn means that the flow of minority carriers is important only when diffusion predominates.

This circumstance may seem very restrictive and might imply that minority carriers are unimportant in describing semiconductor device properties. Actually, the opposite is true. The existence of concentration gradients of excess carriers in operating devices leads to substantial minority carrier diffusion and further, minority carriers are important precisely because of the simplification introduced by being able to drop the conduction term and consider only diffusion. It is not obvious that this is the case but a justification of this must be deferred to a more detailed study. Here we shall assume the minority flux is due entirely to diffusion.

Thus, using only diffusion flux densities and combining (6.40), (6.41), and (6.44), we obtain the continuity equations for minority carriers.

$$\frac{\partial p}{\partial t} = D_h \frac{\partial^2 p}{\partial x^2} - \frac{p - p_o}{\tau_h} + G_x \quad \text{n-type material} \tag{6.45a}$$

$$\frac{\partial n}{\partial t} = D_e \frac{\partial^2 n}{\partial x^2} - \frac{n - n_o}{\tau_e} + G_x \quad \text{p-type material} \tag{6.45b}$$

This completes the development of the continuity equations. Equations (6.45) are used in specific situations to determine how the minority carrier concentrations, $p(x, t)$ in n-type material and $n(x, t)$ in p-type material, vary with position and time.

It may seem insufficient to be able to calculate behavior of only minority carriers. Actually this is a very important capability. Almost everything to be derived in semiconductor devices can be found from the variation in minority carrier concentrations. Furthermore, in most cases $\Delta p = \Delta n$. This means that once the minority carrier concentration is found as a function of x and t, the majority carrier concentration may be written down by inspection if actually needed.

6.5.1   Applications of the Continuity Equations

Consider the use of the continuity equations in determining non-equilibrium carrier concentrations in a semiconductor.

EXAMPLE 6.1

Suppose a homogeneous sample of n-type silicon has been uniformly illuminated for a long time prior to $t = 0$ and at $t = 0$ the illumination is removed abruptly. Assume that the illumination produces uniform photogeneration of hole-electron pairs through the sample. Let this rate of excess generation be G_o. Assume also that the low level injection condition holds. Find p and n just prior to $t = 0$ and for all time after $t = 0$.

Solution

We begin with calculation of the minority carrier concentration and since the sample is n-type, we use (6.45a). This equation is a partial differential equation containing the partial derivatives of $p(x, t)$. Do both independent variables need to be considered or can the equation be rewritten as an ordinary differential equation in x or t alone? Everything about the problem is uniform in space. The sample is homogeneous and the illumination is uniform. Thus in this case p is not dependent on x and $\partial^2 p / \partial x^2 = 0$. The continuity equation then becomes

$$\frac{dp}{dt} = -\frac{p - p_o}{\tau_h} + G_x \tag{6.46}$$

Prior to $t = 0$ the sample is in steady state with $G_x = G_o$. Steady state means $dp/dt = 0$, so we immediately find

$$p(t) = p_o + G_o \tau_h \qquad (t \leq 0) \tag{6.47}$$

At $t = 0$ the illumination is removed so that G_x becomes 0. This terminates the steady state so that $dp/dt \neq 0$. Thus the differential equation becomes

$$\frac{dp}{dt} = -\frac{p - p_o}{\tau_h} \qquad (t \geq 0) \tag{6.48}$$

Solving this equation by standard techniques gives

$$p(t) = p_o + K \exp(-t/\tau_h) \tag{6.49}$$

where K is the arbitrary constant which must always appear in the solution of a first order differential equation. This constant is not really arbitrary in that it must be chosen so that the equation properly describes the variations of p with time. At $t = 0^-$ the value of $p(t)$ is known. Since G_x, p, and p_o are all finite, dp/dt is finite and therefore $p(t)$ is continuous at $t = 0$. There is no discontinuous change in the hole concentration. Using (6.47) and (6.49) the continuity at $t = 0$ thus requires $p_o + G_o \tau_h = p_o + K$ or $K = G_o \tau_h$. Thus (6.49) may be written

$$p(t) = p_o + G_o \tau_h \exp(-t/\tau_h) \qquad (t \geq 0) \tag{6.50}$$

The electron concentration $n(t)$ may now be written with the aid of the condition $p - p_o = n - n_o$. Thus

$$n(t) = n_o + G_o \tau_h \qquad (t \leq 0) \tag{6.51a}$$

$$n(t) = n_o + G_o \tau_h \exp(-t/\tau_h) \qquad (t \geq 0) \tag{6.51b}$$

Equations (6.47), (6.50), and (6.51) describe the hole and electron concentrations as functions of time. They show that a steady generation rate G_o leads to steady-state excess concentrations $G_o \tau_h$ and these excesses decay to zero with a time constant τ_h when the excess generation terminates. This is shown graphically in Fig. 6.16 where the concentrations are plotted against time. To plot n and p to the same scale the $n(t)$ ordinate is broken. This is necessary since n_o is much larger than $p_o + G_o \tau_h$ according to the assumption of low level injection.

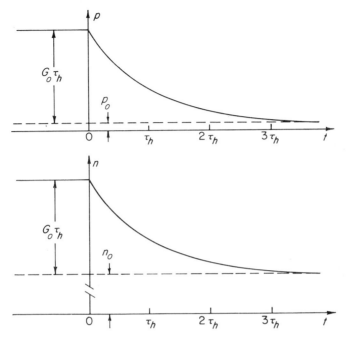

FIG. 6.16 Hole and electron concentration time dependences for Ex. 6.1.

EXAMPLE 6.2

Suppose a homogeneous sample of n-type silicon in thermal equilibrium is, at $t = 0$, subjected to an intense, very brief flash of illumination everywhere in the sample. Let the generation rate corresponding to this flash be represented by an impulse function $G_x = A\delta(t)$. Calculate the hole concentration assuming low level injection.

Solution

The differential equation to use is again (6.46) since there is no spatial dependence to be considered. Prior to the flash thermal equilibrium exists so that $p(t) = p_o$ ($t < 0$). From $t = 0^-$ to $t = 0^+$ the excess generation rate is $A\delta(t)$ and the number of excess hole-electron pairs produced is found by integrating (6.46)

$$\int_{0^-}^{0^+} \frac{dp}{dt}\, dt = -\int_{0^-}^{0^+} \frac{(p - p_o)}{\tau_h}\, dt + \int_{0^-}^{0^+} A\delta(t)\, dt$$

Evaluating the integrals gives

$$p(0^+) - p(0^-) = 0 + A \tag{6.52}$$

Thus the change in $p(t)$ at $t = 0$ simply equals the strength A of the generation impulse. For $t > 0$ the excess generation rate is again zero and (6.48) and (6.49) apply. Repeating (6.49), $p(t) = p_o + K \exp(-t/\tau_h)$ ($t > 0$). To evaluate K we evaluate (6.52) at $t = 0^+$ and equate this to the known value of $p(t)$ at that time. Since $p(0^-) = p_o$ and the increase is simply A, $p(0^+) = p_o + A$. Thus one finds that $K = A$ and

$$p(t) = p_o + A \exp(-t/\tau_h) \qquad (t \geq 0^+) \tag{6.53}$$

The time dependence of the hole concentration thus becomes as shown in Fig. 6.17.

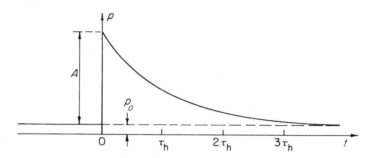

FIG. 6.17   Hole concentration time dependence for Ex. 6.2.

The above examples illustrate the use of the continuity equation when only time dependence must be considered. The next application treats the converse situation when only x-dependence must be considered.

EXAMPLE 6.3
Suppose the left half of a homogeneous sample of n-type silicon is steadily illuminated by light of frequency suitable for production of hole-electron pairs, with excess generation rate G_o everywhere in the left half. Find the steady-state hole concentration for both halves of the sample. Assume the sample is extremely long and the low level injection condition holds.

Solution
Since this is n-type material, (6.45a) again applies. Steady state in the present context means zero time dependence. (If the illumination were varied sinusoidally, steady state would have a different meaning.) Thus $\partial p/\partial t = 0$ and the differential equation again becomes ordinary

$$0 = D_h \frac{d^2 p}{dx^2} - \frac{p - p_o}{\tau_h} + G_o \qquad (x < 0) \tag{6.54a}$$

$$0 = D_h \frac{d^2 p}{dx^2} - \frac{p - p_o}{\tau_h} + 0 \qquad (x > 0) \tag{6.54b}$$

Solving these equations by standard methods yields

$$p(x) = p_o + G_o \tau_h + K_1 \exp(-x/\sqrt{D_h \tau_h})$$
$$+ K_2 \exp(+x/\sqrt{D_h \tau_h}) \quad (x \leq 0) \tag{6.55a}$$

$$p(x) = p_o + K_3 \exp(-x/\sqrt{D_h \tau_h}) + K_4 \exp(+x/\sqrt{D_h \tau_h})$$
$$(x \geq 0) \tag{6.55b}$$

The constants K_1, K_2, K_3, and K_4 are again the arbitrary constants. There are four of them because two different second order differential equations have been solved (one for $x < 0$ and one for $x > 0$.)

The length constant $\sqrt{D_h \tau_h}$ in the exponentials in (6.55) is called the *diffusion length* L_h, i.e., $L_h = \sqrt{D_h \tau_h}$. This parameter is discussed in more detail in Sec. 6.6.2.

For (6.55) to be useful the four arbitrary constants must be determined. The conditions at $x = 0$ provide some information required for this determination. Continuity of $p(x)$ is one condition we can invoke since if $p(x)$ were not continuous the diffusion flow would be infinite; hence $p(0^-) = p(0^+)$. Also the flow itself must be continuous or the flow "into" $x = 0$ would not equal the flow "out" and $p(0)$ would be growing or decreasing with time. Thus $(dp/dx)_{0^-} = (dp/dx)_{0^+}$. In addition, we must insist that $p(x)$ behave reasonably for arbitrarily large values of $\pm x$ (recall that the bar is extremely long).

Consider the implications of this latter requirement. For increasingly negative x the term $K_1 \exp(-x/L_h)$ (since $L_h = \sqrt{D_h \tau_h}$) gets increasingly large. This is not reasonable because the material and generation rate are uniform in the region $x < 0$ and $p(x)$ should approach a uniform distribution as its distance from $x = 0$ increases. We thus conclude that K_1 should be zero to eliminate the divergent behavior of this term. On the other hand the term $K_2 \exp(+x/L_h)$ decays to zero for large negative x so this term is well behaved.

Similar reasoning for large values of x leads to the conclusion that K_4 must equal zero. Thus (6.55) reduce to

$$p(x) = p_o + G_o \tau_h + K_2 \exp(+x/L_h) \quad (x \leq 0)$$

$$p(x) = p_o + K_3 \exp(-x/L_h) \quad (x \geq 0)$$

We use the conditions at $x = 0$ to find K_2 and K_3. For continuity of dp/dx at $x = 0$ we find that K_2 and K_3 are related by

$$(K_2/L_h)e^0 = (-K_3/L_h)e^0 \tag{6.56}$$

so that $K_2 = -K_3$. Requiring continuity of $p(x)$ itself at $x = 0$ then yields

$$K_3 = G_o \tau_h/2 = -K_2 \tag{6.57}$$

Using these expressions $p(x)$ is given by

$$p(x) = p_o + G_o\tau_h - (G_o\tau_h/2)\exp(x/L_h) \qquad (x \leq 0) \qquad (6.58a)$$

$$p(x) = p_o + (G_o\tau_h/2)\exp(-x/L_h) \qquad (x \geq 0) \qquad (6.58b)$$

These equations together describe the steady-state dependence of hole concentration on x throughout the entire bar of material. This dependence is illustrated graphically in Fig. 6.18.

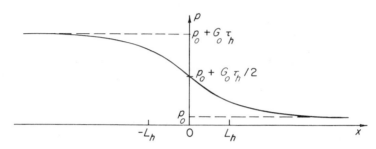

FIG. 6.18   Hole concentration x-dependence for the situation described in Ex. 6.3.

Figure 6.18 shows that $p(x)$ for $x \ll 0$ approaches a uniform distribution dictated by the excess generation whereas for $x \gg 0$ it approaches the thermal equilibrium value p_o. One significance of the diffusion length L_h is apparent. It is the length constant which governs the transition from one uniform distribution to another. The range of the transition from $p \simeq p_o + G_o\tau_h$ to $p \simeq p_o$ extends a few L_h on each side of $x = 0$, the place where G_x changes from G_o to 0.

EXAMPLE 6.4

Suppose the left portion of a homogeneous sample of n-type silicon is subjected to illumination or some other process such that at $x = 0$ there is a steady-state hole concentration $p(0) = K_o$. The right portion is very long and has no excess generation. Assuming low level injection, find the steady-state hole concentration in this right portion.

Solution

This problem is similar to that in Ex. 6.3. Since only the right portion of the sample need be considered the continuity equation to use is simply (6.54b) and the solution is as given in (6.55b). Again the term $K_4\exp(+x/L_h)$ behaves unacceptably so K_4 must be zero. Applying the condition $p(0) = K_o$ then gives

$$p(x) = p_o + (K_o - p_o)\exp(-x/L_h) \qquad (x \geq 0) \qquad (6.59)$$

A plot of this equation is identical with that given in the right half of Fig. 6.18 except that the value of $p(0)$ is K_o rather than $p_o + G_o\tau_h/2$.

6.6 LIFETIME AND DIFFUSION LENGTH

The terms *lifetime* and *diffusion length* have been assigned to the time and length constants arising in the examples in Sec. 6.5. Additional meanings are associated with these quantities as follows.

6.6.1 Lifetime

In Ex. 6.1 we see that the existence of $G_o \tau_h$ excess holes at $t = 0$ is followed by a gradual disappearance of these excess carriers due to recombination when the excess generation is terminated. Evidently recombination occurs immediately after generation for some holes and a long time after for others. The time elapsing between generation and recombination for a particular hole is the life span of that hole. In Ex. 6.2 the excess holes were generated at $t = 0$ and the life span of a hole is simply the time at which it recombines. Thus if the ith hole recombines at t_i, its life span is t_i. This life span t_i varies from zero to very large values because recombination is a chance happening.

In characterizing human populations one sometimes speaks of life expectancy, i.e., how long on the average a person may expect to live. This same concept is useful in discussing the behavior of carriers in a semiconductor. Suppose we calculate the average life span for holes. If the initial number of excess holes per unit volume is $\Delta p(0)$, we need to calculate the total number of hole-seconds (analogous to man-hours or man-years) contributed by these holes and divide by $\Delta p(0)$ to get the average life span for the group.

We have seen that the total recombination rate is $R = p(t)/\tau_h$. This includes recombination of excess holes generated at $t = 0$ and recombination of holes generated thermally at various times. If we subtract the thermal generation rate $G_t = p_o/\tau_h$ from the total recombination rate R the difference is the rate at which excess carriers are recombining. Using this difference we have the number recombining between t and $t + dt$ where dt is infinitesimal, $[(p(t) - p_o)/\tau_h]\,dt$. The hole-seconds contributed by the above number of holes is simply their number times their life span t or $t[(p(t) - p_o)/\tau_h]\,dt$. To obtain the total hole-seconds we integrate this over all values of time from zero to infinity so the contributions of all excess holes are included. Thus

$$\text{total hole-seconds} = \int_0^\infty t[(p(t) - p_o)/\tau_h]\,dt \qquad (6.60)$$

Then divide by $\Delta p(0)$ to obtain

$$\text{average life span} = [1/\Delta p(0)] \int_0^\infty t[(p(t) - p_o)/\tau_h]\,dt \qquad (6.61)$$

Evaluation of this expression is straightforward and shows that *average life span* is identical with lifetime τ_h. With appropriate modification of notation the above conclusions apply equally to electrons in p-type material.

[*Exercise:* Show, by evaluation of (6.61) using the results of Ex. 6.2, that the average life span for a hole in p-type material is simply the lifetime τ_h.]

Lifetime is thus (1) the average life span for excess carriers, (2) a parameter used in calculating the recombination rate R and the thermal generation rate G_t, and (3) the time constant describing the decay of excess carriers.

The values of τ_e and τ_h vary widely depending upon the type of semiconductor, the degree of crystalline perfection, the presence of various impurities, etc. In general the carrier lifetimes in silicon are smaller than those in germanium and larger than those in gallium arsenide. In silicon the values of τ (either τ_e or τ_h) vary between approximately 1 μs and 1 ns.

We see later that several important diode and transistor parameters depend upon τ_e or τ_h. To cite one important example, low values of τ are important in diodes or transistors required to perform fast-switching operations, such as those in high speed computers.

6.6.2 Diffusion Length

Diffusion length L is essentially the space analog of lifetime. It represents the average distance a minority carrier diffuses during its lifetime. This can be shown by calculations similar to those in Sec. 6.6.1. Note this distance is much longer than the mean free path $\mathcal{L}$ because a hole can experience many collisions before recombining with an electron. Note also that the ratio of diffusion length to lifetime is not the thermal velocity v_t because the hole does not travel in a single direction during its lifetime but bounces around in various directions. It thus travels a total path length given by the product of lifetime and thermal velocity but the net distance traveled, that is, the distance the hole diffuses, is much less than this.

In addition, the diffusion length has the analytical meaning introduced in Exs. 6.3 and 6.4; it is the length constant describing the exponential distance variations of minority carriers.

SUMMARY

● Current in semiconductors is made up of conduction current and diffusion current. The conduction current results from an electric field while diffusion current results from gradients in p and n.

● The conduction current is proportional to the electric field intensity, the carrier concentration, and the carrier mobility μ. The mobility is the ratio of the drift velocity to the electric field intensity.

Its numerical value is determined by the lattice scattering and impurity scattering processes that randomize the carrier motion and cause the drift velocity to be proportional to the field intensity.

• The diffusion current is proportional to the carrier concentration gradient and the carrier diffusion constant D. The numerical value of the diffusion constant is determined by the same scattering processes governing the mobility. In fact, these two parameters are related to one another by the Einstein relation $D/\mu = kT/q$.

• In general the carrier concentrations in nonthermal equilibrium situations are found by solving the carrier continuity equations. The general forms of these equations are nonlinear, but in most cases linearizing approximations can be made.

• Two parameters that arise in connection with solutions of the continuity equations are the lifetime and the diffusion length. The lifetime is the average time between a carrier's generation and its recombination. The diffusion length is the average net distance a carrier travels during its lifetime.

• Numerical values for the mobilities and diffusion constants are given in Table 6.1.

Table 6.1. Intrinsic properties of several semiconductor elements and compounds at 300 K.

Property	Si (silicon)	Ge (ger-manium)	GaAs (gallium arsenide)	GaP (gallium phosphide)	Units
E_g: energy gap	1.1	0.66	1.43	2.24	eV
$n_i(300\ K)$: intrinsic concentration	1.5×10^{10}	2.4×10^{13}	$\sim 10^7$	$\sim 10^{-1}$	cm^{-3}
m_e^*/m: electron effective mass ratio	1.1	0.55	0.07	0.5	
m_h^*/m: hole effective mass ratio	0.59	0.37	0.5	0.5	
μ_e: electron mobility	1350	3900	8500	110	$cm^2/(V \cdot s)$
μ_h: hole mobility	480	1900	400	75	$cm^2/(V \cdot s)$
D_e: electron diffusion constant	35	100	220	2.8	cm^2/s
D_h: hole diffusion constant	12	49	10	1.9	cm^2/s
ϵ_r: relative dielectric constant	12	16	11	10	

PROBLEMS

6.1.   A sample of silicon is 0.5 cm^2 in cross section and is 3 cm long. A potential difference of 15 V between ends of the sample produces a uniform electric field. Calculate the conduction current density and the conduction current if the material conductivity is 2 mho/cm.

6.2.   A sample of germanium is 0.25 cm^2 in cross section and is 2 cm long. Application of 3 V between ends of the sample results in a current of 4 A. Assuming the potential distribution is uniform, calculate the conductivity of the material.

6.3.   In a certain sample of germanium the electron mobility is 3900 cm^2/(V · s) and the hole mobility is 1900 cm^2/(V · s). Calculate the particle drift velocities (specify both magnitude and direction) if an electric field of 10 V/cm is applied in the $+x$-direction.

6.4.   A sample of silicon is 0.3 cm^2 in cross section and 4 cm long. It is found that on the average a hole traverses the length of the bar in 10 ms (ten milliseconds) when an external voltage of 8 V is applied. Determine the hole mobility for this sample.

6.5.   A sample of silicon is 0.2 cm^2 in cross section and 3 cm long. The electron concentration is 10^{15}/cm^3. Calculate the electron conduction current density and current if an applied field causes the electrons to drift at a velocity of 900 cm/s.

6.6.   A sample of germanium is 0.3 cm^2 in cross section and 1 cm long. The hole concentration is 10^{14}/cm^3. Find the hole drift velocity if the hole current is 500 mA.

6.7.   A sample of pure silicon is 0.2 cm^2 in cross section and 2 cm long. The temperature is such that n_i = 1.5 × 10^{10}/cm^3. The electron conductivity is 3 × 10^{-9} mho/cm. Calculate the electron mobility.

6.8.   A sample of gallium arsenide is 0.6 cm^2 in cross section and 1 cm long. Calculate the electron conductivity if the electron mobility is 4000 cm^2/(V · s) and the electron concentration is 10^{15}/cm^3.

6.9.   A sample of silicon is 0.2 cm^2 in cross section and 2 cm long. The temperature is 300 K, the donor concentration is 10^{15}/cm^3, and there are no acceptors. The mobilities are μ_h = 400 cm^2/(V · s) and μ_e = 1200 cm^2/(V · s). An external field is applied resulting in a total current of 500 mA.
   a)   Calculate the electron and hole currents.
   b)   Does the ratio of I_h to I_e depend on the magnitude of the total current? Derive a general expression for this ratio. Evaluate numerically for the case at hand.

6.10. Calculate and plot on log-log coordinates the conductivity of p-type silicon as a function of impurity concentration over the range 10^{12}–10^{19}. Assume all impurities ionized and negligible hole-electron pair production.

6.11. Consider two samples of n-type silicon: in the first N_d = 10^{13}/cm^3 and in the second N_d = 10^{17}/cm^3. Assume full ionization and negligible hole-electron pair production. Assume Figs. 6.5 and 6.6 apply.
   a)   Calculate the conductivities at room temperature (300 K).
   b)   Which conductivity shows stronger temperature dependence (on a percentage basis) near room temperature? Explain.
   c)   Sketch the conductivities versus temperature on log-log coordinates over the range 100–400 K.

6.12. In a sample of germanium the electron concentration is found to vary as $n = 10^{14}(1 - 10x + 50x^2)/cm^3$ when x is measured in cm. Calculate the electron flux density at $x = 0.01$ cm if the electron diffusion constant is 80 cm/s. [Ans.: $+7.2 \times 10^{16}$ electrons/(cm$^2 \cdot$ s)]

6.13. A sample of n-type silicon is 0.2 cm^2 in cross section and 3 cm long. The hole concentration is found to vary with distance as $p = p_o + P_1 \exp (-x/L_h)$ where P_1 and L_h are constants having the dimensions of holes/cm^3 and length, respectively. The x-axis runs the length of the sample with $x = 0$ at the left end.
   a) Calculate F_h, J_h, and I_h (due to diffusion only) in terms of D_h, q, p_o, P_1, L_h, x, and/or the area A.
   b) Evaluate J_h algebraically at $x = 0$; and numerically for $D_h = 12$ cm^2/s, $P_1 = 10^{12}/cm^3$, and $L_h = 10^{-3}$ cm. [Ans.: 1.92 mA/cm^2]
   c) Sketch p and J_h as functions of x.

6.14. A sample of p-type silicon is 0.3 cm^2 in cross section and 2 cm long. The electron concentration decreases linearly from a value N_1 at $x = 0$ to zero at $x = W$ where N_1 and W are constants.
   a) In which direction $\pm x$ are the electrons diffusing?
   b) Sketch the electron flux density versus x over the range $x = 0$ to W.
   c) What value must N_1 have if the electron diffusion current is -10 mA? Use 35 cm^2/s for the electron diffusion constant. The value of W is 10^{-4} cm.

6.15. An effective velocity with which particles are diffusing may be calculated by equating the diffusion current density to $J_h = qpv_{diff}$ or $J_e = qnv_{diff}$ where v_{diff} plays the same role in the description of diffusion as the drift velocity plays in the description of conduction.
   a) Calculate the effective diffusion velocity (as a function of distance) for the situation in Prob. 6.13. Sketch v_{diff} vs x.
   b) Repeat a for the situation in Prob. 6.14.

6.16. Holes are flowing in the $+x$-direction at a rate of 2×10^{16} holes/(cm$^2 \cdot$ s). Calculate the corresponding algebraic current density.

6.17. Electrons are flowing in the $+x$-direction at a rate of 3×10^{15} electrons/(cm$^2 \cdot$ s). Calculate the corresponding algebraic current density.

6.18. The x-axis current density due to holes is -10 A/cm^2. Calculate the algebraic hole flux density. In which direction are the particles moving?

6.19. You are doing some calculations requiring application of the Einstein relation. You know the relationship is either $\mu/D = kT/q$ or $D/\mu = kT/q$. You remember the units of μ and D and you recognize that kT/q has the dimensions of voltage (energy divided by charge). With this information use dimensional analysis to determine which formula is correct.

6.20. Discuss how the temperature dependence of a given diffusion constant differs from that of the corresponding mobility. Use the Einstein relation to convert the mobility data in Fig. 6.5 to diffusion constant data.

6.21. Use the Einstein relation to express the mobility in terms of temperature and any two of the three parameters L, v_t, and τ_c (the mean time between collisions).

6.22. A sample of n-type silicon at 300 K is 0.2 cm^2 in cross section and 1.5 cm long. The donor concentration is $10^{15}/cm^3$. Application of 100 mA direct current results in a potential difference of 4.3 V along the length of the sample. Determine the electron diffusion constant for this material. What assumption about the hole conduction current is necessary in the solution of this problem?

6.23. A sample of p-type silicon at an unknown temperature is carrying a hole current density of 30 mA/cm^2. At the left end of the sample ($x = 0$) half the current density is due to conduction and half due to diffusion. The hole concentration is given by $p = 10^{14} + 10^{12} \exp(-\alpha x)$ where $\alpha = 10^4$ cm^{-1}. The potential gradient at $x = 0$ is 19.5 V/cm. Determine the temperature of the sample.

6.24. A sample of silicon has acceptor concentration varying linearly from 10^{18}/cm^3 at the left end to 10^{16}/cm^3 at the right end. The sample is 0.1 cm long. The hole diffusion constant is 12 cm^2/s.

   a) Write an approximate expression for p_o as a function of x and calculate F_h.

   b) Describe the charge unbalance which develops, sketch the resulting space charge density, and indicate the direction of the field produced.

   c) Derive the expression for the electric field intensity $\mathcal{E}$ as a function of x.

   d) Sketch N_a vs x and directly below it sketch $\mathcal{E}$ vs x. Where is $\mathcal{E}$ larger?

6.25. Using the situation described in Prob. 6.24 as a vehicle, carry out an analytic derivation for the Einstein relation for holes. Explain carefully the expression you use for the electric field intensity.

6.26. A homogeneous sample of p-type silicon is uniformly illuminated with a step function of light at $t = 0$. Prior to $t = 0$ thermal equilibrium exists. The light produces hole-electron pairs at a rate such that the percent change in the hole concentration is very small.

   a) Does this problem involve time only, space only, or both time and space?

   b) Evaluate the electron concentration for $t \geq 0$ in terms of lifetime, excess generation rate, and such other parameters and variables as appropriate.

   c) Sketch the results of this evaluation.

   d) Suppose that $\tau_e = 100 \ \mu s$, $D_e = 30$ cm^2/s, $n_o = 10^{18}$/cm^3 and G_x at $x = 0$ is 10^4/(cm$^3 \cdot$ s). Evaluate $n(x, t)$ at $x = 0$, $t = \tau_e$. [Ans.: 6.42×10^9/cm^3]

6.27. A sample of n-type silicon with the two ends designated as $x = 0$ and $x = W$ is steadily illuminated at both ends. *Photogeneration* of hole-electron pairs occurs only at the ends of the sample and in steady state produces $p = P_1$ at $x = 0$ and $p = P_2$ at $x = W$.

   a) Does this problem involve time only, space only, or both time and space?

   b) Calculate the steady-state hole concentration in terms of P_1, P_2, L_h, and such other quantities as appropriate.

   c) Plot p vs x for $P_1 = 100 \, p_o$, $P_2 = 10 \, p_o$, and $L_h = W$.

   d) Repeat c with $L_h = 0.1 \, W$.

   e) Repeat c with $L_h = 10 \, W$.

   [Note: The distribution in e is like that in one region of a transistor. Although the boundary values P_1 and P_2 in the transistor are not produced by photogeneration the mathematics is the same. The distribution is approximately a straight line connecting P_1 and P_2.]

6.28.   Estimate the spread in values of life span for holes in n-type material
        by evaluating σ_τ, the standard deviation, by calculating the root-mean-
        square value of life span and applying $\sigma_\tau = [\tau_{rms}^2 - (\tau_{av})^2]^{1/2}$, where τ_{rms}
        is the rms life span and $\tau_{av} = \tau_h$ is the average life span. [Ans.: $\tau_{rms} =$
        $1.414\,\tau_h$]

6.29.   Groups III and V impurities diffuse in silicon and germanium at high
        temperatures. If a very thin layer of very high concentration of phos-
        phorus is placed on a silicon surface, the distribution of phosphorous
        atoms as a function of distance is $N_d(x, t) = Q(\pi Dt)^{-1/2}\exp(-x^2/4Dt)$
        where t is the time and Q is the total number of phosphorous atoms/cm^2.
        a)   Verify that the equation given is a solution of the continuity equa-
             tion for N_d. (Why may the electric field term be ignored here?)
        b)   The diffusion constant of phosphorus in silicon at 1100°C is 3.8 ×
             10^{-13} cm^2/s. At 1100°C how much time elapses until the concen-
             tration of phosphorous atoms at a depth of 10^{-3} cm reaches 10% of
             the concentration at the surface, i.e., $x = 0$?

6.30.   So long as $\mu_e \neq \mu_h$, the minimum value of the conductivity of a semi-
        conductor is less than the intrinsic conductivity. Show the σ_{min} occurs
        for carrier concentrations given by

        $$n = n_i(\mu_h/\mu_e)^{1/2} \qquad p = n_i(\mu_e/\mu_h)^{1/2}$$

        Show further that $\sigma_{min} = \sigma_i[2b^{1/2}/(b + 1)]$ where $b = \mu_e/\mu_h$.

6.31.   Consider a semiconductor in which two recombination processes are
        present characterized by the lifetimes τ_1 and τ_2. The recombination rate
        due to each is proportional to the excess minority carrier concentration.
        Show that the resultant lifetime τ_t is given by $1/\tau_t = 1/\tau_1 + 1/\tau_2$.

C H A P T E R 7

Junction Diode

IN THE previous chapters the concentrations and motions of charge carriers in n-type and p-type semiconductors and metals have been considered separately. In this chapter we consider what happens when the substances are joined together. Our principal concern is the properties of the *pn* junction where p-type and n-type semiconductors meet. We shall also deal briefly with "contacts," i.e., junctions between metals and semiconductors.

The *pn* junction is the heart of the junction diode. An elementary structural sketch and the diode current-voltage characteristic are given in Fig. 7.1.

The semiconductor portion of the diode is a continuous crystalline lattice in which the impurity doping is changed from acceptor dominance in one portion to donor dominance in the remainder. The boundary (a plane in the structure sketched in Fig. 7.1) between the resulting p-type and n-type regions is called the metallurgical junction. The current-voltage characteristic of the diode is due almost entirely to the behavior of the holes and electrons in the regions near this junction.

At the two ends of the semiconductor crystal, contacts are formed by alloying or depositing a metallic coating. There is a certain amount of "art" involved in making contacts. If they are improperly made they themselves introduce a current-voltage characteristic similar but inferior to that of the junction. Proper formation of these contacts involves selection of the appropriate metal and suitable chemical treatment of the surface prior to applying the metal. In some cases heavy concentrations of impurities are introduced at the surface to improve contact performance. The theory underlying all these steps is beyond the scope of the present discussion. The main point here is that contacts when properly made carry current equally well in either direction and behave like resistances in the range of a fraction of an ohm.

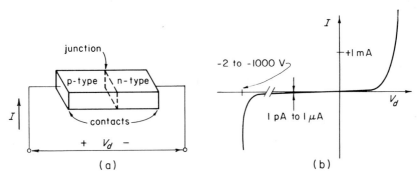

FIG. 7.1   (a) Elementary structure and (b) current-
voltage characteristic of the junction diode.

Let us now turn our attention to a physical understanding of the
junction itself. As before we begin with thermal equilibrium.

7.1   *pn* JUNCTION IN THERMAL EQUILIBRIUM
To obtain a simple clear picture of the thermal equilibrium situation in a *pn* junction it is helpful to perform a thought experiment
and imagine forming the junction by bringing together a p-type and an
n-type piece of semiconductor in such a way that the crystalline structure is continuous across the boundary where they are joined. This is
not the way junctions are really made but it is a convenient way to arrive at an understanding of the junction's thermal equilibrium features.

Consider the two pieces before they are joined. The p-type piece
has many holes and very few electrons and the n-type piece has many
electrons and very few holes. It is important to recognize that both are
electrically neutral. In the p-type piece the ionized acceptors and the
few electrons exactly balance the hole charge and in the n-type piece
the ionized donors and the few holes exactly balance the electron
charge. This statement is the charge neutrality equation (CNE) expressed in words.

Consider next the instant when the two pieces are brought together. At the boundary between them are large concentration gradients. The hole concentration changes abruptly from a large value in
the p-type piece to a very small value in the n-type piece while the electron concentration change is exactly the reverse. These gradients result
in diffusion flows of holes from *p* to *n* and electrons from *n* to *p*. Notice
what this does to the neutrality of the two pieces or regions (as we
should now call them since the pieces are joined to form a single semiconductor crystal). Consider the p-region. As holes leave the p-material
they leave behind negatively charged ionized acceptor atoms which
are of course immobile charges. As electrons enter the p-region they are

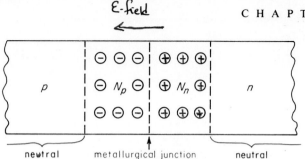

FIG. 7.2   Charge distributions in a *pn* junction.

surrounded by large numbers of holes and immediately recombine. This "exposes" additional acceptor ions, i.e., it leaves the acceptor ions without adjacent positive charges to maintain net neutrality. Thus the net negative charge possessed by the p-region resides in a layer of exposed acceptor ions near the *pn* boundary. Similarly the net positive charge of the n-region resides in a layer of exposed donor ions near the *pn* boundary. These layers are shown schematically in Fig. 7.2.

Thus as noted the p-region takes on a net negative charge and the n-region takes on a net positive charge. These charges are near the boundary and create an electric field across the boundary opposing the flows due to diffusion. The field is directed from the n-region to the p-region.

The force the field exerts on charged particles crossing the boundary pushes some holes back toward the p-region and some electrons back toward the n-region and results in diminished hole and electron flow rates. Charge unbalance continues to develop but at a smaller rate. As time goes on the charge unbalance finally becomes sufficient for the electric field to reduce the net hole and electron flows across the boundary to zero and thermal equilibrium exists. The features of this thermal equilibrium status may be summarized as follows:

1. There are charged regions on either side of the *pn* boundary.
2. The electric field due to these charged regions counteracts the tendency for holes and electrons to diffuse across the boundary.

Note that the existence of an electric field implies a variation of electric potential and of electron potential energy and a potential difference across the boundary. This difference is called the *barrier potential* V_{Bo} because the electric field has established a barrier to the flow of holes from *p* to *n* and the flow of electrons from *n* to *p*. The height of this barrier equals the change in electron potential energy across the barrier and is called the *barrier energy* E_{Bo}. Thus we have a third feature of the *pn* junction in thermal equilibrium:

3. The electric field creates a barrier potential V_{Bo} and a corresponding barrier energy $E_{Bo} = qV_{Bo}$ across the boundary.

The region surrounding the metallurgical junction of the two layers of exposed impurity ions is called here the *space charge layer* (SCL) because of the net charge that exists within it. Several other equally appropriate names are found in the literature: *barrier layer* because of the energy barrier there, *depletion layer* because the electric field there largely depletes the region of mobile carriers, and *transition region* because within it occurs the transition from neutral p-type to neutral n-type material.

Note that the space charge layer lies between two neutral regions. The SCL by definition contains all the departures from neutrality that came about when the junction was formed. Also, the SCL itself has overall neutrality. The negative charge on the p-side of the boundary exactly matches the positive charge on the n-side since the two original pieces of semiconductor are neutral and the regions outside the SCL are neutral.

Let us examine the *pn* junction in thermal equilibrium from the viewpoint of energy. The energy band diagrams of the two original pieces of material are shown in Fig. 7.3.

The two pieces are originally neutral so there is no electric field or potential difference between them. (We are ruling out fields and potential differences due to outside influences.) This means no work is done in taking a test charge from rest at the surface of one piece to rest at the surface of the other, and the surface energies and the bands of the two line up as in Fig. 7.3. Therefore, before the pieces are joined,

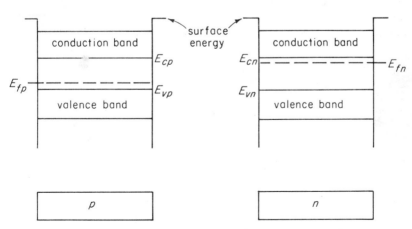

FIG. 7.3   Energy band diagrams for separate neutral p-type and n-type semiconductors.

$E_{cp} = E_{cn}$ and $E_{vp} = E_{vn}$ where these quantities are defined by their locations in Fig. 7.3.

Notice however that $E_{fp} \neq E_{fn}$. The two Fermi levels are different by an amount somewhat less than the energy gap E_g. Recall in Chap. 5 we learned that a system in thermal equilibrium possesses a single Fermi level. Evidently these two pieces together are not in thermal equilibrium even though each piece separately is in equilibrium. This is obvious when we recall what happens when the two pieces are joined. At the instant of contact large flows of holes and electrons occur, charge unbalance builds up, and potential and energy differences arise. System equilibrium is finally attained with zero net hole and electron flows across the boundary, and a barrier potential V_{Bo} and a barrier energy difference E_{Bo} existing across the SCL. What does the new energy band diagram look like? The barrier energy E_{Bo} is a potential energy difference, so the potential energy for electrons E_c must change from one side of the SCL to the other. Considering the need for a single Fermi level in a system in thermal equilibrium, evidently the value of E_{Bo} that causes zero net carrier flow coincides with the value that causes the two Fermi levels to become one, i.e., $E_{fp} = E_{fn} = E_f$.

These features are shown in Fig. 7.4. Notice that relative to the p-region all energies in the n-region have been lowered by an amount E_{Bo} (or we can say that relative to the n-region all energies in the p-region have been raised by an amount E_{Bo}). The Fermi levels coincide and there are transitions in E_c and E_v over the extent of the SCL such that $E_{cp} - E_{cn} = E_{vp} - E_{vn} = E_{Bo}$. In Fig. 7.4 one simplification is made: the upper conduction band edge E_c' and the lower valence band edge E_v' are omitted because there are essentially no free carriers near these energies and their values are thus not important.

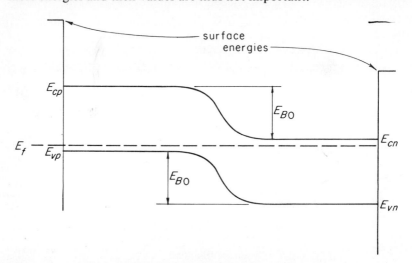

FIG. 7.4   Energy band diagram for a *pn* junction in thermal equilibrium.

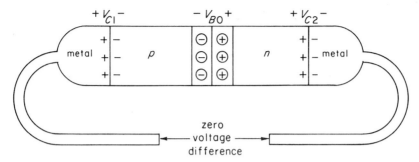

FIG. 7.5   Schematic representation of a *pn* diode
showing the barrier potential V_{Bo} and the contact
potentials V_{c1} and V_{c2}.

Note that the surface energies also differ by E_{Bo}. Does this imply a
voltage difference V_{Bo} between the two surfaces and does this mean we
have discovered a solid-state battery? Yes, there is a voltage difference.
No, we do not have a solid-state battery. To use the "battery" we
would have to connect some conductors or semiconductors to the surfaces and at that instant flows of holes and/or electrons would occur
at the surface connections bringing about contact potentials V_{c1} and V_{c2}
analogous to the barrier potential V_{Bo}. These contact potentials would
be of the appropriate magnitudes and polarities to exactly cancel V_{Bo}
and the net voltage would be exactly zero. This is illustrated in Fig. 7.5
where metal contacts have been formed at the free ends of the p- and
n-regions. The directions of V_{c1} and V_{c2} have been assigned arbitrarily.
Their actual values and polarities depend on the materials involved. In
any case however

$$V_{c1} + V_{c2} = V_{Bo} \tag{7.1}$$

Let us consider how holes and electrons are distributed in the
energy bands and how thermal equilibrium may be viewed in terms of
these distributions. The plots of $f(E)S_c(E)$ and $f'(E)S_v(E)$ in Fig. 5.5
provide this distribution information. These plots are superimposed on
the energy band diagram in Fig. 7.6 where the electron and hole distributions are shown at the edges of the SCL. Inside these distribution
plots we have shaded certain areas corresponding to carriers whose
total energies are such that the barrier energy does not prevent them
from passing through the SCL.[1]

Considering the two electron distribution diagrams, notice that we
have shaded the entire area n_{po} corresponding to electrons in the

---

1. It should be pointed out that the relative areas under these curves are grossly ex-
aggerated. In a typical silicon sample the minority carrier concentration is a factor of
10^{12} smaller than the majority carrier concentration. If Fig. 7.6 were accurately drawn
the areas under the curves would be in this proportion. Also, note that for simplicity the
variations of E_c and E_v within the SCL have been drawn as straight lines. Actually they
are smooth curves, as shown in Fig. 7.4.

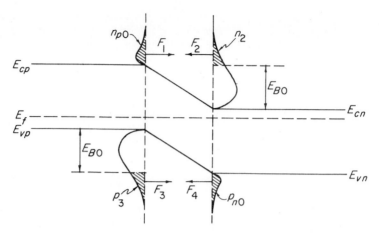

FIG. 7.6   Energy bands and carrier distributions for a
pn junction in thermal equilibrium.

p-region because these electrons are "at the top" of the barrier and do
not view the barrier as an impediment. For them the electric field in
the SCL is an accelerating one. By contrast electrons in the n-region
are "at the bottom" of the barrier and cannot surmount it unless they
have kinetic energy at least as large as E_{Bo}. Thus only the area n_2 above
$E_{cn} + E_{Bo}$ is shaded.

Similar remarks apply to the hole distribution. All holes in the
n-region (the shaded area p_{no} on the diagram) can pass through the SCL
unimpeded because they are accelerated, not decelerated, by the electric field. By contrast holes in the p-region must reside in energy states
at least E_{Bo} down in the valence band to have enough kinetic energy to
surmount the barrier.[2] Thus only the area labeled p_3 is shaded for holes
in the p-region.

We consider the carriers represented by the shaded areas because
they lead to corresponding flows F_1, F_2, F_3, and F_4 proportional to
n_{po}, n_2, p_3, and p_{no}, respectively. Thermal equilibrium exists only if
F_1 balances F_2 and F_3 balances F_4, i.e., $F_1 = F_2 = F_{eo}$ and $F_3 = F_4 =
F_{ho}$, where F_{eo} is the thermal equilibrium value of F_1 and F_{ho} is the
thermal equilibrium value of F_4. To bring about this balancing of hole
and electron flows E_{cn} must be just far enough below E_{cp} so that $n_2 =
n_{po}$ and $p_3 = p_{no}$.[3] If E_{Bo} were too small, then $F_2 > F_1 = F_{eo}$ and $F_3 >$

---

2. A hole at $E = E_v$ has zero kinetic energy. Increasing kinetic energy for holes
means moving down on the electron energy band diagram. It may be helpful to visualize
the hole as an air bubble in a tank of water (the valence band). It tends to stay at the top
and work must be done to move it down.

3. This is not strictly true. As described in App. 7.1 it is actually a pair of related
quantities n_2' and p_3' which must equal n_{po} and p_{no}, respectively. The basic reason is that
some of the carriers comprising n_2 and p_3 have x-directed kinetic energies less than
E_{Bo} even though their total kinetic energies exceed E_{Bo}.

$F_4 = F_{ho}$ thus causing a buildup in charge unbalance, a growing electric field, and an increasing E_{Bo}. Conversely if E_{Bo} were too large, then $F_2 < F_1$ and $F_3 < F_4$. The net flows would reduce the charge unbalance, thereby reducing the electric field and E_{Bo}. Thus the system always tends toward a stable equilibrium in which E_{Bo} is such that $F_1 = F_2$ and $F_3 = F_4$.

7.2   JUNCTION DIODE WITH APPLIED VOLTAGE

With the thermal equilibrium situation described in Sec. 7.1 as a foundation, we can consider the practical case where the diode is subjected to a positive or negative applied voltage. For the present we shall treat the case of constant voltage. (Section 7.5 deals with the time-dependent case.) The junction diode is shown in Fig. 7.7 with a voltage V_d applied and a diode current I defined. Also shown are the contact potentials V_{c1} and V_{c2} and a voltage V_B across the SCL. The voltage V_B is the *barrier voltage*, a generalization of the barrier potential V_{Bo} which is the thermal equilibrium value of V_B. Thus $V_B = V_{Bo}$ when $I = 0$. Resistor symbols R_p and R_n in the diode schematic account for ohmic voltage drops along the neutral portions of the p- and n-regions.

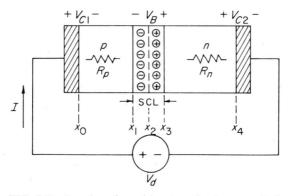

FIG. 7.7   A *pn* junction with external voltage applied.

What happens when V_d is applied and a current I flows? For the present let us regard the $R_p I$ and $R_n I$ voltage drops as negligible; then it is evident that V_d equals the following algebraic summation of the contact potentials and the barrier voltage,

$$V_d = V_{c1} - V_B + V_{c2} \tag{7.2}$$

We assume that the contact potentials do not change appreciably with the current I. Thus V_{c1} and V_{c2} have the same values in (7.2) as in (7.1). But that equation says $V_{c1} + V_{c2} = V_{Bo}$. Thus (7.2) may be written more simply as

$$V_d = V_{Bo} - V_B \tag{7.3}$$

or in incremental notation, with $\Delta V_B \equiv V_B - V_{Bo}$,

$$V_d = -\Delta V_B \tag{7.4}$$

Equation (7.4) indicates that, except for sign, the change in barrier voltage equals the applied voltage. Thus positive V_d leads to reduced V_B while negative V_d leads to increased V_B. [The application of $V_d > V_{Bo}$ does not lead to a negative barrier voltage in spite of what (7.3) indicates because we discover that as V_d approaches V_{Bo} the current I becomes large so the ohmic drops $R_p I$ and $R_n I$ cannot be ignored. Equation (7.3) must be modified to account for $R_p I$ and $R_n I$ in that case.]

We have shown how V_d affects the barrier voltage V_B. Now we wish to know how much current flows when a given V_d is applied. Insight into this can be obtained from Fig. 7.8, a diagram drawn for the case of positive V_d, which is defined as the *forward bias* condition. Since positive V_d reduces V_B (and hence E_B) the energy bands for the n-region are raised relative to where they are in thermal equilibrium. Because of this, the concentration n_2 of electrons energetic enough to surmount the barrier is larger than its thermal equilibrium value n_{po} which means that $F_2 > F_{eo}$. So far as electrons in the p-region are concerned there is no change. The number is still n_{po} so that $F_1 = F_{eo}$. Thus we have a flow unbalance in which $F_2 > F_1$ so there is a net flow of electrons from the n-side to the p-side.

Likewise for holes, p_3 is increased above its thermal equilibrium value p_{no} and $F_3 > F_{ho}$ so there is a net flow of holes from p to n. These

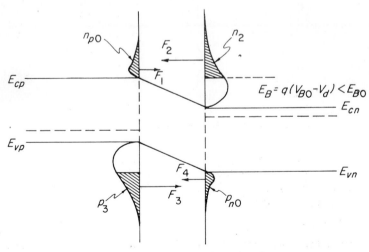

FIG. 7.8   Energy band and carrier distribution diagrams for a junction diode with positive voltage applied (resistance drops are neglected).

flows of holes from p to n and electrons from n to p both produce conventional current from p to n. Thus the current I is positive as expected. (If it were negative with V_d positive, the diode would be delivering power to the external generator—clearly an absurdity.)

The nature of the dependence of I upon V_d is reasoned as follows: the Fermi function causes the curve bounding n_2 on the right to have an exponential character—note for example the integrand in (5.27)—which means that the area n_2 varies exponentially as the lower boundary of the area is raised and lowered. Since the change in the lower boundary results from the band shifting brought about by V_d it is plausible that n_2 and F_2 are increased by exponential factors when compared to their thermal equilibrium values.

Similarly it is plausible that p_3 and F_3 increase exponentially with V_d. Since the net current depends upon the unbalances between F_2 and F_1 and between F_3 and F_4 it appears that the diode current I is proportional to the difference between the exponential function of V_d and its thermal equilibrium value $e^0 = 1$. Thus it is not unreasonable that the $I = f(V_d)$ relationship should be

$$I = I_s[\exp(qV_d/kT) - 1] \tag{7.5}$$

where I_s is a function of material constants such as n_{po}, p_{no}, diffusion constants, etc. The current in forward bias is thus a very sensitive function of the applied voltage.

This equation is logical also for the reverse bias case $V_d < 0$. Negative V_d causes a raising of the energy barrier thereby exponentially reducing n_2, F_2, p_3, and F_3 so that F_2 and F_3 become very small in comparison with F_1 and F_4 (see Fig. 7.9). As a result $F_2 - F_1$ approaches $-F_1$ while $F_3 - F_4$ approaches $-F_4$ and I approaches a negative constant $-I_s$ in (7.5).

The proposal of exponential dependences of n_2, p_3, F_2, and F_3 on V_d is explored further in App. 7.1. The conclusion is that F_2 and F_3 are proportional to $\exp(qV_d/kT)$ so the form of (7.5) is substantiated.

The analysis up to this point has not identified the exact nature of the current-voltage relationship because I_s in (7.5) has not yet been found as a specific function of p_{no}, n_{po}, etc. Also no consideration has been given to "injected electrons" as they enter the neutral p-material and "injected holes" as they enter the neutral n-material. Accordingly let us analyze the carrier motion in those neutral regions.

Consider first the n-material. The pertinent equations are

$$I_h = qA\left(\mu_h p \mathcal{E} - D_h \frac{\partial p}{\partial x}\right) \tag{7.6a}$$

$$I_e = qA\left(\mu_e n \mathcal{E} + D_e \frac{\partial n}{\partial x}\right) \tag{7.6b}$$

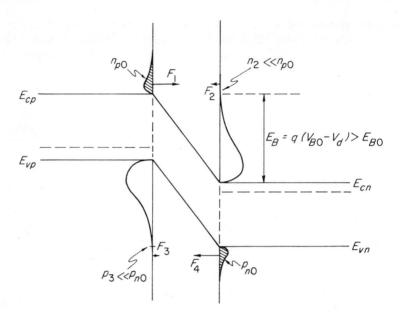

FIG. 7.9   Energy band and carrier distribution
diagrams for a junction diode with negative voltage
applied (resistance drops are neglected).

$$\frac{\partial p}{\partial t} = D_h \frac{\partial^2 p}{\partial x^2} - \frac{p - p_o}{\tau_h} - \mu_h \frac{\partial(p\mathcal{E})}{\partial x} \tag{7.7a}$$

$$\frac{\partial n}{\partial t} = D_e \frac{\partial^2 n}{\partial x^2} - \frac{p - p_o}{\tau_h} + \mu_e \frac{\partial(n\mathcal{E})}{\partial x} \tag{7.7b}$$

$$\epsilon \frac{\partial \mathcal{E}}{\partial x} = \rho = q(p - n + N_d - N_a) \tag{7.7c}$$

The latter three equations in principle permit solving for p, n, and $\mathcal{E}$ as functions of x. Then the first two equations can be used to calculate I_h and I_e and their sum is the total current I.

In practice one cannot proceed in this way for an analytic result since equations (7.7) form a nonlinear set because of the products $p\mathcal{E}$ and $n\mathcal{E}$. In general an accurate solution can be obtained only by solving the equations numerically, using digital computer routines for the solution of simultaneous nonlinear differential equations. On the other hand an adequate analytic solution can be obtained if certain reasonable approximations are made. In (7.6b) the term $qA\mu_e n\mathcal{E}$ is comparable to the total current I. Since we are dealing with n-type material we have $p \ll n$ which means $qA\mu_h p\mathcal{E} \ll qA\mu_e n\mathcal{E}$. Hence the first term in (7.6a) can be discarded since it is not a significant part of the total current I

anywhere in the n-material, and by the same reasoning the last term in (7.7a) can be discarded. Thus the hole current I_h, if significant in size, can be regarded as purely diffusion current and the differential equation for $p(x, t)$ can be treated as linear. Our present concern is with the DC current-voltage relationship so that $\partial p/\partial t = 0$ and $\partial^2 p/\partial x^2$ becomes a total derivative. Thus (7.7a) simplifies to

$$0 = D_h \frac{d^2 p}{dx^2} - \frac{p - p_o}{\tau_h} \tag{7.8}$$

This linear second order differential equation now can be solved for p.

Two boundary conditions are required in the course of the solution. At $x = x_3$ (see Fig. 7.7) there is a boundary condition $p(x_3)$ produced by the arrival of holes from the p-material energetic enough to surmount the barrier. Previously we have suggested that these holes are characterized by p_3 in Fig. 7.8. However it is shown in App. 7.1 that a slightly different quantity $p'_3 = p_{no} \exp(qV_d/kT)$ actually characterizes these holes. This concentration of energetic holes applies throughout the entire p-material and also within the SCL because very little recombination occurs there due to the low electron concentration. It thus applies all the way to $x = x_3$ and gives the boundary condition

$$p(x_3) = p'_3 = p_{no} \exp(qV_d/kT) \tag{7.9}$$

The second boundary condition requires that the hole concentration approach the thermal equilibrium value p_{no} for $x \gg x_3$.

The general solution of (7.8) is readily shown to be

$$p(x) = p_{no} + K_1 \exp(-x/L_h) + K_2 \exp(+x/L_h) \tag{7.10}$$

where as usual $L_h = \sqrt{D_h \tau_h}$. To obtain $p(x) \rightarrow p_{no}$ for increasing x we must set $K_2 = 0$. Then applying (7.9) we have the following (shown in Fig. 7.10),

$$p(x) = p_{no} + p_{no}[\exp(qV_d/kT) - 1] \exp[-(x - x_3)/L_h] \tag{7.11}$$

If (7.11) is now used in (7.6a) omitting the $\mu_h p\mathcal{E}$ term, the hole current I_h is obtained as a function of x.

$$I_h(x) = qAD_h(p_{no}/L_h)[\exp(qV_d/kT) - 1] \exp[-(x - x_3)L_h] \tag{7.12}$$

This equation shows that the hole current decays to zero as one proceeds far into the n-material. At the edge of the neutral n-material $x = x_3$, the hole current is

$$I_h(x_3) = qAD_h(p_{no}/L_h)[\exp(qV_d/kT) - 1] \tag{7.13}$$

This equation also characterizes the hole current within the SCL since we assume there is little recombination or generation there (see Sec. 7.4). What can be said about the electron current? The electron current

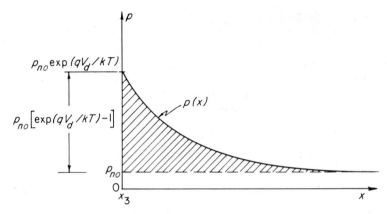

FIG. 7.10   Hole concentration in the n-side of a *pn* junction.

plus the hole current must equal the total current I. Thus

$$I_e(x) = I - I_h(x) \tag{7.14}$$

At $x = x_3$ the hole current is given by (7.13). For $x > x_3$ the hole current diminishes so that $I_e(x)$ increases until it eventually accounts for the total current. (This is not strictly true of course because there is always a tiny conduction hole current $qA\mu_h p\mathcal{E}$; however we have already agreed this is too small to warrant inclusion in our equations.)

Equation (7.14) describes the electron current in terms of the total current I that we are attempting to calculate. We need an independent determination of I_e so that it may be added to I_h to give I. Since $I_h(x_3)$ is known, consider how we might find $I_e(x_3)$. As indicated, the hole current within the SCL is constant at $I_h(x_3)$ because negligible recombination or generation is assumed to occur there. Similarly, the electron current is constant within the SCL, i.e., it is the same at $x = x_1$, $x = x_3$ and everywhere between (see Fig. 7.7 for locations x_1 and x_3). Hence if $I_e(x_1)$ can be found, both $I_e(x)$ and $I_h(x)$ within the SCL will be known.

The calculation of $I_e(x_1)$ involves analyzing the behavior of electrons in p-material which is completely analogous to that for holes in n-material. The general equations are (7.6) and (7.7c) together with continuity equations appropriate to p-type material, i.e.,

$$\frac{\partial p}{\partial t} = D_h \frac{\partial^2 p}{\partial x^2} - \frac{n - n_o}{\tau_e} - \mu_h \frac{\partial (p\mathcal{E})}{\partial x} \tag{7.15a}$$

$$\frac{\partial n}{\partial t} = D_e \frac{\partial^2 n}{\partial x^2} - \frac{n - n_o}{\tau_e} + \mu_e \frac{\partial (n\mathcal{E})}{\partial x} \tag{7.15b}$$

In this case the term containing $n\mathcal{E}$ can be omitted.

One boundary condition for $n(x)$ is

$$n(x_1) = n_2' = n_{po} \exp(qV_d/kT) \tag{7.16}$$

where n_2' is analogous in meaning to p_3' and discussed in App. 7.1. The other boundary condition is $n(x) \rightarrow n_{po}$ for $x \ll x_1$. The resulting solution has $n(x)$ given by (7.16) at $x = x_1$ and decaying to n_{po} within the p-material. The electron current at x_1 is found to be

$$I_e(x_1) = qAD_e(n_{po}/L_e)\,[\exp(qV_d/kT) - 1] \tag{7.17}$$

Since this also applies within the SCL and at $x = x_3$, (7.13) and (7.17) may be added to yield

$$I = qA(D_h p_{no}/L_h + D_e n_{po}/L_e)\,[\exp(qV_d/kT) - 1] \tag{7.18}$$

so that $I_s = qA(D_h p_{no}/L_h + D_e n_{po}/L_e)$. Equation (7.18) or its compact form, (7.5), is known as the *diode equation*. While it is not perfect (see Sec. 7.4) it is accurate enough to be important in making many practical calculations.

The quantity I_s is known as the diode *saturation current* because of the nature of the current-voltage relationship. If (7.18) is plotted on a scale where I is measured relative to I_s and V_d is measured relative to $kT/q = 26$ mV at room temperature, the current-voltage relationship appears as in Fig. 7.11. Observe that I saturates at a limiting value $-I_s$ for V_d less than about $-4kT/q$. Thus I_s is called the saturation current. For positive V_d the characteristic approaches a pure exponential form proportional to the saturation current I_s, i.e.,

$$I = I_s \exp(qV_d/kT) \quad \text{for} \quad V_d > 4kT/q \tag{7.19}$$

Note that I_s varies linearly with the two minority carrier concentrations. Since these concentrations vary inversely with the impurity

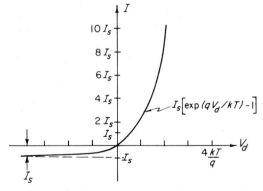

FIG. 7.11   Diode equation at very low currents for $T = 290$ K.

concentrations N_p and N_n ($n_{po} = n_i^2/N_p$ and $p_{no} = n_i^2/N_n$), we see that I_s is determined by the doping. Also since n_i^2 is a strong function of temperature we see that I_s, and hence the I-V_d relationship, has a strong temperature dependence. Ultimately this property provides the fundamental limitation on the operating temperature of pn junction diodes. Because n_i^2, and hence I_s, is so much smaller in silicon than in germanium devices, silicon diodes and transistors can be operated at substantially higher junction temperatures (possibly 175°C compared with 100°C for germanium) and therefore higher power.

At useful temperatures, then, the saturation current I_s is small. At room temperature it ranges from a few hundred microamperes in large area germanium diodes to less than a picoampere in small area silicon diodes. Since the diodes are usually operated with positive currents much larger than this, a higher current scale is used in Fig. 7.12 to show the characteristic as it might be observed in practice.

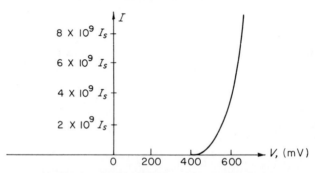

FIG. 7.12   Diode equation plotted using larger current and voltage scales.

Viewed on this scale the diode has an apparent threshold (450 mV in this case) which must be overcome before forward bias current flows. In fact there is not a threshold, but the current is very small for voltages below the apparent break in the characteristic.

7.3   DIODE VOLTAGE EQUATION

In the previous section the focus is on the current I as a function of the voltage. To consider the voltage as a function of the current, one merely solves (7.5) for V_d to obtain the *diode voltage equation,*

$$V_d = (kT/q)\ln(1 + I/I_s) \tag{7.20}$$

Recall that in Sec. 7.2 we elected to neglect the ohmic voltage drops $R_p I$ and $R_n I$. If they are not actually negligible, we must subtract $R_p I + R_n I \equiv RI$ from V_d to obtain the net voltage that affects the barrier voltage and causes current to flow across the junction. Thus in general we should replace V_d by $V_d - RI$ in all prior equations and energy band diagrams. This difference is known as the *junction voltage* because it represents that portion of the applied voltage which alters the barrier voltage. Symbolizing it as V we may rewrite (7.5) and (7.20), the diode and diode voltage equations, respectively, as

$$I = I_s [\exp(qV/kT) - 1] \tag{7.21}$$

$$V = (kT/q) \ln(1 + I/I_s) \tag{7.22}$$

where

$$V \equiv V_d - RI \tag{7.23}$$

Substituting this value for V in (7.22) the diode voltage equation becomes

$$V_d = RI + (kT/q) \ln(1 + I/I_s) \tag{7.24}$$

7.4   PRACTICAL DIODE CHARACTERISTICS

The diode equation (7.21) is a simple theoretical model that is more accurate for certain operations than others. We may categorize the constant voltage operation of diodes by means of the following current or voltage conditions:

1. large forward (positive) currents
2. moderate forward currents
3. small forward currents
4. moderate reverse (negative) voltages
5. large reverse voltages

The diode equation is at its best using moderate forward currents. In this category the agreement between theory and experiment is nearly ideal. In the first category, large forward currents, the diode equation is inaccurate. To restore accuracy the exponential must be changed to $\exp(qV/2kT)$ and the coefficient I_s must be replaced by a much larger number (the reasons for these changes are beyond the level of treatment considered here).[4] However, great accuracy in the current–junction voltage relationship is not important at high currents because the ohmic drop RI tends to be dominant. Hence these changes are seldom made in practice.

In small forward currents, the third category, the diode equation accounts for only that part of the current due to holes and electrons

---

4. Detailed discussion of this may be found in Rajendra P. Nanavati, *Introduction to Semiconductor Electronics*, 1963, McGraw-Hill, New York, pp. 115–19.

surmounting the barrier. There is another part however. Some electrons entering the SCL from the n-region recombine with holes entering the SCL from the p-region. This constitutes an equivalent positive charge transfer all the way across the SCL and implies a new current component. Its calculation is complicated. The result is like the diode equation except that I_s is replaced by a similar quantity I'_s and the exponential is replaced by $\exp(qV/nKT)$ where n can lie between 1 and 2. Thus at low currents

$$I \simeq I_s[\exp(qV/kT) - 1] + I'_s[\exp(qV/nkT) - 1] \qquad (7.25)$$

The relative importance of the two terms in (7.25) depends on the voltage V and the magnitudes of I_s and I'_s. As V increases the second term becomes less significant since in it qV/kT is divided by n, a number greater than one. More important is the comparison of I_s and I'_s. Detailed analysis shows that I'_s is large relative to I_s in diodes made from semiconductors having a large energy gap.[5] Thus at room temperature the second term in (7.25) is dominant in silicon diodes at low forward voltages whereas it is insignificant in germanium devices at all forward voltages. While (7.25) is essential if rather accurate calculations are required it is difficult to apply. Hence in practice we replace (7.25) by

$$I \simeq I''_s[\exp(qV/mkT) - 1] \qquad (7.26)$$

where I''_s and m are chosen empirically to make (7.26) fit experimental data as well as possible over the current range of importance in the application at hand.

In the fourth category, moderate reverse voltages, the diode equation predicts the behavior of germanium diodes with reasonable accuracy but is totally wrong in its description of silicon diodes. In the latter case the reverse current is several orders of magnitude larger than I_s (though still much smaller than in comparable germanium devices) and the reverse current increases with increasing reverse voltage. The reasons for this behavior are similar to those used to describe the I'_s component for the forward current case. In moderate reverse bias a current arises from generation rather than recombination of carriers within the space charge layer. The electric field present under reverse voltage conditions is so successful in stopping n-region electrons and p-region holes that very few of them penetrate into the SCL. The result is that the recombination rate within the SCL drops below the generation rate and the net effect is generation of hole-electron pairs. As these

---

5. This subject is explored more completely in A. S. Grove, *Physics and Technology of Semiconductor Devices,* 1967, Wiley, New York, Chap. 5.

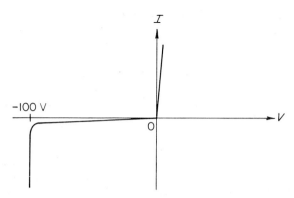

FIG. 7.13   Diode characteristic including the voltage
breakdown region, − 100 V in this example.

pairs are generated the field sweeps the holes into the p-region and the
electrons into the n-region, producing an equivalent positive charge
transfer from n to p and therefore an additional component of negative
current. The size of the current is roughly proportional to the width of
the SCL; the wider the SCL the more total generation takes place. (We
see in Sec. 7.6.2 that the SCL widens as negative voltage is applied to
the diode.) Thus the generation current varies with voltage rather than
being constant. In silicon devices the space charge generation current is
orders of magnitude larger than I_s. Thus a reverse bias measurement
cannot be used to determine I_s; it must be inferred from a forward bias
measurement.

The precise equation for this generation current is not of interest
here. The important point is that the total reverse current I_r is not
even approximately equal to $-I_s$ for silicon devices. Like the recombination current in forward bias, the space charge generation effect is
not of direct practical significance. The total reverse current in silicon
devices is normally so small it makes little difference whether it is
10^{-12} A as deduced from the I_s expression or 10^{-9} A as it might be in
fact.

Finally consider the fifth category, large reverse voltages. As V_d and
V are made increasingly negative a point is reached at which the reverse
current becomes extremely large. This is shown graphically in Fig. 7.13.
The phenomenon of reaching a practical limit on applied voltage is
known as *voltage breakdown*. The voltage at which breakdown occurs
varies from diode to diode depending on the impurity doping levels
used. Breakdown voltages from a few to several thousand volts can be
realized by appropriate device design. The physical processes responsible for voltage breakdown are discussed in detail in Sec. 7.7.

7.5 JUNCTION CURRENTS: CHARGE CONTROL MODEL

Another way of looking at junction current, complementary to that in Sec. 7.2, provides insight into diode behavior under time-varying conditions. In this approach we evaluate minority currents at the edges of the SCL in terms of charge distributions in the neutral regions and combine them to obtain total current.

The starting point for the stored charge viewpoint, or *charge control model,* is the continuity principle. Let us first focus our attention upon the hole current. Consider the volume of material in the neutral portion of the n-region, i.e., between x_3 and x_4 in Fig. 7.7. The continuity principle tells us that (rate of change of hole charge in the region) = (hole current entering at $x = x_3$) − (hole current exiting at $x = x_4$) + (integrated effects of generation and recombination for the region). Letting q_h stand for the total charge due to excess holes in the n-region we have

$$\frac{dq_h}{dt} = I_h(x_3) - I_h(x_4) + qA \int_{x_3}^{x_4} \left(\frac{p_{no}}{\tau_h} - \frac{p_n}{\tau_h}\right) dx \qquad (7.27)$$

Note that in this equation we have written p_{no}/τ_h for the generation rate G_t and p_n/τ_h for the recombination rate R (see Chap. 6).

Now the charge q_h is simply the excess hole concentration $p_n - p_{no}$ integrated over the entire volume between $x = x_3$ and $x = x_4$ and multiplied by $+q$. Thus

$$q_h = q \int_{x3}^{x_4} (p_n - p_{no})A \ dx \qquad (7.28)$$

Comparison of (7.27) and (7.28) reveals that the integral term in (7.27) is simply $-q_h/\tau_h$. Also, the hole current at $x = x_4$ is typically zero because the n-region is normally long enough to ensure that virtually all holes entering at $x = x_3$ recombine before reaching $x = x_4$. Thus, setting $I_h(x_4) = 0$, substituting $-q_h/\tau_h$ for the integral term, and rearranging the order of the terms, (7.27) translates into

$$I_h(x_3) = dq_h/dt + q_h/\tau_h \qquad (7.29)$$

This equation states that (hole current at the edge of the SCL) = (rate at which the stored hole charge in the n-material varies) + (rate at which hole charges in that material recombine).

The nature of q_h and its relationship to the junction voltage V can be seen with the aid of Fig. 7.10 in which the hole concentration p_n vs x is plotted. The shaded area is the integral of $(p_n - p_{no}) dx$ and this area is proportional to the hole charge q_h. This shaded area (and hence q_h) is also proportional to its left-hand "altitude," $p_{no}[\exp(qV/kT) - 1]$. (We now replace V_d by V in light of Sec. 7.3.) Hence as $\exp(qV/kT)$ increases, the altitude and the shaded area increase, thereby increasing q_h.

Quantitatively we use $p(x)$ from (7.11) for p_n in (7.28) and, letting $x_4 \to \infty$ because the n-region is many diffusion lengths long, obtain

$$q_h = qAL_h p_{no} [\exp(qV/kT) - 1] \tag{7.30}$$

Strictly speaking this result and the plot in Fig. 7.11 hold only in the constant voltage case where q_h and the hole distribution do not vary with time. However if the rate of change is not too severe they are also reasonable approximations for time-dependent cases. We thus consider (7.30) to be good for both static and dynamic problems.

A similar analysis of the behavior of electrons in p-material can be undertaken. The results are completely analogous.

$$I_e(x_1) = dq_e/dt + q_e/\tau_e \tag{7.31}$$

$$q_e = qAL_e n_{po} [\exp(qV/kT) - 1] \tag{7.32}$$

By convention the quantity q_e is positive when the voltage V is positive. The actual charge due to the electrons is negative of course; q_e is simply defined as having its sign opposite to that of the actual charge.

The two current components developed above can be used to evaluate the total diode current (except for a capacitance term calculated in Sec. 7.6.2). As in Sec. 7.2, we reason that I_h and I_e vary only slightly within the SCL because generation and recombination (and charge storage for the time-dependent case) are small. Thus we now combine (7.29) and (7.31) to obtain total current in terms of q_h and q_e and their derivatives

$$I = I_h(x_3) + I_e(x_1) = \frac{d}{dt}(q_h + q_e) + \frac{q_h}{\tau_h} + \frac{q_e}{\tau_e} \tag{7.33}$$

Equation (7.33) is applicable to both static and dynamic cases.

Now let us use (7.33) to rederive the diode equation and obtain an alternate expression for I_s. Under static conditions (7.33) reduces to

$$I = q_h/\tau_h + q_e/\tau_e \tag{7.34}$$

This equation indicates that the diode current can be expressed simply as the sum of the recombination currents in the two neutral regions because all excess minority carriers recombine somewhere, and the total current is known to be the sum of the minority currents at the edge of the SCL. To obtain the diode equation we simply substitute into (7.34) the expressions given in (7.30) and (7.32) for q_h and q_e. Factoring the result then yields

$$I = [qA(p_{no}L_h/\tau_h + n_{po}L_e/\tau_e)](\exp(qV/kT) - 1) \tag{7.35}$$

This equation is of the same form as (7.5) and (7.18). The bracketed quantity in (7.35) is again the saturation current I_s. Equations (7.18) and (7.35) can be shown to be equivalent by use of $L_h^2 = D_h \tau_h$ and $L_e^2 = D_e \tau_e$.

Let us now return to the dynamic case. Equation (7.33) is a differential equation relating the current to two unknown charge components. This is simplified considerably if the number of charge components is reduced to one. The time derivative term in (7.33) involves the sum of q_h and q_e. Thus we shall define a total stored charge q_s as

$$q_s = q_h + q_e \qquad\qquad (7.36)$$

The recombination currents q_h/τ_h and q_e/τ_e can also be expressed in terms of q_s. Notice from (7.30) and (7.32) that both q_h and q_e are proportional to $\exp(qV/kT) - 1$. It follows that their sum q_s is also proportional to $\exp(qV/kT) - 1$. Hence q_h/τ_h and q_e/τ_e are both proportional to q_s and their sum can be written as q_s/τ_s where τ_s is a suitably defined constant. Thus (7.33) can be rewritten as the *charge control equation*

$$I = dq_s/dt + q_s/\tau_s \qquad\qquad (7.37)$$

where τ_s is the *effective lifetime*, given by

$$\tau_s = \frac{1 + q_e/q_h}{1/\tau_h + q_e/q_h\tau_e} \qquad\qquad (7.38)$$

[*Exercise:* Verify that (7.36), (7.37), and (7.38) are consistent with (7.33).]

Equation (7.37) is the fundamental equation of the charge control model. By its use the behavior of *pn* diodes in time-varying situations can be understood and predicted. Equation (7.38) is almost never used to determine τ_s. Instead, τ_s is measured experimentally and (7.37) is used to interpret the data. The importance of (7.38) is that it shows τ_s to be a constant and (7.37) is therefore a meaningful simplification of (7.33).

7.6   DYNAMIC EFFECTS

Suppose a *pn* junction is connected in the circuit of Fig. 7.14 with the circuit-driving voltage varying as shown. What current and voltage waveforms are found in this circuit? From the diode equation (7.5) we would predict the waveforms of Fig. 7.15. These are not, however, the results actually found. No real electrical system has ever been built in which the dynamic response could be exactly predicted from static theory. A differential equation rather than an algebraic equation is always required. The waveforms actually found are those in Fig. 7.16.

Two features are noted in these waveforms. First, during the time interval t_1 immediately following the reversal of the driving voltage, the junction voltage remains positive (rather than following the driving voltage) due to the charge storage described in the previous section. Second, during an additional time interval t_2, the current and voltage

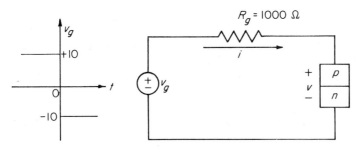

FIG. 7.14   A *pn* junction with step driving voltage.

make smooth transitions to the values predicted from steady-state theory, in a manner reminiscent of *RC* circuits. This we explain in terms of the space charge layer capacitance, Sec. 7.6.2.

7.6.1   Charge Storage Effects

During the time the driving voltage is positive the junction is forward biased. Holes flow from *p* to *n* and electrons flow from *n* to *p* leading to stored charges q_h and q_e. The total stored charge q_s is readily found by (7.37). For $t < 0$, the circuit is in steady state with $I = I_1$ and $dq_s/dt = 0$ so that

$$q_s(0^-) = I_1 \tau_s \qquad\qquad (7.39)$$

At $t = 0$ the driving voltage becomes $-10\,\mathrm{V}$ which immediately

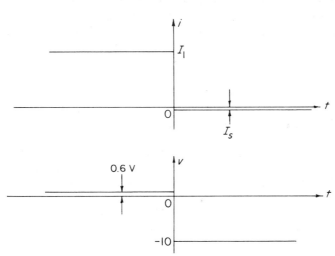

FIG. 7.15   Waveforms predicted for the circuit of Fig. 7.14 on the basis of static theory.

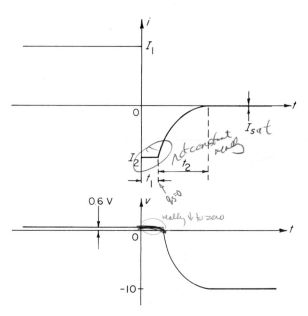

FIG. 7.16   Actual waveforms for the circuit of Fig.
7.14.

changes the current to a negative value I_2.[6] Why does this negative
current occur? Why does the diode voltage V not immediately become
-10 V and permit the current to be zero? The answer lies in the relationship between V and the stored charge q_s. Recall that q_h and q_e are
proportional to $\exp(qV/kT) - 1$, and hence so is q_s. This means that
V cannot change without q_s changing and, also, V must remain positive
so long as q_s is positive.

By (7.39), at $t = 0^-$ the stored charge is $q_s(0^-) = I_1\tau_s$. Unless
an infinite current is available, the stored charge must have the same
value at $t = 0^+$. Since the resistance R_g in the circuit of Fig. 7.14 limits
the current to finite values, then $q_s(0^+) = I_1\tau_s$ also, which means
that $V(0^+) = V(0^-)$. This value of V depends on the type of diode
used; if it is a silicon diode it is in the neighborhood of 0.6 V. Knowing
this we can determine I_1 and I_2 by elementary circuit analysis. From
Kirchhoff's voltage law we have (generator voltage V_g) = (R_gI drop) +
(diode voltage V). (We are presuming that the diode resistance R can
be ignored so it is unnecessary to make a distinction between diode
applied voltage V_d and diode junction voltage V.) Writing this in equa-

6. For this to be strictly true would require zero circuit inductance, which is a
physical impossibility. Inductance can be made very small however and we shall assume
it to be small enough for the current reversal to be essentially instantaneous.

tion form and then solving for the current we have

$$V_g = R_g I + V \qquad (7.40)$$

$$I = (V_g - V)/R_g \qquad (7.41)$$

Given that V is +0.6 V at both $t = 0^-$ and $t = 0^+$ and noting the values of V_g at these two moments we find the currents I_1 and I_2 to be $I_1 = (+10 - 0.6)/1000 = +9.4$ mA and $I_2 = (-10 - 0.6)/1000 = -10.6$ mA. Thus we find that I changes abruptly from +9.4 mA at $t = 0^-$ to -10.6 mA at $t = 0^+$.

As time proceeds q_s and V change. The stored charge decreases because $I < 0$. Hence V drops below the value of +0.6V, but it is still positive so long as q_s is positive. Thus during the time that q_s is dropping from $I_1 \tau_s$ to zero, V is between +0.6 V and 0. The current I is thus between -10.6 mA and -10.0 mA [applying (7.41) once again, this time with $V = 0$]. Thus I is near -10.6 mA during most of the turnoff process and can be regarded as being constant until the instant when $q_s = 0$.

With I constant at I_2 the decrease of q_s from $I_1 \tau_s$ to zero can be calculated; set $I = I_2$ in (7.37) to obtain

$$I_2 = \frac{dq_s}{dt} + \frac{q_s}{\tau_s} \qquad (7.42)$$

We then solve this differential equation, and require that the result give $q(0^+) = I_1 \tau_s$, as follows. The complementary function for (7.42) is $K_1 \exp(-t/\tau_s)$.

Since the left side of (7.42) is a constant we try a constant K_2 for the particular solution to this equation: $I_2 = d(K_2)/dt + K_2/\tau_s$; then $I_2 = 0 + K_2/\tau_s$ and $K_2 = I_2 \tau_s$. The complete solution to (7.42) is the sum of the complementary function and the particular solution; thus

$$q_s(t) = K_1 \exp(-t/\tau_s) + I_2 \tau_s \qquad (7.43)$$

This result must equal $I_1 \tau_s$ at $t = 0$. Thus K_1 and $q_s(t)$ are given by

$$K_1 = (I_1 - I_2)\tau_s \qquad (7.44)$$

$$q_s(t) = (I_1 - I_2)\tau_s \exp(-t/\tau_s) + I_2 \tau_s \qquad (7.45)$$

The expression for the stored charge q_s applies only so long as $i \simeq I_2$. Plotting $q_s(t)$ and also $V(t)$ (which is logarithmically related to q_s) yields the graphs in Fig. 7.17.

The time t_1 defined in Fig. 7.17 is called *storage time* or storage interval since the behavior of the diode is governed by the stored charge q_s. It is important because it indicates how long it takes for the diode to start acting like a reverse biased diode. For $t > t_1$, V moves toward V_g and the current I moves toward zero; see (7.41).

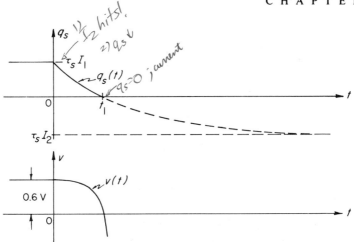

FIG. 7.17   Charge and voltage waveforms for the
diode in Fig. 7.14.

Let us evaluate t_1 for the circuit of Fig. 7.14. Since t_1 is defined as
the moment when q_s reaches zero, let $t = t_1$ in (7.45), set $q_s(t_1) = 0$,
and solve the resulting equation for t_1.

$$q_s(t_1) = (I_1 - I_2)\tau_s \exp(-t_1/\tau_s) + I_2\tau_s = 0$$

$$t_1 = \tau_s \ln[(I_2 - I_1)/I_2]$$

Inserting values for I_1 and I_2 into (7.55), we find t_1 in terms of τ_s.

$$t_1 = \tau_s \ln\{[(-10.6) - 9.5]/(-10.6)\} = \tau_s \ln 1.89 = 0.64\tau_s$$

In this example the storage time t_1 is the same order of magnitude
as the effective lifetime τ_s. This is typical since the relative sizes of I_1
and I_2 are usually such that $\ln[(I_2 - I_1)/I_2]$ lies between 0.3 and 3.0.

Once the storage interval is completed, the voltage V becomes
negative and q_s becomes essentially zero so that dq_s/dt and q_s/τ_s are
negligible. Then (7.37) would lead us to expect that immediately $I = 0$
and therefore $V = V_g = -10\,\mathrm{V}$. In fact however a new current component must be considered. It is a capacitive current $I = C(dV/dt)$ resulting from a capacitance C associated with the junction space charge
layer. Thus for $t > t_1$ the current is governed by an RC decay, as suggested in Fig. 7.16.

7.6.2   Space Charge Layer Capacitance

In Sec. 7.1 the development of the junction space charge layer
(SCL) is discussed. Because the SCL contains few mobile carriers it behaves much like an insulator with a dielectric constant ϵ equal to that
of the semiconducting material. It is not a perfect insulator since car-

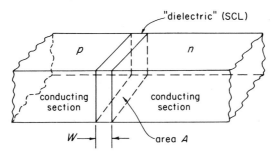

FIG. 7.18   Representation of *pn* junction emphasizing
features pertinent to SCL capacitance.

riers do diffuse through to make up the current described earlier in this
chapter. That current may be thought of as being in parallel with the
capacitance effects we are now considering. Thus one has conducting
sections of material (the neutral p- and n-regions) separated by a dielectric layer. If the SCL width is W, then the SCL acts as a capacitor
with dielectric thickness W.

This may be seen with the aid of Fig. 7.18. The conducting p- and
n-sections act as the plates of a capacitor. If fringing fields can be considered negligible then the capacitance C is

$$C = \epsilon A / W \tag{7.46}$$

which is the usual formula for a parallel-plate capacitance.

This SCL capacitor has one unusual feature. The SCL width W
varies as the junction voltage is changed. We shall show that W is proportional to $V_B^{1/2} = (V_{Bo} - V)^{1/2}$ so that capacitance varies inversely
with $V_B^{1/2}$.

To see this we must examine the electric field and potential variations with distance within the SCL (see Fig. 7.19). In an electric field
the electric flux lines originate on positive charges and terminate on
negative charges. The total acceptor and donor charges are numerically
equal because the diode as a whole is neutral. Thus all flux lines originating on donor ions terminate on acceptor ions. Assuming the geometry is such that flux fringing can be ignored, we may say that these

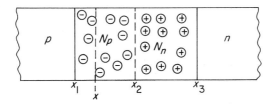

FIG. 7.19   The SCL in detail.

flux lines lie parallel to the x-axis and point in the $-x$-direction. Now we can evaluate electric flux density and field intensity. Consider a plane at some position x between x_1 and x_2. The net charge to the left of this plane is simply $-qAN_p(x - x_1)$, hence the number of flux lines crossing x from right to left is $qAN_p(x - x_1)$. Dividing this by the area A and taking a negative sign to account for the direction of the flux lines yields the electric flux density, and dividing the flux density by the electric permittivity ϵ yields the electric field intensity $\mathcal{E}$

$$\mathcal{E} = -qN_p(x - x_1)/\epsilon \quad \text{for } x_1 \leq x \leq x_2 \tag{7.47}$$

By a similar process

$$\mathcal{E} = -qN_n(x_3 - x)/\epsilon \quad \text{for } x_2 \leq x \leq x_3 \tag{7.48}$$

The simplicity of these results is more apparent when graphed; see Fig. 7.20.

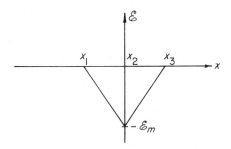

FIG. 7.20   Electric field intensity variation in the space charge layer of the *pn* junction of Fig. 7.19.

With the electric field intensity at x_2 designated as $-\mathcal{E}_m$, we have from (7.47) and (7.48) that $x_2 - x_1 = \epsilon\mathcal{E}_m/qN_p$ and $x_3 - x_2 = \epsilon\mathcal{E}_m/qN_n$. Adding these we find W is

$$W = x_3 - x_1 = (\epsilon\mathcal{E}_m/q)(1/N_p + 1/N_n) \tag{7.49}$$

The barrier voltage V_B is the integral of $-\mathcal{E}\,dx$ from x_1 to x_3. But this is simply the ~~magnitude~~ *area* of the major triangle in Fig. 7.20. Thus

$$V_B = (1/2)\mathcal{E}_m W \tag{7.50}$$

Combining (7.49) and (7.50) we find

$$V_B = (1/2)W(qW/\epsilon)(1/N_p + 1/N_n)^{-1} = (qN/2\epsilon)W^2 \tag{7.51}$$

where $N \equiv N_p N_n/(N_p + N_n)$.

Equation (7.51) is now solved for W and this is used in (7.46) to obtain the capacitance C.

$$C = \epsilon A (qN/2\epsilon V_B)^{1/2}$$
$$= A (q\epsilon N/2V_B)^{1/2}$$
$$= A[q\epsilon N/2(V_{Bo} - V)]^{1/2} \tag{7.52}$$

where $V_B = V_{Bo} - V$. Note how the capacitance varies with the voltage V. As V approaches V_{Bo}, C gets quite large. However V will not reach $V = V_{Bo}$ because the ordinary diode current I as given by (7.21) would become large enough to destroy the diode before $V = V_{Bo}$ would be obtained. If V is negative then C decreases. This voltage-controlled capacitance has important applications in communication circuits where it is desired to adjust the resonant frequency of an LC circuit electronically rather than manually. An example is the automatic frequency control (AFC) found on FM tuners and receivers. In such an application the diode is called a *varactor* (variable reactor.)

Since C is proportional to the junction area, it is small for low power (high-frequency) devices and relatively large for high power (low-frequency) devices. A reasonable range of C for such devices is 5.0–100 pF, measured at 0 V.

An additional important fact about C is that because C varies with V the ordinary charge voltage equation applies only for very small changes in V, that is,

$$\Delta Q = C \Delta V \quad \text{for} \, |\Delta V| \ll V_B$$

For large changes in voltage the proper relationship is

$$\Delta Q = \int_V^{V+\Delta V} C \, dV$$

where the voltage dependence of C is taken into account in the integration.

On the other hand the usual current equation does apply; this is the SCL capacitance current equation

$$i = \frac{dQ}{dt} = \frac{dQ}{dV} \frac{dV}{dt} = C \frac{dV}{dt} \tag{7.53}$$

In (7.53), C is still a function of voltage so that if the variations of C are significant, the analysis of circuits containing this capacitance involves one or more nonlinear differential equations.

Having discussed the SCL capacitance we can complete discussion of the waveforms in Fig. 7.16. As time interval t_1 ends, the excess minority carrier charges vanish and lose control over the junction voltage V, whereupon V tends toward -10 V. The SCL capacitance then causes a significant capacitive current to flow so that V moves gradually rather than instantaneously toward -10 V. The decay during time interval t_2 is thus an RC decay where C is the varying SCL capacitance and R is the circuit resistance.

In general, to find current, use (7.37) (the charge control equation) for a forward biased diode, and (7.53) (the SCL capacitance current equation) for a reverse biased diode.

7.7   VOLTAGE BREAKDOWN

In Sec. 7.4 voltage breakdown is mentioned briefly and illustrated graphically in Fig. 7.13. How does this phenomenon come about? There are two mechanisms by which larger than expected reverse current is obtained. These are the avalanche and the Zener mechanisms. Both are in operation in any given diode so the reverse current is actually the sum of an avalanche current and a Zener current. In most diodes one process overshadows the other.

7.7.1   Avalanche Breakdown

Avalanche breakdown results from what may be called carrier multiplication in the space charge layer. In Fig. 7.21 is a diode energy band diagram constructed for the case of substantial reverse bias, i.e., $V \ll 0$.

Consider an electron in the p-material that diffuses to the SCL and is swept through by the accelerating field there. A typical path in energy and position is indicated in Fig. 7.21. The vertical jumps along the trajectory (numbers 1–8) represent collisions of the electron with the lattice. For simplicity most of the random motion has been averaged so that at each collision the electron energy nearly returns to E_c and the electron progresses always to the right. The random distance between

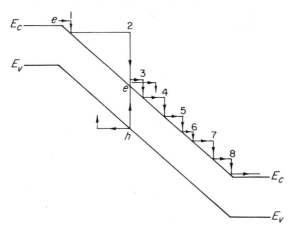

FIG. 7.21   A *pn* junction with avalanche multiplication.

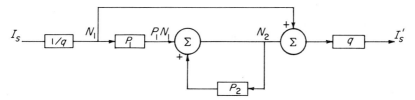

FIG. 7.22   Block diagram showing the interrelated
processes in carrier multiplication.

collisions has been retained however. Most distances are small so that
little kinetic energy is acquired between collisions. However in one randomly selected case a large distance is shown (between the first and
second collisions) so that the kinetic energy obtained is larger than the
energy gap E_g. At the second collision this kinetic energy can transfer
to the lattice so as to free a valence electron and thus create a hole-
electron pair, as shown in Fig. 7.21. The collision in this case is an
ionizing (or generating) collision. When this happens the current exceeds that directly attributable to the original electron. Further, note
that—and this turns out to be crucial—the newly created hole and
electron (*secondary* carriers as contrasted with the original or *primary*
carrier) can likewise be accelerated, suffer collisions, and generate still
other pairs of secondary carriers. The ways these various possibilities
relate to one another and to the resulting current are shown in the
block diagram of Fig. 7.22.

The input variable in this diagram is the saturation current I_s, due
to thermally generated minority carriers, known in the present discussion as primary carriers. The first block in the system is simply the
mathematical conversion from I_s in coulombs per second to N_1 primary
carriers per second. The block P_1 is the probability that a primary
carrier will generate a secondary pair; it depends on V, W, and the
electron mean free path $\mathcal{L}_e$.

The number of secondary pairs produced per second by the primary carriers is evidently $P_1 N_1$ but this is not the total number. We
must also determine the number of secondary pairs produced by secondary pairs. If there are N_2 secondary pairs per second and P_2 is the
probability of a secondary pair producing a secondary pair, then N_2 is
evidently given by the sum of $P_1 N_1$ and $P_2 N_2$, i.e.,

$$N_2 = P_1 N_1 + P_2 N_2 \tag{7.54}$$

This is symbolized in the block diagram by the first summation and the
block labeled P_2.

Now the total current I'_s is that due to the primary carriers and the
secondary pairs. The sum of N_1 and N_2 is thus formed in the second
summation and a multiplication by q is accomplished in the final block

in Fig. 7.22, thus yielding $I_s' = q(N_1 + N_2)$. But from Fig. 7.22 and
(7.54) we also have $N_2 = P_1 N_1 / (1 - P_2)$. Hence I_s' is given by

$$I_s' = q[N_1 + P_1 N_1 / (1 - P_2)]$$

Then noting that $N_1 = I_s / q$ and assuming $P_1 \simeq P_2$ we have

$$I_s' = [(1 - P_2 + P_1) / (1 - P_2)] I_s \simeq [1 / (1 - P_2)] I_s \qquad (7.55)$$

The bracketed quantity in (7.55) is known as the multiplication factor
M. Note that the critical parameter in M is P_2, the probability that a
secondary pair will generate another secondary pair. As this probability
approaches unity, M and I_s' become very large. Probability P_2 is clearly
voltage dependent. The larger the voltage the greater the kinetic energy
gained between collisions and the greater the likelihood that one of the
carriers in a secondary pair will create another secondary pair. The
avalanche breakdown voltage is the value for which $P_2 = 1$.

Thus avalanche breakdown is the result of primary carriers (the
holes and electrons comprising I_s) colliding with the lattice and generating secondary hole-electron pairs which in turn generate additional
secondary pairs. The total current approaches infinity as the probability of one secondary pair generating another approaches unity. A
theoretical calculation of this probability is complicated and is not
pursued here. It is sufficient to simply present two experimental results.
The first result is an empirical equation for the multiplication factor M,

$$M = I_s' / I_s = 1 / [1 - (-V/V_A)^m] \qquad (7.56)$$

where V_A is the observed avalanche breakdown voltage and m is a
quantity between about 2 and 6. This equation is used in several problems at the end of this chapter.

The second experimental result is the dependence of the avalanche
voltage V_A on impurity concentrations. We have seen in (7.51) that the
quantity $N = N_p N_n / (N_p + N_n)$ governs the relationship between the
SCL width and the barrier voltage. Given this fact, one can also see,
from (7.50), that N governs the relationship between the electric field
intensity and the barrier voltage. It therefore is reasonable that N
governs the value of avalanche voltage V_A. Figure 7.23 shows the experimental results for V_A as a function of N for silicon and germanium
diodes. We see that V_A varies from several hundred volts when the
doping is light (N moderate) to a few volts when the doping is heavy
(N large).

Also shown for comparison purposes in Fig. 7.23 is an arbitrary
inverse relationship between V_A and N, which on this log-log coordinate system is a straight line. Examination of the data in Fig. 7.23 suggests that V_A varies roughly as $1/\sqrt{N}$.

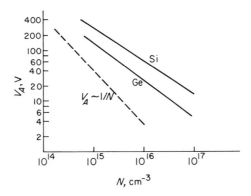

FIG. 7.23   Avalanche breakdown voltage versus
impurity concentration. [Adapted from S. M. Sze, and
G. Gibbons, Avalanche Breakdown Voltages of
Abrupt and Linearly Graded *pn* Junctions of Ge, Si,
GaAs, and GaP, *Appl. Phys. Letters* 8(1966):11]

7.7.2   Zener Breakdown

The Zener mechanism is named after Clarence Zener, who offered
it as a theoretical explanation for the observed breakdown in dielec-
trics. It is a quantum-mechanical process, i.e., to properly explain it
one must refer to electron wave functions and associated electron
quantum states.

As a starting point consider Fig. 7.24, the energy band diagram for
a reverse biased *pn* junction. In particular consider some energy level E_1
which lies in the valence band of the p-material, passes through a forbidden region of width Δx, and lies in the conduction band of the
n-material. Suppose a valence electron in the p-material has energy E_1.
The exact nature of its wave function is hard to state; however we can
reason in somewhat qualitative terms. In both the p- and n-materials

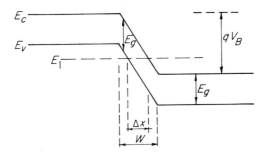

FIG. 7.24   Energy band diagram for a reverse biased
pn junction.

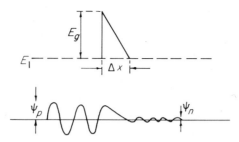

FIG. 7.25   Effective energy barrier and wave function
for an electron at E_1 in Fig. 7.24.

the wave function is oscillatory since the energy lies in allowed bands.
In the region marked Δx the wave function must be a decaying exponential since this is a forbidden region. Since the electron at E_1 is
initially in the p-material, the wave function should be large in the
p-side, decay to a very small value at the edge of the n-material, and
then oscillate with small amplitude in the n-material. The barrier and
wave function are sketched in Fig. 7.25.

The wave function shown is not drawn to a realistic scale. Actually
the peak amplitude in the n-side ψ_n should be much smaller than the
peak amplitude in the p-side ψ_p. However small ψ_n may be, though, it
is not zero. There is a finite probability that the electron will sometime
appear on the n-side rather than on the p-side. When this happens
tunneling has occurred; the electron has tunneled through the forbidden region rather than being reflected back from it (see Sec. 3.5).
The tunneling probability P_{tun} is given by

$$P_{tun} = |\psi_n / \psi_p|^2 \qquad (7.57)$$

This probability is much less than unity. But consider the number
of electrons having this small tunneling probability. A typical semiconductor has $N_s \simeq 10^{23}$ atoms/cm^3 and there are four valence electrons per atom so the number of electrons involved is large. To be more
quantitative consider the valence electron current incident on the left
side of the forbidden region in Fig. 7.24. In general current is given by

$$I = q A \, nv \qquad (7.58)$$

where q is the electron charge, A is the cross-sectional area, n is the
electron concentration, and v is the electron velocity. In the present
case we have $2N_s$ electrons/cm^3 with $+x$ velocities (and $2N_s$ with $-x$
velocities). Thus $n_{inc} = 2N_s$.

In kinetic theory the average kinetic energy in the x-direction is
$kT/2$. Thus the average velocity is approximately $v = v_t = (kT/m)^{1/2}$.
Combining the values of n_{inc} and v in (7.58) we find

$$I_{inc} = qA(2N_s)v_t \qquad (7.59)$$

Taking 10^{23} atoms/cm³, an area of 10^{-2} cm², and a room temperature thermal velocity of 6×10^6 cm/sec we find $I_{inc} \simeq 2 \times 10^8$ A. We thus see that even with $P_{tun} \ll 1$ an appreciable tunneling current could result. For example with $P_{tun} = 10^{-10}$ the tunneling current would be $I_{tun} = P_{tun} I_{inc} = 20$ mA.

Evidently the size of the tunneling current depends on the barrier thickness Δx. An approximate analysis (see App. 7.2) using the barrier shown in Fig. 7.25 yields the following tunneling probability,

$$P_{tun} = \exp[-(4/3)(2mE_g/\hbar^2)^{1/2} \Delta x] \tag{7.60}$$

This equation may be used to estimate the value of Δx required to obtain a particular value of P_{tun}. For $P_{tun} = 10^{-10}$ with $E_g = 1.1$ eV, one finds that Δx must be 3.2×10^{-7} cm $= 32$ Å.

The manner in which Δx is determined by the barrier voltage V_B can be seen from Fig. 7.24. The slope of E_c within the SCL is given by qV_B/W, and also by $E_g/\Delta x$. Hence we see that

$$\Delta x = (E_g/q)(W/V_B) \tag{7.61}$$

Now the SCL width W is itself dependent on V_B as seen in (7.51). If that equation is solved for W and the result is combined with (7.61) the result is

$$\Delta x = (E_g/q)(2\epsilon/qN V_B)^{1/2} \tag{7.62}$$

Thus the tunneling distance Δx varies as $(NV_B)^{-1/2}$. Hence to attain a particular value of Δx, a certain value of the product NV_B is required. Any combination of N and V_B yielding the required product then produces the desired Δx and hence the desired P_{tun}. We may obtain a given tunneling current with large V_B and small N or with small V_B and large N (V_B is inversely proportional to N).

The *Zener breakdown* voltage is now defined. An arbitrary tunneling current much larger than I_s is chosen and the voltage producing that tunneling current is defined as the Zener breakdown voltage V_Z. Selecting 20 mA for example implies $P_{tun} \simeq 10^{-10}$ and $\Delta x \simeq 32$ Å. The latter, via (7.62), implies a specific value for NV_B. Since V_B is inversely proportional to N and $V_Z \simeq V_B$, then V_Z is inversely proportional to N, as shown in Fig. 7.26.

Also shown in Fig. 7.26 is the avalanche voltage V_A vs N. As seen, V_A and V_Z depend somewhat similarly on N. Both breakdown voltages are large when N is small, and both are small when N is large. However, the avalanche voltage changes less rapidly with N. The straight-line portion of the V_A-N graph indicates something like a $1/\sqrt{N}$ relationship as contrasted with $1/N$ for the V_Z vs N.

Since the avalanche and Zener mechanisms are both possible, what is the actual breakdown voltage for a given diode? Is it the sum of the two voltages V_A and V_Z? The average? The smaller of the two? None of

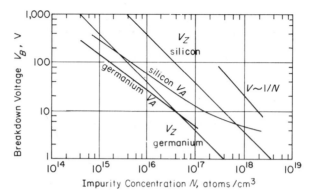

FIG. 7.26   Zener and avalanche breakdown barrier
voltages in silicon and germanium *pn* junctions.

the above! The total reverse current is the sum of the avalanche current
and the Zener current. If either current gets large the diode is in breakdown. This means that the smaller of the two voltages V_A and V_Z governs, and thus avalanche breakdown is the breakdown mechanism in
most diodes. In Fig. 7.26 we see that $V_A < V_Z$ everywhere except at
very large N. Thus Zener breakdown is observed only in diodes with
breakdown at voltages less than about 6–7 V.

Junction diodes are used in many different applications. Often one
diode characteristic is of particular importance and the device design is
then optimized with respect to that characteristic. In the next sections
we discuss various types of diodes, giving the most significant device
parameters and indicating in a qualitative way how these parameters
can be obtained.

7.8   RECTIFIER DIODES

A rectifier diode is a *pn* junction with doping levels and mechanical
housing designed to yield the following characteristics:

1. low forward voltage drop at some rated current such as 0.1 A, 1 A,
   or 10 A
2. negligible reverse current for reverse voltage smaller than or equal to
   a rated peak reverse voltage (PRV) such as 100 V, 500 V, or 1000 V
3. negligible charge storage and capacitance effects at frequencies up to
   a few thousand hertz
4. sufficient heat dissipation capability so the power dissipated during
   forward and reverse operations does not cause the junction temperature to rise above 100°C (germanium) or 200°C (silicon)

[*Exercise*. Discuss how doping levels affect the forward voltage drop in terms of (a) junction voltage and (b) bulk resistance.]

[*Exercise*. Discuss whether the doping levels required for low forward voltage drop are compatible with attaining a very high PRV.]

7.9   REGULATOR DIODES

A regulator diode is a *pn* junction diode designed to have:

1. a well-defined avalanche or Zener breakdown voltage
2. a very steep *I-V* characteristic at breakdown
3. thermal capability to permit continuous operation in breakdown at rated power and temperature conditions such as 100 mW, 1 W, or 50 W with an ambient temperature of 25°C

Regulator diodes are manufactured with breakdown voltages ranging from a few to hundreds of volts. One particularly interesting case has breakdown voltage of around 5–6 V. Figure 7.26 reveals that avalanche and Zener voltages are about equal in this case which means the avalanche and tunneling currents are comparable. This is noteworthy because the two currents have opposite temperature dependences that yield zero net temperature dependence for the total current. If the applied voltage is held constant and the temperature is raised, the tunneling current increases while the avalanche current decreases or, equivalently, the Zener voltage decreases and the avalanche voltage increases.

The Zener voltage decreases because the energy gap E_g decreases with increasing temperature (see Fig. 5.9, for example). From (7.60) and (7.62) it can be shown that P_{tun} remains constant if the ratio of E_g^3 to V_B is constant. Thus as E_g decreases V_B also decreases if the tunneling current is held constant.

The avalanche voltage increases because the rise in temperature increases lattice vibrations, which increase chances of carrier collisions, which decrease the mean free path, which increases the voltage required for avalanche.

The temperature dependences of the two voltages cancel exactly at one particular value of total current and cancel approximately for currents near this value. Practically speaking one can obtain a temperature dependence as small as about $\pm 50 \ \mu V/°C$.

7.10   BACKWARD DIODES

It may have occurred to the reader, in studying Zener breakdown (Sec. 7.7.2), that for a sufficiently high impurity concentration N the barrier voltage V_B could equal the junction barrier potential V_{Bo} so that Zener breakdown would occur at virtually 0 V reverse bias. Such a

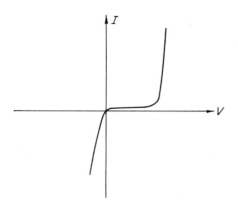

FIG. 7.27   Current-voltage characteristic for a silicon
backward diode.

diode would have the *I-V* characteristic of Fig. 7.27. This diode is
known as a backward diode because it actually conducts better with reverse bias than with forward bias.

To describe more precisely the characteristic shown in Fig. 7.27,
consider the energy band diagram for the backward diode shown in
Fig. 7.28 for zero, forward, and reverse bias.

Note that the position of the Fermi level is slightly different from
the other cases discussed. Specifically it lies at rather than near the edge
of the energy gap and equals E_v in the p-material and E_c in the n-
material. Then even a slight reverse bias causes occupied valence states
in the p-material to line up with unoccupied conduction states in the
n-material, and a tunneling current exists as indicated in Fig. 7.28c. For
forward bias no lining up occurs and the only current is due to ordinary
diffusion processes. Thus little current flows until the voltage reaches
about 200 mV (germanium) or 600 mV (silicon).

The unusual position of the Fermi level is explained as follows.
Consider first the p-material. As acceptor concentration is increased,
interaction between acceptor atoms becomes appreciable and the impurity levels split into a narrow band. When the splitting causes this
band to touch the regular valence band the union becomes an effective
valence band whose upper edge is called E_v in Fig. 7.28. Since the number of holes in this band must be quite large the difference $E_f - E_v$ must
be smaller than in less doped materials. The particular level of doping
used for the backward diode yields essentially $E_f = E_v$. Similar remarks
apply for the n-material where high donor concentration leads to an
impurity band that merges with the conduction band and brings about
$E_f = E_c$. The highly doped materials used in the backward diode are
known as *degenerate* semiconductors, because the majority carrier distributions differ fundamentally from those in intrinsic and moderately

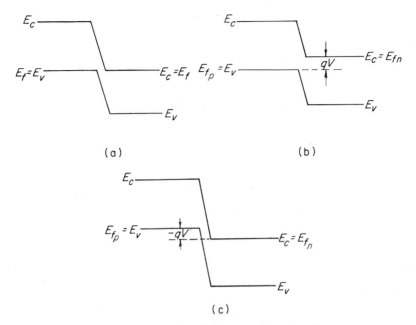

FIG. 7.28   Energy band diagram of a *pn* junction
backward diode with (a) zero bias, (b) small forward
bias, and (c) small reverse bias.

doped semiconductors where the state occupancy falls off in a simple
exponential manner. In the degenerate semiconductor the quantity l in
the Fermi function equation is not negligible compared to the exponential for energies near the majority carrier band edges and the
variation with energy is thus fundamentally different. See (5.15) and
(5.22).

[*Exercise:* Is the CPE, (4.8), valid for a degenerate semiconductor?
Hint: Consider whether (5.30), (5.39), and (5.41) are valid.]

7.11   TUNNEL DIODES

Consider what happens if the doping levels are increased even beyond those in the backward diode. From the discussion of Sec.
7.7.2 we might say that the barrier voltage required for Zener breakdown becomes smaller than V_{Bo} so breakdown occurs even for small
forward bias. This statement is not especially helpful. We would do
better to consider the actual physical behavior. The energy band diagrams for a sequence of bias conditions and the corresponding current-
voltage characteristic are given in Figs. 7.29 and 7.30.

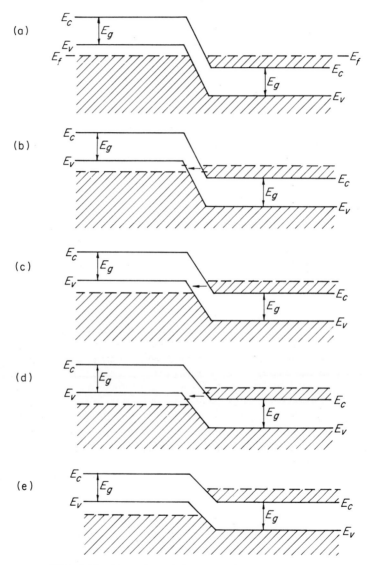

FIG. 7.29 Energy band diagrams for a *pn* junction
tunnel diode for (a) zero bias, (b) V_1, (c) V_2, (d) V_3, and
(e) V_4.

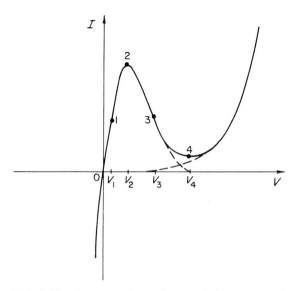

FIG. 7.30 Current-voltage characteristic corresponding to the tunnel diode energy band diagrams of Fig. 7.29. Points numbered 0–4 correspond to (a)–(e), respectively, of Fig. 7.29.

Note that due to the very high doping the Fermi level lies in the majority carrier energy bands, i.e., in the valence band of the p-material and in the conduction band of the n-material. This means many empty states are in the p-side valence band (between E_f and E_v) and many filled states are in the n-side conduction band (between E_c and E_f). To illustrate these features the levels below the Fermi level are cross-hatched to emphasize that they are mostly filled as contrasted with those above the Fermi level that are mostly empty. Because the barrier is very thin the tunneling probability is significant. In thermal equilibrium there is some tunneling in each direction but the net effect is zero. As forward bias $V = V_1$ is applied (Fig. 7.29b), an overlap between filled states on the n-side and empty states on the p-side is created and there is a net tunneling flow indicated by the arrow. This accounts for the current at V_1 in Fig. 7.30. As the bias is increased to $V = V_2$ (Figs. 7.29c and 7.30) the overlap and the tunneling current reach a maximum. For further increase in forward bias $V = V_3$, the overlap decreases again and a reduced tunneling current results. As the overlap reaches zero again at $V = V_4$ the tunneling current vanishes and only conventional diffusion currents exist. Thus for $V \geq V_4$ the ordinary diode characteristic applies.

[*Exercise:* Draw the tunnel diode energy band diagram for $V < 0$.]

The unique feature of the tunnel diode is the fact that the current is not a monotonic function of voltage but instead is a function with two regions of positive slope and one of negative slope. Thus voltage is a multivalued function of current for a certain range of currents. This fact is sometimes exploited in high speed switching circuits.

7.12   HIGH SPEED DIODES

Many communication and computing applications require a diode that is essentially ideal, i.e., unidirectional, in the presence of rapidly varying signals. The diode must be able to change quickly from the highly conducting forward bias condition to the virtually nonconducting reverse bias condition with a transition time of a few nanoseconds or less. The critical quantities in this case are capacitance and charge storage effects. Forward voltage drop, breakdown voltage, and power capability are usually not of concern since the signals are relatively small—a few volts and a few milliamperes perhaps.

Capacitance is proportional to the diode cross section so small area devices are used. Impurity concentrations also directly affect capacitance.

[*Exercise:* Discuss whether low or high doping is used to obtain small capacitance. What does this do to the breakdown voltage and to the two components of forward voltage drop, resistive and junction?]

Charge storage effects surprisingly do not depend on area but only upon the lifetimes of minority carriers on the two sides of the junction. Control of lifetime in silicon diodes is accomplished by introducing an impurity like gold in addition to the donor and acceptor impurities. The extra impurity introduces additional energy levels into the energy gap. These levels increase the rate of recombination and thereby speed up the process of getting rid of stored charge when the diode is taken from forward to reverse bias.

[*Exercise:* Discuss whether the lifetimes should be made as large or as small as possible.]

7.13   SCHOTTKY DIODES

When a diode with extremely small capacitance and charge storage is required, a Schottky diode is often used in lieu of a *pn* junction. This is a metal-semiconductor junction formed by evaporating a small metallic contact onto moderately doped n-type material to obtain a rectifying contact with a current-voltage relationship identical to the *pn* junction diode equation (7.21). Because the area is small there is little capacitance. There is also negligible charge storage because virtually all the current is carried by conduction electrons. Thus there is no significant injection of holes into the n-type semiconductor and hence no waiting for holes to recombine before the diode can block reverse current and voltage.

SUMMARY

- A *pn* junction is formed in a semiconductor crystal where the doping changes from a predominance of p-type impurities to a predominance of n-type impurities.

- At the boundary between the p- and n-regions there is a space charge layer (SCL), part on each side of the boundary. The space charge layer contains ionized impurity atoms but essentially no mobile carriers. The space charge implies an electric field within the layer directed from *n* to *p* and the field in turn implies a potential variation that acts as a barrier to the flow of holes from *p* to *n* and of electrons from *n* to *p*.

- When an external voltage is applied, the height of the potential barrier is increased or decreased and a net current flows. The current (under constant voltage conditions) is given by $I = I_s[\exp(qV/kT) - 1]$.

- Under dynamic conditions the effects of stored charge outside the SCL must be taken into account. Also a capacitance is associated with the SCL because it acts much like a dielectric separating two conducting regions. Because of this capacitance and the stored charge effects, a *pn* junction does not immediately block the reverse current when used in a circuit that attempts to suddenly change the current from forward to reverse. There is a storage interval, during which the junction acts more or less like a short circuit, followed by a decay interval during which the SCL capacitance charges to a steady-state reverse bias condition.

- At large reverse voltages the reverse current becomes large due to either Zener breakdown or avalanche breakdown. Zener breakdown occurs in heavily doped junctions with thin space charge layers. The breakdown is due to a tunneling of electrons directly from the valence band of the p-material to the conduction band of the n-material. Avalanche breakdown occurs in less heavily doped junctions with thicker space charge layers. In these tunneling is insignificant and breakdown is due to high energy collisions that create large numbers of hole-electron pairs within the space charge layer by breaking valence electrons free from their covalent bonds.

- Junctions so heavily doped that the Zener breakdown voltage approaches zero and yet exhibiting normal forward characteristics are known as backward diodes. The backward conduction is a tunneling current.

- Junctions even more heavily doped exhibit tunneling in both forward and reverse operation. The forward tunneling, i.e., from the n-side conduction band to the p-side valence band, gives rise to a multivalued forward characteristic.

PROBLEMS

7.1. A section of silicon contains 10^{16} donors/cm^3. Calculate E_{cn} in terms of E_f and kT where E_{cn} means E_c in n-type material.

7.2. A section of silicon contains 10^{16} acceptors/cm^3. Calculate E_{cp} in terms of E_f and kT where E_{cp} means E_c in p-type material.

7.3. Calculate the height of the energy barrier E_{Bo} at a pn junction composed of the materials described in Probs. 7.1 and 7.2. [Ans.: 0.7 eV]

7.4. Derive an analytic expression for the barrier potential V_{Bo} in terms of kT/q, n_i^2, N_p, and N_n.

7.5. A particular silicon junction diode has the following dimensions and material properties: cross section = 10^{-3}cm^2, length of p-region = length of n-region = 0.1 cm, $N_p = N_n = 10^{17}$/cm^3, $\tau_h = \tau_e = 10^{-7}$ sec, mobilities given in and diffusion constants calculable from the data in Fig. 6.6.
   a) Calculate I_s for the junction.
   b) Calculate the bulk resistances.

7.6. Theoretically the diode voltage equation is $V_d = RI + (kT/q) \ln(1 + I/I_s)$. In practice this holds quite well for $I \gg I_s$ except that sometimes kT/q has to be modified; i.e., even though one knows that $kT/q = .026$ V, say, this value does not make the equation fit experimental data best. The data are found to fit

$$V_d = RI + (mkT/q) \ln(1 + I/I_s) \quad \text{for } I \gg I_s$$

   where m is a dimensionless number between one and two.
   a) Given $I \gg I_s$, show that this equation can be simplified to $V_d = RI + A \ln I + B$.
   b) Select appropriate data from the following table and determine values for R, A, and B. Explain why the points you select give more accurate or better values of R, A, and B than some other combinations.

I	0	10^{-6}	10^{-5}	10^{-4}	10^{-3}	10^{-2}	10^{-1}	0.2	0.4	0.6	1.0	A
V_d	0	0.207	0.276	0.345	0.415	0.493	0.652	0.773	0.994	1.205	1.621	V

   c) From the values of A and B calculated above, determine m and I_s. [Ans.: $m = 1.15$, $I_s = 10^{-9}$ A]
   d) Over what range of I is V_d a linear function of $\ln I$ within an error of 1%? Specify both upper and lower limits.
   e) If one applies $V_d = -1$ V, will $-I = I_s$ found above? Explain. [Ans.: no, because of generation in the SCL]

7.7. A silicon diode with negligible resistance is found to obey the diode equation exactly. (In terms of the discussion in Prob. 7.6, $m = 1.0$.) When the diode carries 100 mA, the voltage is 0.7 V.
   a) Calculate I_s.
   b) Calculate absolute change and percent change in voltage as I is varied $\pm 75\%$ from 100 mA.

7.8. A silicon diode with $R = 3 \, \Omega$ obeys the diode equation and has a 0.4 V drop when the current is 1 mA. Calculate the power being dissipated when the current is 200 mA.

7.9.   A silicon diode with negligible resistance has $I_s = 10^{-12}$ A at room temperature. In silicon n_i^2 is approximately proportional to exp $[(T - 300)/7.1]$.

   a)   Express $I_s(T)$ in terms of $I_s(300)$ and an appropriate exponential function.

   b)   Substitute the above result into the diode equation to obtain a relation involving V_d, I, and T as variables and $I_s(300)$ as a constant. Assume $I \gg I_s$.

   c)   Calculate the change in voltage ΔV_d for a temperature increase $\Delta T = 10$ K if the current I is held constant at 10 mA. How does the result change if I is held constant at 1 A? What is the percent change in V_d? Calculate $\Delta V_d / \Delta T$ from your results.

   d)   Calculate the change in current ΔI for a temperature increase $\Delta T = 10$ K if the voltage is held constant at the value producing $I = 10$ mA at 300 K. What is the percent change in I? Calculate $(\Delta I/I)/\Delta T$.

7.10. Suppose $n_i^2(T)$ is written as $n_i^2(T) = n_i^2(T_o) \exp [(E_g/k)(1/T_o - 1/T)]$.

   a)   Express $I_s(T)$ in a similar form (explaining the basis for this).

   b)   Assuming $I \gg I_s$, rewrite the diode equation in terms of V_d, R, I, T, and $I_s(T_o)$.

   c)   Calculate $(\partial V_d/\partial T)_I$ and then set $T = T_o$.

   d)   Discuss briefly whether $\partial R/\partial T$ is positive or negative.

   e)   Assuming $\partial R/\partial T \simeq 0$, evaluate $(\partial V_d/\partial T)_I$ for silicon if $(kT_o/q) \ln [I/I_s(T_o)] = (1/2)(E_g/q)$ and $T_o = 300$ K.

7.11. The hole charge q_h stored in n-type material, corresponding to the plot in Fig. 7.10, is simply the charge of one hole times the number of excess holes in the entire n-type region. In symbols

$$q_h = q_A \int_{x_3}^{\text{end of n-region}} (p_n - p_{no}) \, dx$$

   a)   Solve the continuity equation for the steady-state hole distribution graphed in Fig. 7.10 in terms of $p_n(x_3)$, p_{no}, x, and L_h. (Reference to Ex. 6.1 may be helpful since this problem and that example have many similarities.) Assume the length of the n-region is many times L_h.

   b)   Calculate q_h in terms of q, A, $p_n(x_3)$, p_{no}, and L_h. Explain why you can replace "end of n-region" by "∞."

   c)   Express q_h in terms of q, A, p_{no}, L_h, and the applied junction voltage V. {Ans.: $q_h = qAL_h p_{no}[\exp(qV/kT) - 1]$}

   d)   Write by inspection expressions for the electron charge in the p-region analogous to those written in b and c.

7.12. A junction diode is operated as shown in the following circuit. Switch S has been in position A long enough for a steady state to exist. The steady-state conditions are $V = 0.7$ V, $I = 113$ mA, $q_h = q_e = 10^{-9}$ C. At $t = 0$ the switch is moved to position B.

   a)   Recognizing that the junction voltage cannot change significantly at $t = 0$ (since it is tied to q_h and q_e which cannot change instantaneously), calculate $I(0^+)$. [Ans.: -187 mA]

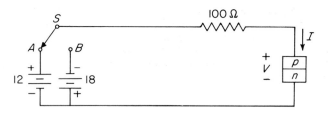

b) Recognizing that q_h and q_e supply the charge that carries I across the SCL, estimate the storage time (t_1 in Fig. 7.16) during which I remains constant at $I(0^+)$. Pretend there is negligible recombination during t_1 so that all q_h and q_e can be assumed to cross the SCL.

c) Assuming q_h and q_e decrease linearly with time over the interval t_1, calculate the junction voltage V at $t = 0.25\,t_1$, $0.5\,t_1$, $0.75\,t_1$, and t_1 and plot V vs t. [Note: The relationships between q_h, q_e, and V are developed in Prob. 7.11. The quantity $qAL_h p_{no}$ can be abbreviated as q_{ho} and evaluated from the data given in this problem; likewise, $q_{eo} = qAL_e n_{po}$]

7.13. a) Using the results of Prob. 7.11, show that the static diode current may be written as $I = q_h/\tau_h + q_e/\tau_e$.

b) Given this expression, explain why materials with small lifetimes are preferred for making high speed diodes.

7.14. For the junction of Prob. 7.3, calculate the SCL width, electric field intensity, and capacitance for $V = 0$ and $V = -10$ V. The junction area is $10^{-3}\,\text{cm}^2$.

7.15. A silicon junction has $N_a = 10^{18}/\text{cm}^3$ on one side and $N_d = 10^{15}/\text{cm}^3$ on the other. The junction area is $10^{-3}\,\text{cm}^2$.

a) Calculate the barrier potential if $kT = 0.026\,\text{eV}$. [Ans.: 0.758 V]

b) For $V = 0$ calculate the thickness of each side of the SCL and calculate the portion of V_{Bo} appearing across each part.

7.16. Suppose one wishes to design a junction diode having a small capacitance.

a) Discuss the effects of choosing impurity concentrations with
   (1) N_p and N_n both large
   (2) N_p and N_n both small but $> 4\,n_i$
   (3) one large and one small

b) Denoting the capacitances for these three cases as C_1, C_2, and C_3, respectively, evaluate the ratios C_1/C_2 and C_3/C_2 for the following impurity concentrations: large, $10^{18}/\text{cm}^3$; and small, $10^{12}/\text{cm}^3$. [Ans.: 1000 and 1.414]

7.17. This problem concerns alternate forms for the basic C-V relationship expressed in (7.52).

a) Show that for a suitable definition of K, the relationship between C and V can be written as $C = K/(V_{Bo} - V)^{1/2}$. Evaluate K (including units) if $V_{Bo} = 0.8$ V and $C = 50$ pF for $V = 0$. [Ans.: $K = 44.7\,\text{pF} \cdot \sqrt{V}$]

b) Show that the relationship between C and V can also be written as $C = C_o[V_{Bo}/(V_{Bo} - V)]^{1/2}$ where C_o is the value of C when $V = 0$.

c) Show that the relationship between C and V can also be written as $C = C_1[(V_{Bo} - V_1)/(V_{Bo} - V)]^{1/2}$ where C_1 is the value of C when

V equals some specified voltage V_1. Use this expression to calculate the capacitance of a diode with $V = -10$ V if that diode has $V_{Bo} = 0.8$ V and $C = 100\,\text{pF}$ when $V = -1$ V. [Ans.: 40.8 pF]

d)   Sketch C vs V and label the points $(0,\ C_o)$ and $(V_1,\ C_1)$.

7.18.   Suppose that for some fictitious junction, C is found to vary with V as given in the following graph.

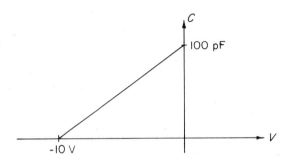

a)   Evaluate the charge required to change V from -10 V to -5 V. [Ans.: 125 pC]

b)   Evaluate the charge required to change V from -5 V to 0 V. [Ans.: 375 pC]

7.19.   A silicon junction is to be symmetrically doped and have a breakdown voltage of 100 V. Determine the impurity concentration needed. Will the mechanism of breakdown be avalanche or Zener?

7.20.   A silicon junction has 10^{18} acceptors/cm^3 on one side and 10^{15} donors/cm^3 on the other.

a)   Determine the breakdown voltage. [Ans.: 300 V]

b)   Across which region will most of the voltage appear? [Ans.: the n-region]

7.21.   A silicon junction diode exhibits the following reverse bias current voltage behavior.

I'_s	2.0	2.3	10	50	100	250	500	off scale	μA
$-V$	1	35	70	74	74.5	74.8	74.9	75	V

a)   What are the values of V_A and I_s for this diode?

b)   Devise and execute a procedure for finding m of (7.56) for this diode.

c)   Verify your values for V_A, I_s, and m by calculating I'_s at several values of $-V$ in the above table.

7.22.   The reverse characteristic of a junction diode is specified by $V_A = 50$ V, $I_s = 2 \times 10^{-7}$ A, and $m = 4.7$. Calculate the power dissipated when $V = -49.9$ V.

7.23.   a)   Show from (7.56) that the *dynamic diode impedance*

$$Z_d \equiv \frac{d(-V)}{dI'_s} \simeq \frac{V_A I_s/m}{(I'_s)^2} \quad \text{for} -V \simeq V_A$$

b)   For the diode of Prob. 7.22, evaluate Z_d for $I'_s = 20$ mA.

7.24. Suppose the barrier thickness Δx in Fig. 7.24 is such that the transmission probability P_{tun} is 3×10^{-11}, there are 10^{22} atoms/cm^3 with four valence electrons each, and the energy range common to the p-side valence band and the n-side conduction band is such that 20% of the p-side valence electrons have the probability P_{tun} of being transmitted. Assuming $v_t = 10^7$ cm/sec and a diode cross section of 10^{-3}cm^2, calculate the Zener current.

APPENDIX

This appendix examines in detail (1) the carriers actually able to surmount the energy barrier in a *pn* junction, and (2) the tunneling probability involved in Zener breakdown. The discussion and results here supplement Secs. 7.1, 7.2 and 7.7.2.

A7.1   Energetic Carrier Analysis

In Sec. 7.1 the carrier flow rates F_1, F_2, F_3, and F_4 are described in terms of four carrier concentrations n_{po}, n_2, p_3, and p_{no}. (See Fig. 7.6.) These are characterized as being the concentrations of carriers with sufficient total energy to pass through the barrier region. It is then suggested that equality of the thermal equilibrium values of n_2 and p_3 with n_{po} and p_{no}, respectively, leads to zero net hole and electron flows— two essential conditions of thermal equilibrium. Specifically it is reasoned that $n_{2o} = n_{po}$ produces $F_1 = F_2$ thus giving zero net electron flow, and $p_{3o} = p_{no}$ produces $F_3 = F_4$ thus giving zero net hole flow. This reasoning is correct qualitatively but contains a quantitative flaw.

It is correct to say that $F_1 = F_2$ and $F_3 = F_4$ are required for thermal equilibrium and also that $F_1 \propto n_{po}$ and $F_4 \propto p_{no}$. However it is not quite correct to say that $F_2 \propto n_2$ and $f_3 \propto p_3$.

The problem is this: some of the carriers comprising n_2 and p_3 cannot in fact surmount the barrier. In Fig. 7.6, n_2 and p_3 have been defined such that the kinetic energy of each carrier is greater than the barrier energy. (Recall that E_{cn} and E_{vp} play the roles of potential energy for the n_2 electrons and the p_3 holes, respectively.) However, simply having kinetic energy greater than barrier energy is not enough. The x-directed kinetic energy must be greater than the barrier energy because the barrier force is directed along the x-axis and affects only the x-directed carrier velocity.

Thus, of the n_2 electrons there is some subset n_2' that has sufficient x-directed kinetic energy to surmount the barrier. The electron flow rate F_2 is proportional to this quantity. Likewise, of the p_3 holes there is a subset p_3' to which F_3 is proportional. In thermal equilibrium we then have $n_2' = n_{po}$ and $p_3' = p_{no}$ which lead to $F_2 = F_1$ and $F_3 = F_4$.

The concentration n_2' may be calculated in a manner analogous to that used for calculating n_o in Chap. 5: multiply the appropriate density of states function $S_c(E)$ by the appropriate Fermi function $f(E)$ and integrate over the range of energies occupied by the n_2' electrons. The appropriate Fermi function is of course that for electrons in n-material. From (5.15) or (5.22),

$$f(E) = \{1 + \exp[(E - E_{fn})/kT]\}^{-1} \equiv f_n(E) \tag{A7.1}$$

The appropriate density of states function is not $A_c(E - E_{cn})^{1/2}$ since that function includes all electrons comprising n_2, not just those comprising n_2'. The quantum states in which the n_2' electrons reside are clearly those which exist on both sides of the junction, i.e., those quantum states whose wave functions do not decay to zero in the p-material. But this is simply all the conduction band quantum states for the p-material. The distribution of these states in energy is given by

$$S_c(E) = A_c(E - E_{cp})^{1/2} \equiv S_{cp}(E) \tag{A7.2}$$

Thus E_{cp} rather than E_{cn} is used in $S_c(E)$.

The product $f_n(E)S_{cp}(E)$ is now to be integrated from $E_{cn} + E_B$ to ∞, the range of energies occupied by the n_2' electrons. A plot of the product is superimposed on the energy band in Fig. A7.1 for the special

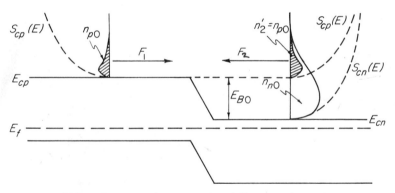

FIG. A7.1   Junction energy band diagram (thermal equilibrium case) illustrating use of $S_{cp}(E)$ to calculate n_2'.

case of thermal equilibrium (hence the o subscripts). Also shown for comparison are $f_p(E)S_{cp}(E)$ from which n_{po} is computed and $f_n S_{cn}(E)$ from which n_{2o} and n_{no} are computed. The integral reads as follows

$$n_2' = \int_{E_{cn}+E_B}^{\infty} \frac{A_c(E - E_{cp})^{1/2}\, dE}{\{1 + \exp[(E - E_{fn})/kT]\}} \tag{A7.3}$$

To evaluate this integral we must approximate the Fermi function by neglecting unity in comparison with the exponential. Thus (A7.3) becomes

$$n_2' = \int_{E_{cn}+E_B}^{\infty} \exp\left[-(E - E_{fn})/kT\right] A_c(E - E_{cp})^{1/2} dE \qquad (A7.4)$$

The lower limit $E_{cn} + E_B = E_{cp}$. This means that the right side of (A7.4) is almost identical with the expression that is used for calculating n_{po}. Only the subscript on the Fermi energy is different. If $\exp(E_{fn}/kT)$ is factored out of the integral and if the integral is multiplied by $\exp(-E_{fp})$ and $\exp E_{fp}$ the result is

$$n_2' = \exp\left[(E_{fn} - E_{fp})/kT\right] \int_{E_{cp}}^{\infty} \exp\left[-(E - E_{fp})/kT\right] A_c(E - E_c)^{1/2}$$
$$(A7.5)$$

The integral in this expression is now exactly that for n_{po}. The exponential before the integral depends on the difference between the Fermi levels in the two materials. In thermal equilibrium (Fig. A7.1) the Fermi levels are equal and the exponential becomes unity. Thus in thermal equilibrium $n_{2o}' = n_{po}$ as asserted earlier.

The nonequilibrium cases are shown in Fig. A7.2. The Fermi levels in general differ by qV_d where V_d is the applied voltage, i.e.,

$$E_{fn} - E_{fp} = qV_d \qquad (A7.6)$$

Using this and the fact that the integral equals n_{po}, (A7.5) becomes

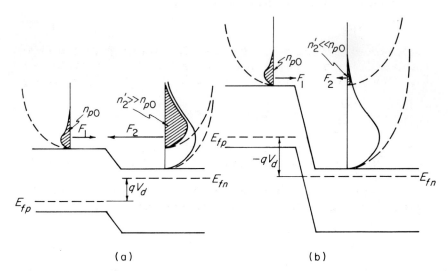

FIG. A7.2   Diagrams corresponding to Fig. A7.1 for nonequilibrium cases: (a) $V_d > 0$, leading to $n_2' \gg n_{po}$ and (b) $V_d < 0$, leading to $n_2' \ll n_{po}$.

$$n'_2 = n_{po} \exp(qV_d/kT) \tag{A7.7}$$

Thus for $V_d > 0$ we find $n'_2 \gg n_{po}$ and $F_2 \gg F_1$. On the other hand for $V_d < 0$ we find $n'_2 \ll n_{po}$ and as a result $F_2 \ll F_1$.

The calculations for p'_3 are completely analogous to those given for n'_2. The result is

$$p'_3 = p_{no} \exp(qV_d/kT) \tag{A7.8}$$

Given the dependences of n'_2 and p'_3 upon the applied voltage and accepting on an intuitive basis that $F_2 \propto n'_2$ and $F_3 \propto p'_3$, it becomes clear that F_2 and F_3 are proportional to $\exp(qV_d/kT)$ as stated in (7.5) and (7.6).

A7.2   Tunneling Probability Analysis

To calculate the probability of an electron tunneling through an energy barrier we need to evaluate the decay of the electron wave function within the barrier. The differential equation for this wave function is Schrödinger's equation,

$$\frac{d^2\psi}{dx^2} + \frac{2m}{\hbar^2} [E - U(x)]\psi = 0 \tag{A7.9}$$

The exact nature of the solution to this differential equation depends upon $E - U(x)$. However, in general we expect a sort of exponential decay. Let us therefore write

$$\psi = \exp\phi \tag{A7.10}$$

where ϕ is some function of x. By use of (A7.10) we in effect transform the problem from finding $\psi(x)$ to finding $\phi(x)$. Once $\phi(x)$ is known, the tunneling probability P_{tun} can be calculated in terms of ϕ by writing

$$P_{\text{tun}} = \left| \frac{\psi(x_2)}{\psi(x_1)} \right|^2 = \exp\{2[\phi(x_2) - \phi(x_1)]\} \tag{A7.11}$$

where x_1 and x_2 are the boundaries of the energy barrier. From this equation we see that the change in ϕ from one side of the barrier to the other must be obtained.

To find ϕ we substitute (A7.10) into (A7.9) and then divide by $\exp\phi$. This yields the following differential equation for ϕ.

$$\frac{d^2\phi}{dx^2} + \left(\frac{d\phi}{dx}\right)^2 + \frac{2m}{\hbar^2} [E - U(x)] = 0 \tag{A7.12}$$

From (A7.10) we note that ϕ is logarithmically related to ψ, which means that rapid variations of ψ translate into slow variations of ϕ. The higher order derivatives of a slowly varying function tend to be very small. Thus we may assume

$$\frac{d^2\phi}{dx^2} \ll \left(\frac{d\phi}{dx}\right)^2 \tag{A7.13}$$

and solve (A7.12) for $d\phi/dx$, thereby obtaining

$$\frac{d\phi}{dx} = -(2m/\hbar^2)^{1/2}[U(x) - E]^{1/2} \tag{A7.14}$$

Multiplying (A7.14) by dx and integrating from x_1 to x_2 then yields

$$\phi(x_2) - \phi(x_1) = -(2m/\hbar^2)^{1/2} \int_{x_1}^{x_2} [U(x) - E]^{1/2} dx \tag{A7.15}$$

Thus the tunneling probability is given by

$$P_{\text{tun}} = \exp\{-2(2m/\hbar^2)^{1/2} \int_{x_1}^{x_2} [U(x) - E]^{1/2} dx\} \tag{A7.16}$$

The triangular barrier of Fig. 7.25 with the boundaries x_1 and x_2 labeled is reproduced in Fig. A7.3. For convenience in characterizing $U(x)$ we let $x_2 = 0$ which means $x_1 = -\Delta x$. For this case the difference

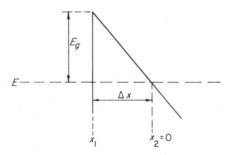

FIG. A7.3   Triangular barrier seen by electrons in *pn* junction.

$U(x) - E$ is given by

$$U(x) - E = -(E_g/\Delta x)x \tag{A7.17}$$

which applies for x between x_1 and x_2. Inserting this expression into (A7.16) leads to P_{tun} for the triangular barrier,

$$P_{\text{tun}} = \exp[-(4/3)(2mE_g/\hbar^2)^{1/2}\Delta x] \tag{A7.18}$$

It is interesting to compare this result with those for barriers of other shapes; Fig. A7.4 shows a square-topped and a parabolic barrier. For the square-topped barrier the quantity $U(x) - E$ simply equals E_g

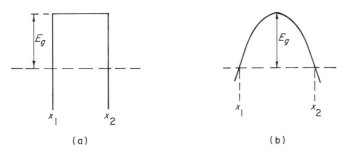

FIG. A7.4   (a) Square-topped energy barrier and (b) parabolic energy barrier.

so that (A7.16) immediately yields

$$P_{tun} = \exp\left[-2(2mE_g/\hbar^2)^{1/2}\,\Delta x\right] \qquad (A7.19)$$

For the parabolic case we select $x = 0$ midway between x_1 and x_2 so that

$$U(x) - E = E_g - [4E_g/(\Delta x)^2]x^2 \qquad (A7.20)$$

Using this in (A7.16) then yields

$$P_{tun} = \exp\left[-(\pi/2)(2mE_g/\hbar^2)^{1/2}\,\Delta x\right] \qquad (A7.21)$$

Comparison of (A7.18), (A7.19), and (A7.21) reveals that in each case the exponent is proportional to $-(2mE_g/\hbar^2)\,x$, and the constants of proportionality do not differ a great deal. They vary from 1.33 in the triangular case to 1.59 in the parabolic case to 2.0 in the square-topped case. Thus the tunneling probability is not strongly dependent on the shape of the barrier. So long as the barrier thickness Δx and height E_g are correctly identified one gets about the right answer for the tunneling probability.

The approximation involved in (A7.13), (A7.14), and (A7.16) is known as the WKB approximation for Wentzel, Kramers, and Brillouin, who each proposed it independently in 1926 as an approximate solution for the Schrödinger equation. For further discussion of the approximation the reader is referred to Moll[7] and Sze.[8]

---

7. J. L. Moll, *Physics of Semiconductors,* 1964, McGraw-Hill, New York, p. 242.
8. S. M. Sze, *Physics of Semiconductor Devices,* 1969, Wiley, New York, p. 161.

CHAPTER 8

Junction Transistor

8.1 INTRODUCTION

In late 1947 researchers at the Bell Telephone Laboratories discovered in a semiconductor experiment an effect which subsequently led to the invention of the junction transistor. The experiment involved probing the surface of a piece of germanium with a pair of fine gold wires. Under certain conditions a small voltage variation applied to one wire resulted in larger voltage variation at the other wire; in other words, voltage amplification was taking place. This experimental setup was refined somewhat and became known as the "transistor." Quite unlike modern transistors, it was a "point contact" transistor, named after the pointed gold wire contacts which pressed against the germanium base. One wire was known as the emitter, the other the collector. The characteristics of this device were unstable and unpredictable and hence point contact transistors were not very satisfactory for industrial electronics application.

Theoretical consideration of the point contact transistor led to the conclusion that a much better device would result if the point contacts were replaced by *pn* junctions. Several years of materials processing research were required before this theoretical conclusion was confirmed in fact, and in 1951 the commercial feasibility of the junction transistor was proven. The name *junction transistor* is a simplified form of *bipolar junction transistor* (BJT), bipolar because there are two polarities of carriers. In this chapter we shall further simplify it to *transistor*.

The general structure of this device may be described as a three-layer sandwich of p-type and n-type materials resulting in two *pn* junctions. Since the center layer may be either p-type or n-type material there are two kinds of devices: *pnp* and *npn*. The names assigned to the layers are those originating with the point contact transistor. The center layer is the *base*, one outer layer is the *emitter*, and the other outer layer is the *collector*. Ohmic electrical contacts are made to these layers

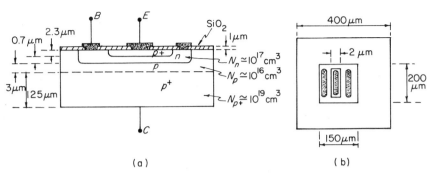

FIG. 8.1   (a) Cross section and (b) top view of a
typical silicon *pnp* planar transistor.

and the currents flowing into the layers from the external leads are
called the *base current* I_B, the *emitter current* I_E, and the *collector current* I_C.

The details of the physical structure of a given transistor depend
upon the fabrication methods used in its manufacture (see Chap. 9). By
far the most commonly used semiconductor is silicon and the structure
with highest performance capabilities is the planar structure.

Since in discussing transistor parameters we often need to note
certain unique properties of the structure, we sketch in Fig. 8.1 a low-
power medium-frequency planar transistor. The particular device
shown is capable of handling approximately 100 mW of power and has
a maximum frequency of operation of about 500 MHz. A number of its
features cannot be made clear until fabrication methods are discussed.
At that point certain modifications are made in the sketch, but the
general features illustrated here are correct. Note that a *pnp* transistor
is shown. The silicon dioxide (SiO_2) over the junctions makes the device stable by shielding the sensitive junction regions from ambient
contamination. The impurities are added to the host semiconductor
material using solid-state diffusion processes. Because the emitter and
collector junctions are parallel planes (except near the edges) the device
is called a planar transistor. The darkened areas above the emitter and
collector regions are deposited metals which provide contact to these
regions. The dimensions and dopings shown are those required for
the desired characteristics.

Figure 8.1 is a reasonably accurate sketch of a practical transistor.
It is inconvenient to reproduce each time we refer to it so we will customarily use a simple rectangular structure for illustrative purposes.
This structure and the accepted circuit symbols for the junction transistor are shown in Fig. 8.2. However, it is important to keep in mind

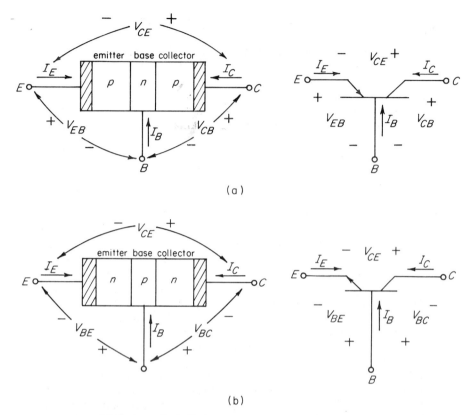

(a)

(b)

FIG. 8.2 Simplified physical structure and conventional circuit symbols for (a) *pnp* transistor and (b) *npn* transistor.

the actual structure when considering factors influencing electrical parameters of the transistor.

Our principal interest in the transistor is its electrical characteristics. What characteristics would we find for the *pnp* structure of Fig. 8.2a? What magnitudes and directions of terminal currents might be expected when (1) $V_{EB} > 0$ and $V_{CB} > 0$, i.e., both junctions forward biased; (2) $V_{EB} < 0$ and $V_{CB} < 0$, i.e., both junctions reverse biased; (3) $V_{EB} > 0$ and $V_{CB} < 0$, i.e., one junction forward biased and one reverse biased? From our study of the junction diode our answers probably would be:

1. I_E and I_C both large and positive, I_B large and negative
2. I_E and I_C both small and negative, I_B small and positive
3. I_E large and positive, I_C small and negative, and I_B large and negative

[*Question:* Do you agree with these expectations? Why or why not?]

   If a transistor is tested experimentally our first two predictions are fulfilled. In the third case, however, some unexpected results are obtained. The current I_E is large and positive but I_C is large and negative while I_B is small and negative. In other words the large current entering the emitter terminal has exited, not through the base terminal as might be expected, but through the collector terminal! As a result $-I_C$ is approximately equal to $+I_E$ and $-I_B \ll I_E$.

   What is the explanation? What are the describing equations? We shall answer these questions in the next few sections.

8.2   PHYSICAL BEHAVIOR OF THE TRANSISTOR

   Let us continue discussing the conditions above, i.e., $V_{EB} > 0$ and $V_{CB} < 0$. Consider first the emitter current I_E. At the emitter-base junction (usually called the emitter junction) the barrier is lowered so that holes flow into the n-type base and electrons flow into the p-type emitter. Let the hole current across the space charge region be called $I_h(0)$ and the analogous electron current $I_e(0)$. The total emitter current is thus $I_h(0) + I_e(0)$. Figure 8.3 shows an expanded portion of the structure in Fig. 8.2a together with a diagram illustrating the various components of current existing within the transistor. The arrowheads indicate directions of particle flow.

   Now the holes comprising $I_h(0)$ create a hole concentration gradient between $x = 0$ and $x = W$ and thus begin diffusing across the base region. If W is rather small there is a good chance that a hole will diffuse the entire distance without recombining and thus a substantial hole current $I_h(W)$ exists at $x = W$. These holes enter the SCL of the collector-base junction, find an accelerating field, are swept into the collector, and cause a substantial current to flow out of the collector terminal giving rise to the principal component of the collector current I_C. (The other component of I_C is diodelike and is discussed later in this section.)

   Finally, consider the base current I_B. From Kirchhoff's current law we know that $-I_B$ must equal the difference between I_E and $-I_C$. From Fig. 8.3 it may be seen that I_B is required to (a) supply the electrons injected into the emitter and recombined there, (b) supply the electrons lost in recombining with the holes in the base, and (c) accept the electrons arising from the generation term G_1. We shall find that I_B is small for a well-designed transistor so that the emitter and collector currents are nearly equal.

[*Question:* We have been assuming $V_{CB} < 0$, which produces an accelerating field. Would the field be decelerating if $V_{CB} > 0$? Explain. (Ans.: No, $V_{CB} > 0$ reduces the height of the barrier but does not elim-

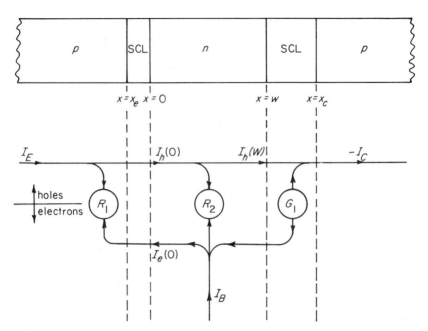

FIG. 8.3   Expanded portion of Fig. 8.2a together
with a diagram showing the several hole and electron
currents and the net generation and recombination
processes that connect them.

inate it or reverse its direction. Therefore the direction of the electric
field is not changed.)]

The current $I_h(W)$ is readily seen to be proportional to the emitter
current which causes it. Hence we shall write

$$I_h(W) = \alpha_F I_E \tag{8.1}$$

where α_F is a dimensionless constant of proportionality (discussed in
Sec. 8.3).

Thus far we have not considered the diode properties of the
collector-base pn junction. The reverse saturation current of this junction is called I_{co} (analogous to I_s in the previous chapter). Thus the collector current contains a component given by $I_{co}[\exp(qV_{CB}/kT) - 1]$,
where V_{CB} is the collector-base voltage. If this component is combined
with $I_h(W)$ from (8.1) we have the collector current,

$$I_C = -\alpha_F I_E + I_{co}[\exp(qV_{CB}/kT) - 1] \quad \text{for low voltage} \tag{8.2}$$

Note that $-I_{co}$ is the collector current that flows when the emitter is
open circuited ($I_E = 0$) and the collector-base junction is reverse biased

$[\exp(qV_{CB}/kT) \ll 1]$. The signs in this equation reflect the fact that the direction for positive diode current (from p to n) agrees with that chosen for I_C (into the transistor) whereas the $\alpha_F I_E$ current flows out of the transistor and hence must be subtracted from the diode current.

A qualifying low voltage condition is included in (8.2) because an additional process, avalanche multiplication, has not yet been taken into account. This process is included in G_1 in Fig. 8.3. As the carriers comprising the terms in (8.2) pass through the collector-base SCL they are accelerated by the field there. If this field is large (high negative V_{CB}) the carriers generate new hole-electron pairs via avalanche multiplication thus increasing the total collector current. The effect then is that both terms in (8.2) are multiplied by the multiplication factor M described in the previous chapter. This factor depends of course on the collector-base voltage. Thus we have

$$I_C = -M\alpha_F I_E + MI_{co}[\exp(qV_{CB}/kT) - 1] \tag{8.3}$$

where

$$M = [1 - (-V_{CB}/BV_{CBO})^n]^{-1} \tag{8.4}$$

and BV_{CBO} is collector-base avalanche breakdown voltage (thus BV). As before, n is a parameter between two and six.

8.3 CURRENT GAIN, ALPHA

The parameter α_F is the *common-base current gain*. This term arises from the idea of I_E as an input, the variable part of I_C as an output, and the ratio of output to input being gain. "Common-base" refers to the fact that the base terminal is common to the circuitry producing I_E and that carrying I_C. This is illustrated in Fig. 8.4. The makeup of α_F can be determined by recalling from Sec. 8.2 that

$$I_E = I_h(0) + I_e(0) \tag{8.5}$$

Since only the $I_h(0)$ term is useful in producing collector current we

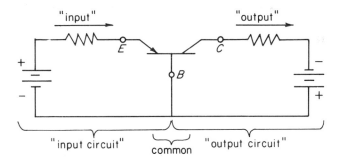

FIG. 8.4 Common-base transistor circuit.

are interested in the ratio of $I_h(0)$ to the total emitter current. Thus we define

$$\gamma_e = \frac{I_h(0)}{I_h(0) + I_e(0)} = \frac{1}{1 + I_e(0)/I_h(0)} \qquad (8.6a)$$

The parameter γ_e is known as emitter-base junction efficiency, or simply *emitter efficiency*. To evaluate γ_e we need $I_e(0)$ and $I_h(0)$, the electron and hole components of I_E. The electron component can be found from the diode equation (7.35) since it is just the electron current at the space charge edge in the p-type emitter. The calculation of $I_h(0)$ is complicated by the fact that the base width W is characteristically much less than the diffusion length of a minority carrier in the base region. In this case $I_h(0) = (qp_{no}D_h/W)[\exp(qV/kT) - 1]$. Note that it differs from the corresponding current in the usual diode equation only in that base width W has replaced diffusion length L_h. Using the expressions for $I_e(0)$ and $I_h(0)$, we find

$$\gamma_e = (1 + D_e W N_n / D_h L_e N_p)^{-1} \qquad (8.6b)$$

where N_p and N_n are the net doping in the emitter and base, respectively. Note that γ_e is independent of V_{EB} and depends only on diffusion constants, diffusion length, base width, and impurity concentrations. By proper choice of N_p and N_n the transistor manufacturer can obtain values of γ_e in the range 0.99–0.999.

[*Question:* If $\gamma_e \simeq 1$ is desired, what relative values of emitter and base doping should be chosen?]

As noted above $I_h(0)$ contributes to I_C. However not all of $I_h(0)$ contributes; some holes recombine while diffusing across the base. Hence we are interested in the hole current at $x = W$ and the ratio of this to $I_h(0)$. This ratio is the *base transport factor* and is expressed as

$$\gamma_b = I_h(W)/I_h(0) \qquad (8.7a)$$

It can be shown by analysis (which we shall not develop) that

$$\gamma_b \simeq 1 - (1/2)(W/L_h)^2 \qquad (8.7b)$$

providing that W is small compared to L_h in the base. With the narrow base widths (less than 1 μm) easily achieved with today's device technology, γ_b can be held in the range 0.99–0.999.

We now can express $I_h(W)$ in terms of I_E. This expression is

$$I_h(W) = [I_h(W)/I_h(0)][I_h(0)/I_E]I_E = \gamma_b \gamma_e I_E \qquad (8.8)$$

Comparing this with (8.1) we see that

$$\alpha_F = \gamma_b \gamma_e \qquad (8.9)$$

Thus α_F is composed of two factors, each slightly less than unity. Hence at low voltages where (8.2) applies the common-base current gain is slightly less than unity. At higher voltages it is seen from (8.3) that the effective gain is $M\alpha_F$ rather than just α_F. Hence for V_{CB} large enough to yield $M \geq 1/\alpha_F$, the effective gain $M\alpha_F \geq 1$. (Since a typical value for $1/\alpha_F$ might be 1.02 it is apparent that $M\alpha_F \geq 1$ occurs even for values of $-V_{CB}$ substantially less than BV_{CBO}.) This is not desirable for two important reasons: (1) the current gain α_F will fluctuate with variations in collector voltage and (2) in certain transistor operating conditions voltage breakdown occurs when $M\alpha_F = 1$. Hence it is usually necessary to operate the transistor with $-V_{CB} \ll BV_{CBO}$.

To achieve α_F very close to unity, from (8.9) it is clear that during fabrication of the transistor both γ_b and γ_e must be made nearly equal to unity. To produce γ_e near unity requires virtually all the emitter current to be carried by holes across the emitter-base junction. In other words the ratio $I_e(0)/I_h(0)$ must be very small. See (8.6a). From (8.6b) we see that γ_e depends mainly on N_n and N_p. To make γ_e near unity one would thus dope the emitter heavily and the base lightly.

To produce γ_b near unity requires as little recombination as possible in the base region. This means making the base width W very small and the diffusion constant D_h and lifetime τ_h large so that $W \ll L_h$. This conclusion is consistent with (8.7b).

[*Questions:* Is large or small base doping called for to make D_h large and τ_h large? Are these requirements compatible with each other and with the requirements for producing γ_e near unity? (Ans.: small, small, yes, yes)]

Note that large values of γ_e and γ_b imply small base current. Large γ_e ensures small electron flow into the emitter while large γ_b means little recombination of electrons with holes diffusing across the base. Each effect contributes to a small I_B. Manufacturers can routinely produce transistors with γ_e and γ_b in the range 0.99–0.999 and hence α_F in the range 0.98–0.998.

8.4   CURRENT GAIN, BETA

In many applications the arrangement in Fig. 8.5 is preferred over the common-base circuit of Fig. 8.4. In this circuit the base and collector currents are the input and output variables and the emitter terminal is common. Since the base current is small compared to the collector current, it is expected that the current gain is higher in the common-emitter circuit. This is borne out in the equations below.

To conveniently describe the transistor in this application we need an equation analogous to (8.2) relating I_C to I_B. Such an equation may be found by using Kirchhoff's current law to reexpress I_E in (8.2) in

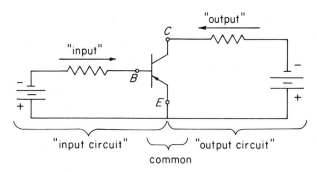

FIG. 8.5   Common-emitter transistor circuit.

terms of I_B and I_C. Thus we write the following [see Fig. 8.1 to verify (8.10)].

$$I_E = -(I_C + I_B) \tag{8.10}$$

$$I_C = +\alpha_F(I_C + I_B) + I_{CO}[\exp(qV_{CB}/kT) - 1] \tag{8.11}$$

$$I_C = [\alpha_F/(1 - \alpha_F)]I_B + [I_{CO}/(1 - \alpha_F)][\exp(qV_{CB}/kT) - 1] \tag{8.12}$$

We now have I_C expressed in terms of I_B and a diode action term. The coefficient of I_B, namely $\alpha_F/(1 - \alpha_F)$, is the current gain in this case, i.e., it is the *common-emitter current gain* β_F.

$$\beta_F = \alpha_F/(1 - \alpha_F) \tag{8.13}$$

[*Exercise:* Prove that $\alpha_F = \beta_F/(1 + \beta_F)$ and $1 - \alpha_F = 1/(1 + \beta_F)$.]

   Given (8.13) and the identities in the above exercise we can rewrite (8.12) in a more convenient form, namely,

$$I_C = \beta_F I_B + (1 + \beta_F)I_{CO}[\exp(qV_{CB}/kT) - 1] \quad \text{for low voltage} \tag{8.14}$$

This equation does not apply for high negative V_{CB} since it is derived from (8.2).

   Proceeding as above but beginning with (8.3) we obtain, taking into account avalanche multiplication,

$$I_C = \frac{M(1 - \alpha_F)}{(1 - M\alpha_F)} \{\beta_F I_B + (1 + \beta_F)I_{CO}[\exp(qV_{CB}/kT) - 1]\} \tag{8.15}$$

This equation allows one to see that voltage breakdown occurs in the common-emitter configuration not when $M \to \infty$ but when $M\alpha_F \to 1$. Thus the common-emitter breakdown voltage BV_{CEO} is smaller than BV_{CBO}. In fact, using (8.4) together with the breakdown condition $M\alpha_F = 1$ one obtains

$$BV_{CEO} = BV_{CBO}/(1 + \beta_F)^{1/n} \tag{8.16}$$

Thus for a transistor with $BV_{CBO} = 100$ V, $\beta_F = 80$, and $n = 4$, the value of BV_{CEO} is given by $BV_{CEO} = 100/(81)^{1/4} = 100/3 = 33.3$ V.

Consider now some typical values for the parameters and variables in (8.14). The current gain β_F shows a very wide range; transistors are manufactured with β_F as low as 5 and as large as 1000. For a particular transistor-line, production tolerances of $\pm 33\%$ or $\pm 50\%$ are typical. In addition β_F is temperature dependent, varying roughly 1–2% for each °C change. As noted before, the parameter I_{CO} corresponds to I_s of the previous chapter. Thus at room temperature I_{CO} is very small, about a microampere in a typical germanium transistor and a few nanoamperes in a silicon transistor. This means, especially in silicon transistors, the second term in (8.14) can usually be neglected for all negative V_{CB} and for positive V_{CB} less than about $+0.5$ V, the voltage required for significant current in a silicon *pn* diode. However I_{CO} like I_s is strongly temperature dependent. Therefore at higher temperatures the I_{CO} terms may become important, especially in germanium transistors.

A tolerance of $\pm 50\%$ on beta seems extreme considering the precision normally attainable in present-day technologies. A clue to the cause for these variations is found in (8.13). From that equation it is apparent that beta is largely determined by the amount alpha differs from unity. A small percent change in α_F implies a much larger percent change in $1 - \alpha_F$ which in turn means a large percent change in beta.

For example, suppose a particular transistor line had variations in production leading to alpha varying $\pm 1\%$ from 0.99, i.e., $\alpha_F = 0.99 \pm 0.0099$. Calculating the maximum and minimum beta values corresponding to this alpha variation we find

$$\beta_F(\text{min}) = \frac{0.9801}{1 - 0.9801} = 49 \qquad \beta_F(\text{max}) = \frac{0.9999}{1 - 0.9999} = 9999$$

Thus beta would have a center value of about 5000 and a tolerance of about $\pm 98\%$!

From the above example one can see how large variations in β_F come about and that a $\pm 50\%$ tolerance is quite reasonable. In fact fabrication techniques cannot always do even this well. The $\pm 50\%$ tolerance is often obtained by testing and sorting after fabrication. Units falling outside the accepted range are assigned other type numbers.

8.5 COMPLETE DC MODEL

To facilitate the discussion, (8.2) was developed in the context of a forward biased emitter junction so that a large positive I_E would exist. It can be shown to hold also if $V_{EB} < 0$ so that I_E is small and/or negative. Thus (8.2), repeated below and renumbered for convenience, is true in general (except at high voltage).

$$I_C = -\alpha_F I_E + I_{CO}[\exp(qV_{CB}/kT) - 1] \qquad (8.17a)$$

To complete the model, a comparable equation involving V_{EB} is required. If the collector junction is forward biased, holes are injected into the base, diffuse across the base, and come out the emitter terminal, thus giving a term proportional to I_C. In addition the emitter current contains a diode term involving V_{EB}. Thus we would write

$$I_E = -\alpha_R I_C + I_{EO}[\exp(qV_{EB}/kT) - 1] \qquad (8.17b)$$

This equation is identical in form with (8.17a); α_R and α_F have the same nature, and I_{EO} and I_{CO} have the same nature. Quantitatively the equations differ because the transistor is not symmetrical. In general $\alpha_R < \alpha_F$ and $I_{EO} < I_{CO}$. A useful relationship among these four parameters is stated here without proof. It is

$$\alpha_F I_{EO} = \alpha_R I_{CO} \qquad (8.18)$$

Equations (8.17) are variations of a pair of equations derived on a very general basis by Ebers and Moll.[1] The Ebers-Moll equations are

$$I_E = I_{ES}[\exp(qV_{EB}/kT) - 1] - \alpha_R I_{CS}[\exp(qV_{CB}/kT) - 1] \qquad (8.19a)$$

$$I_C = -\alpha_F I_{ES}[\exp(qV_{EB}/kT) - 1] + I_{CS}[\exp(qV_{CB}/kT) - 1] \qquad (8.19b)$$

They are derived by solving (8.17) simultaneously and making the following definitions:

$$I_{ES} \equiv I_{EO}/(1 - \alpha_F\alpha_R) \qquad I_{CS} \equiv I_{CO}/(1 - \alpha_F\alpha_R) \qquad (8.20)$$

From (8.19) we see that $-I_{CS}$ is the collector current which flows when the emitter-base junction is short-circuited, $\exp(qV_{EB}/kT) = 1$, and the collector-base junction is reverse biased, $\exp(qV_{CB}/kT) \ll 1$. The S in the subscript arises because I_{CS} is described in terms of a short-circuit condition. A similar definition applies to I_{ES}. Since (8.17) and (8.19) are alternate forms of the same basic information, the pair to be used depends upon the situation. The important feature of (8.19) is that both I_E and I_C are expressed in terms of junction voltages rather than each other.

In many applications it is useful to express the emitter and collector currents in terms of the base current. This may be accomplished by first using Kirchhoff's current law to write

$$I_B + I_C + I_E = 0 \qquad (8.21)$$

which is then used to eliminate I_E from (8.17a) and I_C from (8.17b) to obtain

$$I_C = \beta_F I_B + (1 + \beta_F)I_{CO}[\exp(qV_{CB}/kT) - 1] \qquad (8.22a)$$

$$I_E = \beta_R I_B + (1 + \beta_R)I_{EO}[\exp(qV_{EB}/kT) - 1] \qquad (8.22b)$$

The first of these equations is (8.14) in Sec. 8.4.

---

1. J. J. Ebers, and J. L. Moll, Large-signal Behavior of Junction Transistors, *Proc. IRE* 42(1954): 1761–72.

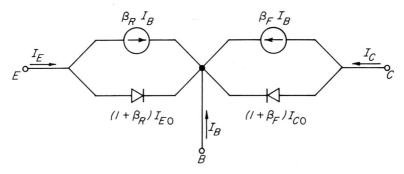

FIG. 8.6   The *pnp* base current controlled equivalent circuit.

Frequently it is useful to have the information in (8.22) presented by either current-voltage graphs or an equivalent electrical network known as an *equivalent circuit*. The equivalent circuit corresponding to (8.22) is given in Fig. 8.6. It is verified by using Fig. 8.6 to find the dependence of I_C and I_E upon V_{CB} and V_{EB}. The resulting equations should be identical to (8.22); if they are then Fig. 8.6 is indeed an accurate model of the device.

This equivalent circuit consists of two current generators controlled by the base current I_B. Thus we designate this circuit as *base current controlled*. The two remaining elements in the circuit are *pn* diodes obeying equations of the form (7.35). From that equation we see it is I_s that distinguishes one *pn* diode from another. Thus in Fig. 8.6 we have assigned diode labels $(1 + \beta_R)I_{EO}$ and $(1 + \beta_F)I_{CO}$, the saturation currents required for the circuit to conform to (8.22). Labeling the diode with its value of I_s is analogous to labeling a resistor with its resistance R. The resistor symbol is understood to imply the current-voltage relationship $I = V/R$; by the same token the diode symbol is understood to imply $I = I_s[\exp(qV/kT) - 1]$.

The important graphic current-voltage characteristics for the *pnp* transistor are obtained by using the equivalent circuit. Two such examples are the base I_B vs V_{BE} or I_B vs V_{EB} characteristic and the collector I_C vs V_{CE} characteristic. Figure 8.6 shows that I_B depends on both V_{EB} and V_{CB}. Hence a graph of I_B vs V_{EB} must specify something about V_{CB} (or about V_{CE} which is related to V_{CB} by Kirchhoff's voltage law). In Fig. 8.7 curves corresponding to three V_{CB} conditions are plotted for a silicon *pnp* transistor. For amplifier applications the important condition is $V_{CB} \leq +0.5$ V. Then the current through the collector-base diode is not significant. In this case we know from physical considerations that I_B is proportional to I_E since $-I_B$ consists of (a) a current $(1 - \gamma_e)I_E$ due to carriers injected from base to emitter and (b) a current $(1 - \gamma_b)\gamma_e I_E$ due to carriers injected from emitter to base and recombining there. In equation form $I_B = -I_E/(\beta_F + 1)$. Thus the

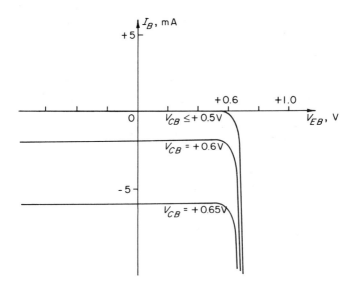

FIG. 8.7   Base characteristics for a silicon *pnp* transistor.

I_B-V_{EB} curve has the same exponential form as I_E-V_{EB} but with I_B reduced in magnitude by the factor $(\beta_F + 1)^{-1}$. This is illustrated in Fig. 8.7.

The curve turns down in Fig. 8.7 rather than up as in Fig. 7.12 because the sign convention chosen for I_B is opposite to the actual current direction in the *pnp* transistor. (Transistor manufacturers commonly replot such data with negative "up" so the curves fall in the first quadrant and thus do resemble Fig. 7.12.) The curves for $V_{CB} = +0.6$ V and $V_{CB} = +0.65$ V are displaced versions of the first curve. Constant forward voltage on the collector-base diode adds a constant (negative) current component to I_B thus shifting the curves down by an amount equal to $(\beta_F + 1)$ times the diode current. The curves for a germanium transistor are similar in form except that, because I_{EO} and I_{CO} are several orders of magnitude larger, the voltages V_{EB} and V_{CB} must be reduced by about 0.4 V to obtain the values of I_B shown in Fig. 8.7.

The collector characteristic I_C vs V_{CE} also consists of a set of curves usually made for a series of values of base current I_B. Three curves for a *pnp* transistor ($\beta_F = 50$, $\beta_R = 10$) are shown in Fig. 8.8, with $I_B = -1$ mA, -2 mA, and -3 mA. The nature of these curves may be seen as follows. For $I_B < 0$ the current generators in Fig. 8.6 tend to circulate current around the two loops in the forward bias directions for the diodes. Thus when $|I_C|$ is small, both diodes are forward biased and V_{CE} is the difference between the drops across the two diodes. If I_C is made increasingly positive the current through the collector-base diode

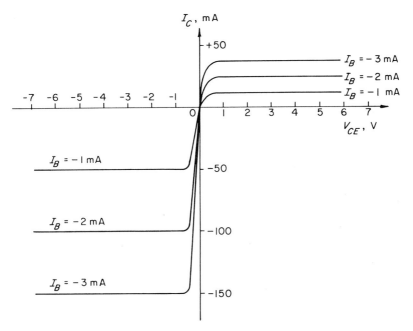

FIG. 8.8   Collector characteristics for *pnp* transistor
with $\beta_F = 50$ and $\beta_R = 10$.

increases while current reduction occurs in the emitter-base diode because the current due to I_C is opposite to the $-\beta_R I_B$ current through that
diode (remember that $I_B < 0$). When I_C is increased such that $I_C + I_B = -\beta_R I_B$ the emitter diode ceases conducting and $V_{CE} = V_{CB} \simeq +0.6$ V.
Attempting to increase I_C further simply causes $V_{CE} > +0.6$ V; the
emitter diode voltage reverses and the diode current becomes $-(1 + \beta_R)I_{EO}$, a negligible amount in most cases. Thus I_E remains constant
at $\beta_R I_B$ and I_C remains constant at $-(1 + \beta_R)I_B$. (The latter comes
directly from Kirchhoff's current law.) For negative I_C and V_{CE} analogous events occur: as I_C is made increasingly negative the emitter
diode current increases while the collector diode current decreases, and
when $I_C = \beta_F I_B$ the collector diode current equals zero and $V_{CE} = V_{BE}$.
For more negative V_{CE} the collector diode is reverse biased and carries
no significant current. Thus I_C is constant at $\beta_F I_B$.

So far we have considered only negative values for I_B. The reason
for this can be seen from Fig. 8.6. When $I_B > 0$ a current $(1 + \beta_F + \beta_R)I_B$ must be accounted for by the sum of the reverse currents of the
diodes. (Apply Kirchhoff's current law at the central node in Fig. 8.6.)
Since the sum $(1 + \beta_F)I_{CO} + (1 + \beta_R)I_{EO}$ is very small, no significant
positive I_B is possible. (We assume neither of the junctions is driven to
voltage breakdown.) The collector current obtained when I_B equals this

small positive limit $[(1 + \beta_F)I_{CO} + (1 + \beta_R)I_{EO}]/(1 + \beta_F + \beta_R)$ is not distinguishable from zero on the scale used in Fig. 8.8. The same is true when $I_B = 0$.

Let us now compare performances in first and third quadrants. For a given base current more collector current is obtained by operating in the third quadrant because $\beta_F \gg \beta_R$. Operation in the third quadrant means $V_{CE} < 0$, which with $I_B < 0$ leads to $V_{CB} < 0$ and $V_{EB} > 0$. This means holes are flowing from emitter to collector—the normal direction. This operation is called the *forward mode* (also called normal or active mode), and thus the subscript F on α_F and β_F.[2] On the other hand first quadrant operation means $V_{CE} > 0$, $V_{CB} > 0$, and $V_{EB} < 0$. Thus holes flow from collector to emitter—opposite to the normal direction. This mode is the inverse or *reverse mode,* hence the subscript R on α_R and β_R.

Care should be taken not to confuse the terms forward mode and reverse mode with forward bias and reverse bias. The latter terms are applied to junctions, forward bias leading to a large positive junction current and reverse bias leading to a small negative junction current. Each mode implies a pair of junction conditions. The forward mode features a forward biased emitter junction and a reverse biased collector junction. The reverse mode features the opposite conditions.

One last point should be made regarding collector characteristics. Manufacturers seldom publish data for the reverse mode because it is used only in a few special applications. Consequently the third quadrant data in Fig. 8.8 is customarily replotted by reversing the directions of the negative axes.

Having examined analytical and graphic descriptions of the transistor under DC conditions, we now turn to the time-varying case. The essential questions to be dealt with are how rapidly the collector current can be changed and how rapid changes can be accomplished. In Sec. 8.6 an analytical model based on charge distributions in the transistor is discussed. This model provides a basis for analysis of time-varying situations. In Sec. 8.7 a more specialized model, the hybrid-pi, is developed for use in transistor amplifiers, etc., where linear operations are being performed.

8.6   CHARGE CONTROL MODEL

In Sec. 7.6 we noted that SCL capacitance and charge storage are the two effects that limit the speed of response of a junction diode. This is also true for the transistor. Our goal is to develop an analytical

---

2. In the Ebers and Moll article N and I for *normal* and *inverse* were used. The notation here is that used in a series of books prepared by the Semiconductor Electronics Education Committee.

model which incorporates these two effects simply and accurately. We begin with charge storage.

Under static conditions the current components at a junction can be evaluated if the concentrations of the minority carriers at the edges of the junctions are known. Ignoring SCL capacitance, the same statement holds in the time-varying case. Thus we consider the distributions of minority carriers in the emitter, base, and collector of the transistor. The distributions depend on junction voltages. Recall from Chap. 7 that minority carrier concentration at the edge of an SCL is the thermal equilibrium value of the concentration multiplied by $\exp(qV/kT)$, where V is the voltage applied to the junction. Let us consider a *pnp* transistor operating in the forward mode—emitter junction forward biased and collector junction reverse biased. The carrier concentrations at the space charge edges are then

$$p_n(0) = p_{no}\exp(qV_{EB}/kT) \equiv p_e \tag{8.23}$$

$$n_p(x_e) = n_{po}\exp(qV_{EB}/kT) \tag{8.24}$$

$$p_n(W) = p_{no}\exp(qV_{CB}/kT) \equiv p_c \tag{8.25}$$

$$n_p(x_c) = n_{po}\exp(qV_{CB}/kT) \tag{8.26}$$

and are sketched in Fig. 8.9 where the positions 0, x_e, W, and x_c are defined. Note that the collector junction being reverse biased (presumably more than a few kT/q) leads to $p_n(W) \simeq 0 \simeq n_p(x_c)$. [For simplicity we have used the symbol n_{po} in (8.24) and (8.26) for both the emitter and collector regions. In fact they may and most often do have quite different values.]

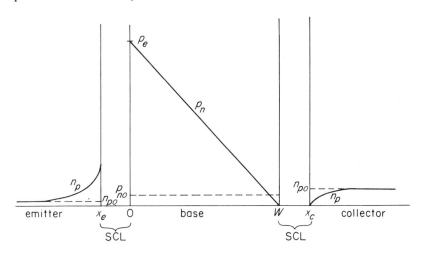

FIG. 8.9 Minority carrier distributions in a *pnp* transistor biased in the active mode ($V_{EB} > 0$, $V_{CB} < 0$).

Given these boundary conditions the carrier distributions in the neutral regions may be plotted. This is done for the forward mode in Fig. 8.9. These distributions can be obtained from the solution to the continuity equation subject to the boundary conditions given in (8.23)–(8.26). Rather than deriving the results we shall simply state them. In the collector and emitter regions, assuming each region is several diffusion lengths long, the concentrations decay exponentially from their boundary conditions to the thermal equilibrium values.

In the base the concentration must change smoothly from the boundary condition at $x = 0$ to that at $x = W$. From a solution of the continuity equation this variation is

$$p_n(x) = p_{no} + A \exp(x/L_h) + B \exp(-x/L_h) \tag{8.27}$$

where L_h is the hole diffusion length in the base region. Recall that the base region is thin and lightly doped. This means W (and therefore x) is small and L_h is large. As a result the exponentials in (8.27) are nearly linear throughout the base region and $p_n(x)$ is a straight line (almost). In more physical terms, because $W \ll L_h$ almost no holes recombine as they cross the base. This implies an almost constant diffusion current everywhere in the base. This in turn means the slope of $p_n(x)$ must be almost constant which is equivalent to a straight-line relationship.

Now let us relate currents to minority carrier distributions. The minority carriers in the emitter and collector regions contribute only small components to the emitter and collector currents. This is true in the emitter since minority carrier concentration there is kept low to obtain γ_e large (near unity). In fact, the design of a transistor to achieve high current gain is based on the emitter current consisting almost entirely of minority carrier flow into the base region. Recall this is achieved by doping the emitter much more heavily than the base. The component of collector current due to minority carriers in the collector is, in the forward mode, simply a part of the small reverse current of the collector-base junction and thus is typically very small. Therefore it is reasonable to consider the collector and emitter currents as arising solely from minority carrier flow in the base region.

Ignoring SCL capacitance effects and the small current components just discussed and assuming base width to be small compared to diffusion length in the base, we see that emitter and collector currents are very nearly equal in magnitude. The emitter current is due to the hole diffusion flow at $x = 0$; the collector current is due to hole diffusion flow at $x = W$. Thus both currents are proportional to $p_n(0)/W$, the slope of the hole distribution in the base. [Note: $p_n(0) \equiv p_e$ in Fig. 8.9.]

Consider the collector current specifically. The excess stored charge q_A in the base is proportional to the area of the triangle in Fig. 8.9, i.e., to $p_n(0) W/2$. [The subscript A signifies active mode, which is synonymous with forward mode; we use the symbol q_A rather than q_F to avoid conflict with conventions used in the books authored by the Semiconductor Electronics Education Committee (SEEC); see reference in footnote 3 for instance.] Since both q_A and the collector current are proportional to $p_n(0)$, they must be proportional to each other. Since the constant of proportionality between a charge and a current is a time we write

$$-i_C = q_A/\tau_F \tag{8.28}$$

(The minus sign comes from the positive sense chosen originally for i_C.) We can guess at the factors that influence τ_F. In steady state, q_A is constant. Since $-i_C$ is proportional to q_A, the magnitude of i_C must be equal to the rate at which the charge to maintain a constant q_A flows into (and therefore out of) the base. The constant of proportionality depends then on the length of time a hole spends in the base region. This in turn depends on the time it takes a hole to diffuse across the base and is inversely proportional to D_h and proportional to the width of the base region W. These two conclusions are borne out in the following exercises.

[*Exercise:* Express q_A in terms of A, q, $p_n(0)$, and W, where A is the cross section of the transistor and $p_n(0)$ is defined in Fig. 8.9 and (8.23). (Ans.: $q_A = Aqp_n(0)\,W/2)$]

[*Exercise:* Express $-i_C$ in terms of A, q, $p_n(0)$, W, and D_b, where $D_b = D_h$ in base region. (Ans.: $-i_C = AqD_hp_n(0)/W$)]

[*Exercise:* From the results of these two exercises evaluate τ_F.].

Let us next evaluate the base current by Kirchhoff's current law. At one side of the base region there is an entering hole current $I_h(0)$. At the other side there is an exiting current $I_h(W)$. Any difference between these two must be accounted for by i_B. More specifically, ignoring $I_e(0)$ and $I_e(W)$,

$$-i_B = I_h(0) - I_h(W) \tag{8.29}$$

To evaluate the right side of (8.29) we can use logic analogous to that in the derivation of the continuity equation (see Sec. 6.5). Considering the charge q_A due to excess holes in the base region we may write: (time rate of change of hole charge) = (hole current into base) − (hole current out of base) + q(total rate of hole generation in base) − q(total rate of hole recombination in base). In symbolic form this is

$$\frac{dq_A}{dt} = I_h(0) - I_h(W) + Aq \int_0^W (G_t - R)\,dx \tag{8.30}$$

in which G_t is the thermal generation rate and R is the recombination rate in the base region. It is assumed that there are no other sources of generation in this case.

The integral in (8.30) will be negative and represents the net recombination of holes summed over the entire base region. Thus the integral must be proportional to q_A, the total excess charge stored in the base region. We have seen that the rate of recombination in a uniformly doped semiconductor is proportional to the excess carrier concentration and inversely proportional to lifetime. Most often the base region of the transistor is not uniformly doped (see discussion pertaining to Fig. 8.2a). This (and other considerations) implies that the constant of proportionality between q_A and the net recombination rate in the base is closely related to τ_h but not equal to it, except in the ideal case. We shall call the effective lifetime τ_A and write $\int_0^W Aq(R - G_t)\, dx = q_A/\tau_A$. Thus, using (8.29), i_B may be written

$$i_B = -\left(\frac{dq_A}{dt} + \frac{q_A}{\tau_A}\right) \tag{8.31}$$

This equation is basic to the charge control model. It states that the charge given to the base of the transistor by i_B supplies those carriers lost by recombination q_A/τ_A and furnishes those carriers needed to change the charge stored in the base dq_A/dt.

We have been examining the forward mode of the device—emitter forward biased and collector reverse biased. Another way transistors are often used, especially important in switching applications, is the *saturation mode,* where both junctions are forward biased and the emitter is more strongly biased. In that case, in a *pnp* transistor, holes flow into the base region across both the emitter and collector junctions. For a given i_C the charge stored in the base is increased over its value in the active case. This circumstance is illustrated in Fig. 8.10. The symbols used are defined by (8.23)–(8.26).

Once again this distribution is obtained from a solution to the continuity equation. The form of the solution again is that in (8.27) but with different boundary conditions so the values of the constants are different. Again assuming $W \ll L_h$, the distribution is linear implying a small amount of recombination in the base.

Now let us relate the currents to this distribution. It is helpful to redraw the base distribution as shown in Fig. 8.11. Consider first the collector current. Ignoring SCL capacitance effects and the electron current at the collector junction, i_C is due simply to the hole diffusion current at $x = W$. This means it is proportional to H/W, the magnitude of the slope of the hole distribution. Now the stored charge in the base is proportional to the area of the triangle plus that of the rectangle in Fig. 8.11, i.e., to $HW/2 + H'W$. The stored charges corresponding to these areas are q_A and q_S, respectively. Both q_A and the

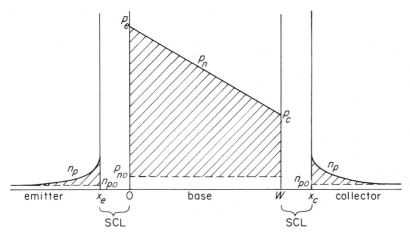

FIG. 8.10   Minority carrier distributions in a *pnp*
transistor with both junctions forward biased ($V_{EB} >$
$V_{CB} > 0$).

collector current are proportional to H and are thus proportional to
each other. This means we may still write $-i_C = q_A/\tau_F$ where τ_F is the
same parameter discussed earlier.

Let us next find the base current appropriate to this case. Proceeding exactly as before we recognize that i_B is the difference between
the rate of charge flow into and out of the base. Thus we still have
(8.29), $-i_B = I_h(0) - I_h(W)$. The rate of change of stored charge in
the base is deduced exactly as was (8.31) to obtain

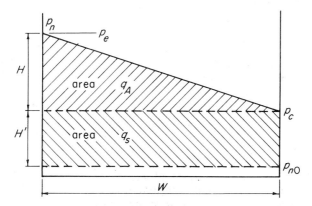

FIG. 8.11   Hole distribution from Fig. 8.10 redrawn
and resolved into rectangle and triangle components.

$$i_B = - \left(\frac{dq_A}{dt} + \frac{dq_S}{dt} + \int_0^W A q (R - G_t) \, dx \right) \tag{8.32}$$

In form this equation is precisely that of the forward case. How does it differ? First we must account for the time rate of change of q_S. Second, the integral is different. Instead of only the charge component q_A we now must consider an added stored charge due to the forward biased collector and denoted by q_S. There is recombination associated with q_S that leads to an increase in the magnitude of i_B. Examining Fig. 8.1 it seems evident that the holes coming into the base from the collector have a different environment from those coming from the emitter. It is reasonable therefore for the lifetime τ_S associated with q_S to be different from that associated with q_A. We shall write

$$i_B = - \left(\frac{dq_A}{dt} + \frac{dq_S}{dt} + \frac{q_A}{\tau_A} + \frac{q_S}{\tau_S} \right) \tag{8.33}$$

(Incidentally, τ_A and τ_S are usually experimentally rather than theoretically determined.) Equation (8.33) again describes the charge control model of the transistor. It is more general than (8.31) since it involves the forward mode as a special case with the collector junction reverse biased and hence $q_S = 0$.

The basic charge control model is now developed and embodied in (8.28) and (8.33). These equations are not complete because SCL capacitance effects are not taken into account. Before complicating the model with those let us demonstrate the significance of the charge control approach.

EXAMPLE 8.1

Suppose a silicon *pnp* transistor with $\beta_F = 50$ is operating as shown in Fig. 8.12. Before $t = 0$ the base current is zero and the circuit is in a DC steady state. It is a routine problem in DC analysis to show that this means $v_{BE} \simeq 0$, $i_C \simeq 0$, and $v_{CB} \simeq v_{CE} \simeq -12$ V. At $t = 0$ the base current steps to -0.1 mA and v_{BE}, i_C, v_{CB}, and v_{CE} all change, eventually reaching some new steady state. The charge control model is concerned with predicting how rapidly the changes occur and what important features characterize the final steady state. (The reader acquainted with the "load-line" method of electronic circuit analysis may wish to use Fig. 8.13 in determining the steady-state conditions at $t = 0^-$ and $t = \infty$.)

Consider the collector current i_C. Equation (8.28) indicates that i_C is determined by charge component q_A; (8.33) in turn relates q_A to the base current i_B and the other component q_S. Evidently some information must be given regarding q_S since otherwise (8.33) contains two unknowns and cannot be solved. Recall that q_S is proportional to p_{no} $\exp(q v_{CB}/kT)$. At $t = 0$ since $v_{CB} = -12$ V it is evident that q_S is very

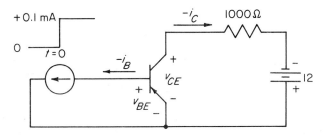

FIG. 8.12 Simple transistor switching circuit.

nearly zero and therefore

$$i_B = - \left(\frac{q_A}{\tau_A} + \frac{dq_A}{dt} \right) \qquad \text{(Ex. 8.1.1)}$$

This is a linear first order differential equation. To solve it we use a standard differential equation method (such as complementary function plus particular solution) and then fit the solution to an initial condition. For the complementary function we try the universal solution $K_1 e^{rt}$ and write

$$0 = - \left(\frac{K_1 e^{rt}}{\tau_A} + K_1 \frac{de^{rt}}{dt} \right) \qquad \text{(Ex. 8.1.2)}$$

We find that $r = -1/\tau_A$. For the particular solution we try a constant K_2 since the nonhomogeneous term i_B is a constant for $t \geq 0^+$. Using

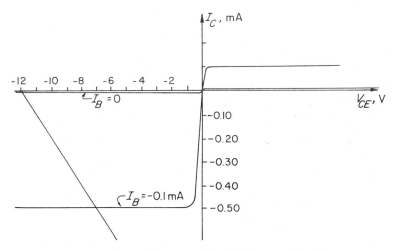

FIG. 8.13 Collector and circuit characteristics for the transistor and circuit of Fig. 8.12.

this we have

$$i_B = I_B = - \left(\frac{K_2}{\tau_A} + \frac{dK_2}{dt} \right) \qquad \text{(Ex. 8.1.3)}$$

from which we find immediately $K_2 = -I_B \tau_A$. Combining the complementary solution with the particular solution we have the complete solution,

$$q_A = K_1 \exp(-t/\tau_A) - I_B \tau_A \qquad \text{(Ex. 8.1.4)}$$

The constant K_1 can be determined if $q_A(0^+)$ is known.

We have seen that at $t = 0^-$, the collector current is zero. From (8.28) we see that this implies $q_A(0^-) = 0$. Now the base current I_B is finite which means q_A cannot change discontinuously and thus $q_A(0^+)$ also equals zero. Applying this condition to the above equation yields the required solution for q_A, namely,

$$q_A = I_B \tau_A [\exp(-t/\tau_A) - 1] \qquad (t \geq 0) \qquad \text{(Ex. 8.1.5)}$$

Having found how q_A varies with time we can determine the variation of i_C with time by using (8.28) again. Thus we find

$$i_C = -q_A/\tau_F = -(I_B \tau_A/\tau_F)[\exp(-t/\tau_A) - 1]$$
$$= (\tau_A/\tau_F)I_B[1 - \exp(-t/\tau_A)] \qquad \text{(Ex. 8.1.6)}$$

This indicates that i_C rises from zero and levels off at a steady-state value $\tau_A I_B/\tau_F$. This steady result is that predicted from the DC equations, specifically (8.22a), with $V_{CB} < 0$. That equation indicates that $I_C = \beta_F I_B$. (Recall that in developing the charge control equations we neglected the effect of the reverse collector voltage on the collector current.) Hence we discover that

$$\tau_A/\tau_F = \beta_F \qquad (8.34)$$

$$i_C = \beta_F I_B[1 - \exp(-t/\tau_A)] \qquad \text{(Ex. 8.1.7)}$$

The time dependences of i_B, q_A, and i_C are sketched in Fig. 8.14. Implicit in these curves is an important property of the transistor and its performance as a switching device. Probably the single largest application of semiconductor devices in general and transistors in particular is in circuits performing digital computations. In such circuits transistors are continuously switched from one state of operation to another. The most important capability of the device then is that of changing states rapidly since the speed of performance of logical operations is limited by how quickly the devices involved can be switched. Several parameters characterize various aspects of the transistor's switching performance.

In this example we meet the first of these. Suppose a transistor is in a nonconducting state (off, $I_B = 0$) and I_B is increased by a step caus-

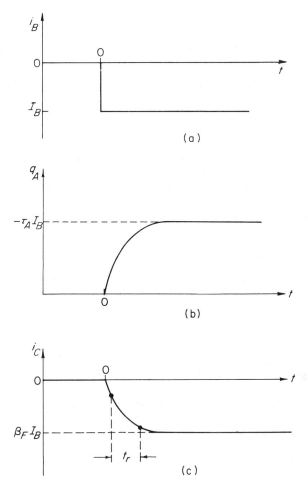

FIG. 8.14   Charge and current waveforms for the
circuit of Fig. 8.12 and Ex. 8.1 (note that I_B is negative).

ing the transistor to conduct. When this occurs q_A and i_C increase with
time and finally attain steady values (see Fig. 8.14). It is apparent that
it takes some time for i_C to increase from its initial value zero to its final
value $\beta_F I_B$; the more rapidly this transition occurs, the faster the transistor can operate. A measure of this speed is a parameter called the
risetime t_r, the time required for the collector current of the transistor
to increase from 10% to 90% of its final value (see Fig. 8.14). We can
calculate t_r using (Ex. 8.1.7). Since the final value of i_C is $\beta_F I_B$ we have
$t_r = t_2 - t_1$ where the times t_2 and t_1 are defined by $0.1\beta_F I_B = \beta_F I_B[1 -
\exp(-t_1/\tau_A)]$ and $0.9\beta_F I_B = \beta_F I_B[1 - \exp(-t_2/\tau_A)]$. Solving for t_1 and

t_2 and finding their difference we obtain

$$t_r = 2.2\tau_A \qquad\qquad\qquad\qquad\qquad \text{(Ex. 8.1.8)}$$

Since we usually want t_r to be as short as possible, it is important to look briefly at the factors which govern its value. From (8.34) we see that $\tau_A = \beta_F \tau_F$ and hence for the circuit of the above example $t_r \propto \beta_F \tau_F$. This proportionality implies at least two things. There will be a conflict if one desires high speed operation and high current gain (the larger the β_F of the transistor the larger the t_r, which means slower operation). Also the fundamental control over risetime lies in τ_F. The range of β_F expected from transistors is relatively narrow (possibly a factor of 10, say 50–500) while the range of τ_F is at least two orders of magnitude. For this reason τ_F is usually the more important of the two parameters and the one we shall look at.

In an exercise following (8.28) it is shown that $\tau_F = W^2/2D_b$ where W is the width of the neutral base region and D_b is the diffusion constant of minority carriers in the base region. Again D_b is relatively constant so the principal variation in τ_F arises because of W. It can be shown rather easily that $W^2/2D_b$ is the average transit time of a minority carrier across the base region. Thus a small W corresponds to a high-frequency transistor. The range of values of W in present-day transistors is about 0.2–2 μm. The smaller W is, the lower the risetime t_r.

On this basis we can compute a typical value of t_r. Assume $\beta_F = 100$, $W = 0.7$ μm, and $D_b = 10$ cm^2/s; then $t_r = 54$ ns. Transistors designed to produce high output power rather than to operate at high frequencies have longer risetimes while very high-frequency devices operating at low power have shorter risetimes, possibly as much as 100 times shorter.

Regardless of how fast a device can operate, the circuit or system designer always is able to use a faster device. Can the risetime be decreased? Yes, through *saturated switching*.

EXAMPLE 8.2

To decrease the risetime t_r, from an intuitive viewpoint it seems we should increase the base current. A larger base current changes the stored base charge faster and hence increases the rate of change of i_C, thus reducing the risetime t_r. In this example let us suppose that at $t = 0$ the base current steps to -1.0 mA rather than -0.1 mA. How does this affect our analytical solution?

Keep in mind that (Ex. 8.1.1)–(Ex. 8.1.7) are based on the condition $q_S \simeq 0$. That condition holds only so long as v_{CB} is negative or only slightly positive, say less than $+0.5$ V, so that $p_{no} \exp(qv_{CB}/kT)$ is negligible compared to p_{no}. Thus we must consider how to determine when that circumstance is no longer true.

The collector-base voltage v_{CB} is related to the other terminal voltages v_{EB} and v_{CE} by Kirchhoff's voltage law, i.e.,

$$v_{CB} = v_{CE} + v_{EB} \tag{Ex. 8.2.1}$$

Recalling that $q_A \propto p_{no} \exp(qv_{EB}/kT)$, we realize that when q_A is significant, v_{EB} must be significantly positive, say $+0.7$ V. Evidently the condition $v_{CB} \leq +0.5$ V implies a corresponding restriction on the collector-emitter voltage, namely,

$$-v_{CE} \geq +0.2 \text{ V} \tag{Ex. 8.2.2}$$

But applying Kirchhoff's voltage law to the circuit of Fig. 8.12 immediately leads to

$$-v_{CE} = +12 + 1000i_C \tag{Ex. 8.2.3}$$

If (Ex. 8.2.2) and (Ex. 8.2.3) are combined the following restriction on i_C is evident:

$$-i_C \leq +(12 - 0.2)/1000 = +11.8 \text{ mA} \tag{Ex. 8.2.4}$$

Thus (Ex. 8.1.7) holds only until that equation predicts a value of -11.8 mA for i_C. Thus if $\beta_F(1 \text{ mA}) > 11.8$ mA, i.e., $\beta_F > 11.8$, the solution holds only for $0 \leq t \leq t_1$, where t_1 is the moment when i_C reaches the value -11.8 mA. In this case $\beta_F = 50$.

What about $t > t_1$? Then $v_{CB} > +0.5$ V and $v_{CE} < -0.2$ V. The increase in v_{CB} above $+0.5$ V implies the collector-base junction is becoming significantly forward biased and q_S is now increasing with time. We must therefore use (8.33) rather than (Ex. 8.1.1) to analyze the changes occurring. But this seems to lead to an insoluble problem since (8.33) contains two unknowns q_A and q_S. Is q_A actually unknown at this point? No, its value at $t = t_1$ is certainly known. Furthermore, and this is crucial, i_C and q_A are now constant! The collector current has reached -11.8 mA $\simeq -12$ mA. From Fig. 8.12 or (Ex. 8.2.3) it is evident that the circuit is incapable of supplying more than $i_C = -12$ mA, the Norton current for the 12 V–1000 Ω collector circuit. Thus for $t \geq t_1$ the collector current varies by no more than 0.2 mA (less than 2%) and may be regarded as constant. Then from (8.28) it is immediately seen that q_A is likewise constant at $q_A(t_1) = (12 \text{ mA})\tau_A$. This means that (8.33) now reduces to

$$I_B = -\frac{q_A(t_1)}{\tau_A} + \frac{q_S}{\tau_S} + \frac{dq_S}{dt} \tag{Ex. 8.2.5}$$

in which $q_A(t_1)/\tau_A = 12$ mA. Note that dq_A/dt is absent because q_A is constant so that its derivative is zero. This equation may now be solved routinely subject to the initial condition $q_S(t_1) = 0$. A graph of this solution is given in Fig. 8.15 along with graphs of q_A and $-i_C$ vs t.

Driving the transistor into saturation resulting in decreased risetime has not yet been demonstrated. To do so recall that (Ex. 8.1.7) is

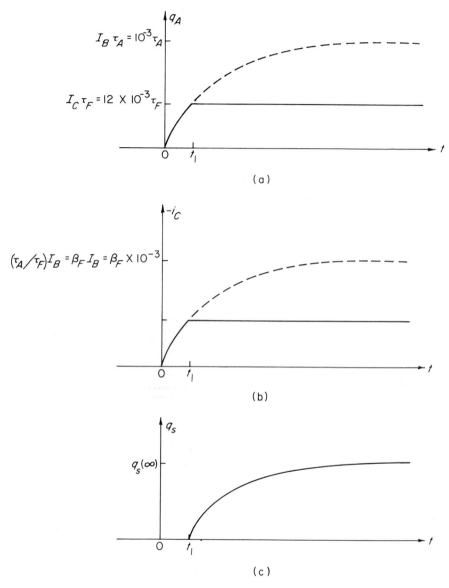

FIG. 8.15   Charge and current waveforms for the
circuit of Fig. 8.12.

valid until the collector current reaches its circuit limited value. Let us suppose that a base current I_B is applied and the collector current obtained is I_C, where we specifically do not assume $\beta_F I_B = I_C$, rather that $\beta_F I_B \geq I_C$. If then (Ex. 8.1.7) is used as before to calculate risetime it is found that

$$t_r = \tau_A \ln \frac{1 - 0.1\, I_C/\beta_F I_B}{1 - 0.9\, I_C/\beta_F I_B} \qquad \text{(Ex. 8.2.6)}$$

Note that if $\beta_F I_B = I_C$ this reduces to (Ex. 8.1.8) as it should. On the other hand if $\beta_F I_B > I_C$ then $t_r < 2.2\tau_A$ and t_r becomes progressively smaller with larger I_B. If for example $\beta_F I_B = 5I_C$ then $t_r = 0.18\tau_A$, a reduction in t_r by a factor greater than 10. Clearly t_r can be made increasingly smaller but only at the expense of requiring increasingly larger driving currents. Eventually the cost of supplying I_B becomes greater than the benefit of the reduced risetime. However it is evident that saturated switching substantially reduces risetimes. This benefit is not "free"; we see later in this section how it is paid for.

A brief review of modes is in order. During the time interval $0 \leq t \leq t_1$ the transistor is operating in the forward or active mode. In the active mode the emitter junction is forward biased but the collector-junction is not, so that $q_A > 0$ but $q_S = 0$.

For the time interval after $t = t_1$ on the other hand the transistor operates in the saturation mode. This mode features forward bias on both junctions so that both q_A and q_S are positive (this condition implies that v_{CE} is low). Thus the saturation mode differs from the active mode in that $q_S > 0$ in saturation. An additional feature is that q_A is constant because the external circuit constrains i_C to a constant value. In summary the properties of the two modes are given as follows:

Active Mode	*Saturation Mode*
q_A = variable	q_A = constant > 0
q_S = constant = 0	q_S = variable
EB junction forward biased	Both junctions forward biased
CB junction reverse biased	

Let us summarize our knowledge about the charge control viewpoint:

1. The collector current is determined by the active base charge q_A and is given by $i_C = -q_A/\tau_F$.
2. This charge component q_A is governed by the base current and is found from solution of the base current charge control equation specialized to the active mode where the charge component q_S is zero.
3. If the collector current reaches a circuit limited value the transistor

enters the saturation mode in which variations in base charge are accounted for by the saturation base charge q_S. These variations may be found from solution of the base current charge control equation specialized to the saturation mode, i.e., with q_A constant.

From this summary and the examples that led to it we discover an important principle of transistor operation: the speed with which the collector current can be changed depends directly on the speed with which charge is "pumped" into (or out of) the base by means of current in the base circuit. The charge control model is not yet complete but this principle continues to hold in the final version.

To complete the transistor switching sequence we must consider the turn-off process. Suppose the transistor is in the saturation mode which means that both q_A and q_S are greater than zero. The charge distribution in the base is shown in Fig. 8.11. To turn off the transistor the charges q_A and q_S must be extracted from the base region by applying a positive step in base current to the transistor in Fig. 8.12. The variation of q_S and q_A with time are determined by (8.33). We shall not carry out this analysis (similar to turn-on analysis) but rather describe the process qualitatively.

During the initial portion of the turn-off sequence, i_C and q_A remain constant until q_S reaches zero. Then, with i_B still constant, the charge represented by q_A is extracted (see Fig. 8.16). Note that a portion of the turn-off time is needed to withdraw q_S. With this time interval (termed storage time, analogous to t_s in Sec. 7.6.1) we "pay for" the decrease in risetime achieved by driving the transistor into saturation. The risetime can be decreased further and further by increasing the input base current step, but at the expense of ever larger q_S and storage time.

The turn-off time is composed of two parts, storage time t_s and fall time t_f. Equation (8.33) can be used to find both t_s and t_f, the former by solving the equation with q_A constant and the latter by solving it with $q_S = 0$. It should be apparent that, for a particular transistor driven by a given base current to a specified collector current, both t_s and t_f can be decreased by increasing the magnitude of the base current used to turn off the device. Typical values of t_s and t_f are in the range of a few nanoseconds to a few hundred nanoseconds.

To complete the charge control model we must include the effects of SCL capacitance. This is simply a matter of adding $C(dV/dt)$ terms to (8.28) and (8.33); thus

$$i_B = -\left(\frac{q_A}{\tau_A} + \frac{q_S}{\tau_S} + \frac{dq_A}{dt} + \frac{dq_S}{dt}\right) + C_e \frac{dv_{BE}}{dt} + C_c \frac{dv_{BC}}{dt} \qquad (8.35)$$

$$i_C = -\frac{q_A}{\tau_F} + C_c \frac{dv_{CB}}{dt} \qquad (8.36)$$

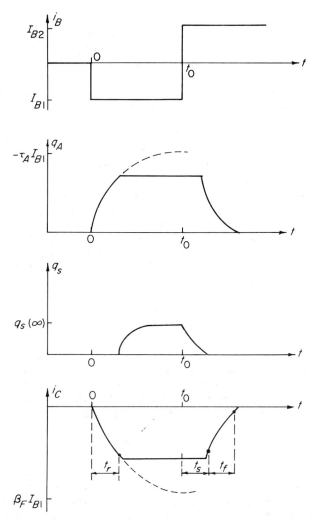

FIG. 8.16 Currents and charges involved in a complete saturated switching sequence for a *pnp* transistor. Note the way the risetime t_r, storage time t_s, and fall time t_f are defined.

where C_e is the emitter junction capacitance and C_c is the collector junction capacitance.

[*Exercise:* Verify that signs and voltages in the capacitance terms in (8.35) and (8.36) are correct.]

The addition of these capacitance terms produces an unfortunate circumstance—(8.35) is no longer a linear differential equation because the capacitances are voltage dependent. Problem 8.15 illustrates an approximate method for analyzing this nonlinear situation.

The model developed in this section is accurate in a broad range of time-varying situations. However there is a feature missing which sometimes is important. In the base current equation (8.35), the term $-dq_S/dt$ represents the current component that arises when the saturation charge is changing due to a change in the collector-base junction voltage. If (8.35) and (8.36) were exact then Kirchhoff's current law $i_E + i_B + i_C = 0$ would force us to conclude that all the current dq_S/dt flows in via the emitter and out via the base with none flowing in or out via the collector, since i_C is apparently independent of q_S. This is surely not true. The charge q_S arises because of forward bias on the collector-base junction so at least part of the current dq_S/dt must be supplied to the base by the collector rather than the emitter. But (8.36) contains no such term and hence is in error when the current dq_S/dt is significant in comparison with the other terms in that equation. The model can be made accurate by considering from the beginning the emitter and collector contributions to the rate of change of base charge. Such a model is described by Gray et al.[3] On the basis of their analysis it can be shown that a reasonable first approximation is simply to add a term $0.5(dq_S/dt)$ to the right side of (8.36).

Some situations for which the model of the present section does apply do not call for all the power the model has. These situations are characterized by junction voltages changing so little that the nonlinear dependences of q_A, q_S, C_e, and C_c may be approximated via first order Taylor's expansions. These situations are called "small signal linear cases" and frequently involve several transistors and many resistors, capacitors, and inductors. In such cases incorporating the charge control equations into the analysis is overly complicated even though correct. We would prefer a circuit model for the transistor, i.e., a combination of sources and passive components which give the same behavior for the time-varying portions of the currents and voltages as the actual transistor. This model would replace the transistor in the circuit and then conventional network analysis would lead to the currents and voltages of interest. Such a model is developed in the next section.

8.7 HYBRID-PI CIRCUIT MODEL

Let us characterize the small signal situation somewhat more completely and then develop a small signal circuit model which relates rather directly to the physical processes in the transistor.

3. Paul E. Gray et al., *Physical Electronics and Circuit Models of Transistors,* 1964, Wiley, New York, Chap. 10.

In small signal applications one almost always finds the total currents and voltages consisting of comparatively large DC components and small time-varying components. Expressing this in symbolic form for the base current i_B we have

$$i_B = I_B + i_b \tag{8.37}$$

where I_B is the DC term and i_b is the time-varying term (often called the AC term). Similarly for i_C, v_{BE}, and v_{BC} we write

$$i_C = I_C + i_c \tag{8.38}$$

$$v_{BE} = V_{BE} + v_{be} \tag{8.39}$$

$$v_{BC} = V_{BC} + v_{bc} \tag{8.40}$$

For small signal conditions to apply, the time-varying components must be small enough to be related by linear differential equations despite the nonlinear relationships existing among the total currents and voltages. As a specific example consider the relation of I_E to V_{EB}. The emitter current depends upon the emitter-base voltage V_{EB} by an exponential relation,

$$i_E = I_{ES}\{\exp[q(V_{EB} + v_{eb})/kT] - 1\} \simeq I_{ES} \exp[q(V_{EB} + v_{eb})/kT] \tag{8.41a}$$

the approximation following from the assumption of forward bias $qV_{EB}/kT \gg 1$.

This expression may be separated into the product of I_{ES} and two exponentials,

$$i_E \simeq [I_{ES} \exp(qV_{EB}/kT)] \exp(qv_{eb}/kT) \tag{8.41b}$$

From this expression it is clear that i_E is not linearly related to V_{EB} since the assumption that $qV_{EB}/kT \gg 1$ implies that $\exp(qV_{EB}/kT)$ is a nonlinear function. Our immediate concern is with the dependence of i_E upon v_{eb}, the time-varying component of v_{EB}. Under what circumstances are i_E and v_{eb} linearly related? We can see by writing a series expansion for the exponential involving v_{eb}.

$$\exp \frac{qv_{eb}}{kT} = 1 + \frac{qv_{eb}}{kT} + \frac{1}{2}\left(\frac{qv_{eb}}{kT}\right)^2 + \frac{1}{3!}\left(\frac{qv_{eb}}{kT}\right)^3 + \cdots$$

If $(qv_{eb}/kT) \ll 1$ then the approximate expression $\exp(qv_{eb}/kT) \simeq 1 + qv_{eb}/kT$ is valid. In that case $i_E \simeq [I_{ES}\exp(qV_{EB}/kT)] [1 + qv_{eb}/kT]$ and i_E *and* v_{eb} are linearly related. The nonlinearity arising from $\exp(qv_{eb}/kT)$ has been removed.

The magnitude of v_{eb} permitted in the small signal case is somewhat arbitrary and depends on what is implied by the condition $qv_{eb}/kT \ll 1$. Actually we wish qv_{eb}/kT to be much larger than the following terms in the series. Since with $qv_{eb}/kT < 1$ the terms become successively smaller we need only ensure $qv_{eb}/kT \gg (1/2)(qv_{eb}/kT)^2$. Let us assume this condition is met if $qv_{eb}/kT \geq 10(1/2)(qv_{eb}/kT)^2$. Then the maximum allowable value of v_{eb} in the small signal case is

$$(v_{eb})_{max} = (1/5)(kT/q) \tag{8.42}$$

At room temperature $kT/q = 0.025$ V, thus $(v_{eb})_{max} = 5$ mV.

We noted in the previous section that the charge control model could be used in small signal cases, so we can use it to develop the desired small signal circuit model. Begin by considering the basic charge control equations (8.28) and (8.33). This means we shall temporarily omit the SCL capacitances. Since the collector is to be reverse biased the charge q_S will be zero. Thus the basic charge control equations reduce to

$$i_B = -\frac{q_A}{\tau_A} - \frac{dq_A}{dt} \tag{8.43}$$

$$i_C = -(q_A/\tau_F) \tag{8.44}$$

A circuit model interrelates the currents and voltages of a device. Hence we wish to consider how the voltages v_{BE} and v_{CE} affect i_B and i_C. (We select these voltages and currents because they are of principal interest in common-emitter operation, which affords the largest current and power gains.)

As a first approximation i_B and i_C are independent of v_{CE} so long as the collector remains reverse biased. Thus we simply need to consider the effect of v_{BE} on q_A. Recall that q_A is proportional to p_e, the hole concentration at the edge of the emitter junction SCL. This concentration is in turn proportional to $\exp(qv_{EB}/kT)$. Suppose v_{be} is positive. This means $\Delta v_{BE} > 0$ and $\Delta v_{EB} < 0$. Therefore q_A decreases, i.e., Δq_A is negative. Since v_{be} is specified to be small, $\exp(qv_{EB}/kT)$ varies linearly with v_{be} and thus Δq_A is proportional to v_{be}. The constant of proportionality has the dimensions of capacitance, thus

$$\Delta q_A = -C_d v_{be} \tag{8.45}$$

where C_d is the constant of proportionality and equals the ratio of the change in charge stored in the base region to the change in voltage which caused it. The motion of charge through the base is due to diffusion so C_d is often referred to as a *diffusion capacitance*. Calculations of C_d based on a linear distribution of charge in the base region show that typical values of C_d are in the range 100–1500 pF. An expression for C_d in terms of the device physical parameters is deduced later in this section.

To find i_b and i_c we increment (8.43) and (8.44) to obtain

$$i_b = \Delta i_B = -\frac{\Delta q_A}{\tau_A} - \frac{d}{dt}(\Delta q_A) \tag{8.46}$$

$$i_c = \Delta i_C = -\Delta q_A/\tau_F \tag{8.47}$$

From (8.45) we find

$$i_b = \frac{C_d}{\tau_A} v_{be} + C_d \frac{dv_{be}}{dt} \tag{8.48}$$

$$i_c = (C_d/\tau_F)v_{be} \tag{8.49}$$

From (8.48) and (8.49) it is seen that the electrical behavior of the transistor is characterized in terms of C_d, C_d/τ_A, and C_d/τ_F. Let us relate these as far as possible to the physical properties of the transistor. Consider first C_d/τ_F. From (8.49), $C_d/\tau_F = i_c/v_{be}$. The right side of this relation is a ratio, the change in output current i_c due to a change in input voltage v_{be}, in units of conductance. This parameter is the *transconductance* g_m of the transistor. The transconductance is an important and fundamental parameter of many electron devices since it is a measure of output response to an input signal. For junction transistors g_m has a remarkably simple form,

$$g_m = (q/kT)|I_C| \tag{8.50}$$

This result is derived in Prob. 8.16b. Note that g_m is fixed when the DC collector current is known.

Referring next to (8.48), consider C_d/τ_A, the input conductance i_b/v_{be} of the transistor. The reciprocal of this conductance is often designated as r_π.[4] Thus using the relation discussed in the previous paragraph $C_d/\tau_F = g_m$ we find

$$r_\pi = \tau_A/C_d = \tau_A(1/\tau_F g_m) = \beta_F/g_m \tag{8.51}$$

The relation between τ_A, τ_F, and β_F is given in (8.34).

An interesting expression can now be developed for the diffusion capacitance C_d. From $g_m = i_c/v_{be}$ and (8.49) we can express C_d in terms of g_m and τ_F,

$$C_d = \tau_F g_m \tag{8.52}$$

We have in Ex. 8.1 that τ_F is the average time required for a minority carrier to diffuse across the base region, and $\tau_F = W^2/2D_b$ in terms of the physical parameters of the transistors. The diffusion capacitance C_d is large if the base width is large.

With the parameters developed, (8.48) and (8.49) may be rewritten as

$$i_b = \frac{1}{r_\pi} v_{be} + C_d \frac{dv_{be}}{dt} \tag{8.48'}$$

$$i_c = g_m v_{be} \tag{8.49'}$$

---

4. In the designation of the components of the hybrid-pi equivalent circuit we follow the generally accepted notation. For example, see Gray et al., *Physical Electronics*.

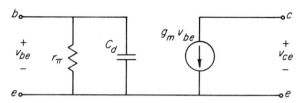

FIG. 8.17   Circuit model of a transistor corresponding to (8.48') and (8.49').

It is easy to devise a circuit that obeys this pair of equations. The input (base) current is divided between a capacitance C_d and a resistance r_π in parallel. The collector current flows from collector to emitter, depending on v_{be} and independent of v_{ce}. This requires a controlled current source. The resulting equivalent circuit is shown in Fig. 8.17.

Having obtained the parameters r_π, C_d, and g_m, let us compute typical values of these quantities using realistic physical properties of a medium frequency *pnp* planar silicon transistor. Let us assume $\beta_F = 50$, $W = 0.7\,\mu\text{m}$, $D_b = 10 \text{ cm}^2/\text{s}$, and a collector DC current of 20 mA. Then $g_m = (q/kT)|I_C| = 0.80$ mho, $C_d = g_m(W^2/2D_b) = 196$ pF, and $r_\pi = \beta_F/g_m = 63\,\Omega$.

Let us next account for the junction SCL capacitances. To do this we simply connect the emitter junction capacitance C_e from *b* to *e* and the collector junction capacitance C_c from *c* to *b* to obtain the circuit of Fig. 8.18.

This circuit is almost the complete small signal circuit model for the transistor. The principal matters as yet unaccounted for are ohmic resistances in the base, collector, and emitter regions. To evaluate these resistances, consider again the structure illustrated in Fig. 8.1a. The resistance associated with the emitter is small since the emitter is characteristically heavily doped to obtain a high current gain through high emitter efficiency. Further, the cross-sectional area through which the emitter current flows is relatively large. The collector region is relatively lightly doped but this region is so thin that resistance is low. Note in

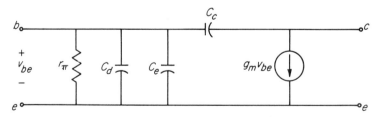

FIG. 8.18   Circuit of Fig. 8.17 with junction capacitances added.

Fig. 8.1a that the much thicker lower portion of the device, the substrate, is very heavily doped and therefore has a very small resistance. The resistance of the collector region is reduced further by its large cross section.

Finally we consider the resistance met by the base current. Recall that i_B has two principal components—one required to make up recombination losses and the other to supply the electrons (in a *pnp* transistor) that flow into the emitter region. The flow of electrons in each case is from the base contact into the narrow base region. The resistance to this flow is large for two reasons: (1) the base is relatively lightly doped to increase emitter efficiency so as to produce a high current gain and (2) the width of the base region is small to increase the transport factor γ_b and to create good high-frequency response. This width W is the distance to be traveled by holes diffusing from emitter to collector. Unfortunately W is a cross-sectional dimension where base current is concerned. (Note that i_B must flow across-the-page in Fig. 8.1a in order to reach the central portion of the base region.) Thus small W leads a small area perpendicular to i_B and hence promotes high base resistance. Both low doping and narrow base width cause the base resistance to be significant in its effect upon the transistor characteristics.

The base resistance causes the base-emitter junction voltage to differ from the terminal base-emitter voltage. Relabeling the b terminal of Fig. 8.18 as b' and calling the external terminal b we have a terminal voltage v_{be}, a junction voltage $v_{b'e}$ controlling the current generator, and a base resistance r_x connecting the internal and external base points. This is shown in Fig. 8.19 where we also have combined C_d and C_e into C_π and relabeled C_c as C_μ to conform to accepted convention.

The careful observer will note two unexplained elements r_μ and r_o shown with dashed connections in Fig. 8.19. A more rigorous analysis would show that the base and collector currents depend slightly upon v_{ce}. Resistances r_μ and r_o are included to account for these dependences

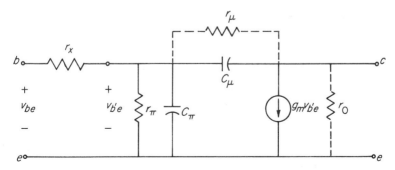

FIG. 8.19   Complete hybrid-pi circuit model.

but in most applications they may be ignored. The reason r_μ and r_o exist is that τ_F and q_A depend on the base width W which in turn depends on the collector-base voltage. This may be explained as follows. Suppose v_{CB} is made more negative, thereby increasing the reverse bias on the collector junction. This widens the collector SCL. But that occurs at least in part at the expense of the base width. The distance W is simply the distance from the edge of the emitter SCL, $x = 0$ in Fig. 8.3, to the edge of the collector SCL. Thus variations in v_{CE} mean variations in v_{CB}, W, and hence τ_F and q_A. These variations in turn mean that i_B and i_C vary somewhat with v_{CE}.

The base resistance r_x, in contrast with g_m, r_π, and C_π, is relatively constant for a given transistor type. It does depend somewhat on the collector current and, as seen above, is affected by the DC value of v_{CB}. For transistors used in small signal applications r_x typically falls in the 50–200 Ω range.

8.8   *npn* TRANSISTOR

Thus far in this chapter all discussion has related to the *pnp* transistor. Convenience is the principal reason for this choice. Since holes are positively charged, the directions of flow and current are the same, thus permitting a clearer picture of effects occurring in the device. In practice *npn* silicon transistors are easier to manufacture than *pnp* devices so the majority of transistors manufactured today are *npn*. Thus it is important to give sufficient consideration to the *npn* transistor to make the similarities and differences apparent.

So far as physical behavior is concerned the roles of holes and electrons are interchanged everywhere in the device. The reader is therefore invited, or perhaps even advised, to carefully reconsider the first seven sections of this chapter in terms of the *npn* transistor. If this is done the following results are obtained. The DC equations for collector and emitter currents are

$$I_E = -\alpha_R I_C - I_{EO}[\exp(qV_{BE}/kT) - 1] \tag{8.53}$$

$$I_C = -\alpha_F I_E - I_{CO}[\exp(qV_{BC}/kT) - 1] \tag{8.54}$$

or equivalently

$$I_E = -I_{ES}[\exp(qV_{BE}/kT) - 1] + \alpha_R I_{CS}[\exp(qV_{BC}/kT) - 1] \tag{8.55}$$

$$I_C = \alpha_F I_{ES}[\exp(qV_{BE}/kT) - 1] - I_{CS}[\exp(qV_{BC}/kT) - 1] \tag{8.56}$$

In terms of I_B these currents are expressed as

$$I_E = \beta_R I_B - (1 + \beta_R)I_{EO}[\exp(qV_{BE}/kT) - 1] \tag{8.57}$$

$$I_C = \beta_F I_B - (1 + \beta_F)I_{CO}[\exp(qV_{BC}/kT) - 1] \tag{8.58}$$

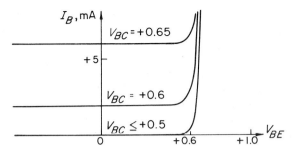

FIG. 8.20   Base characteristics for a silicon *npn* transistor.

At high voltages the collector current is given by

$$I_C = - M\alpha_F I_E - MI_{CO}[\exp(qV_{BC}/kT) - 1] \qquad (8.59)$$

$$I_C = \frac{M(1 - \alpha_F)}{(1 - M\alpha_F)} \{\beta_F I_B - (1 + \beta_F)I_{CO}[\exp(qV_{BC}/kT) - 1]\} \qquad (8.60)$$

These equations are of the same form as those for the *pnp* but the signs of some terms are different. Parameters α_F, α_R, I_{CO}, I_{EO}, I_{CS}, and I_{ES} are all defined to be positive quantities as before.

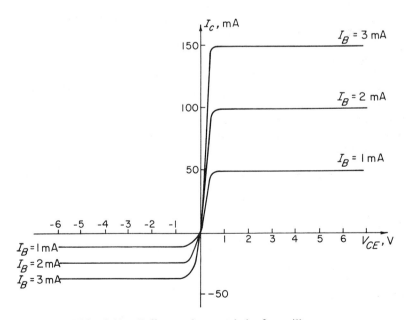

FIG. 8.21   Collector characteristics for a silicon *npn* transistor.

The graphic characteristics of interest are I_B vs V_{BE} and I_C vs V_{CE}. These are shown in Figs. 8.20 and 8.21.

For this transistor the first quadrant, i.e., positive I_C and V_{CE}, is the normal operating region while for the *pnp* it is the third quadrant, i.e., negative I_C and V_{CE}.

The charge control equations are

$$i_B = \frac{q_A}{\tau_A} + \frac{q_S}{\tau_S} + \frac{dq_A}{dt} + \frac{dq_S}{dt} + C_e \frac{dv_{BE}}{dt} + C_c \frac{dv_{BC}}{dt} \tag{8.61}$$

$$i_C = \frac{q_A}{\tau_F} + C_c \frac{dv_{CB}}{dt} \tag{8.62}$$

provided one defines q_A and q_S as positive quantities. In the *npn* transistor the stored minority charge is electronic and hence negative. Thus q_A and q_S are defined as the opposites of the negative quantities they represent. An alternate equivalent interpretation is to interpret q_A and q_S as excess majority charges. The excess minority and majority charges in the base are always equal and opposite because of charge neutrality requirements.

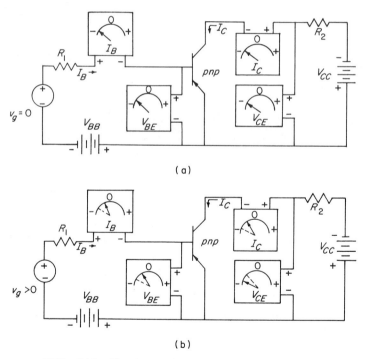

(a)

(b)

FIG. 8.22   Simple *pnp* circuit with bidirectional current meters and voltmeters with (a) $v_g = 0$ and (b) $v_g > 0$.

The hybrid-pi model (Fig. 8.19) and (8.50), (8.51), and (8.52) apply *with no change whatsoever.* The relationships among variations in i_B, i_C, V_{BE}, and V_{CE} are identical in *pnp* and *npn* transistors. To see this is true consider the pair of experiments illustrated in Figs. 8.22 and 8.23.

In each circuit, DC sources are connected to put the transistor in the active mode, i.e., with forward biased emitter and reverse biased collector. Bidirectional current and voltage meters are connected to measure I_B, I_C, V_{BE}, and V_{CE}. Zero is in the center of each scale; a deflection to the right of center means the variable is positive while deflection to the left of center means the variable is negative. With the v_g sources in the base circuits set equal to zero certain DC conditions are established. The meters indicate the four variables being monitored are all negative in the *pnp* circuit and all positive in the *npn* circuit. What now happens when $v_g > 0$ is established in each circuit?

In the *pnp* circuit v_g opposes V_{BB} so the net forward bias on the emitter is reduced. This means $\Delta V_{EB} < 0$ or $\Delta V_{BE} > 0$. Thus V_{BE} becomes less negative and the meter needle swings toward zero as shown in Fig. 8.22b. Reduced forward bias means the base and collector cur-

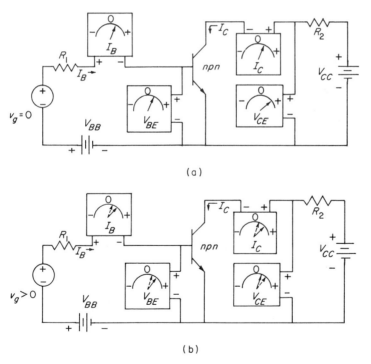

(a)

(b)

FIG. 8.23   Simple *npn* circuit with bidirectional current meters and voltmeters with (a) $v_g = 0$ and (b) $v_g > 0$.

rents decrease, i.e., the meter needles move toward zero. Algebraically this means $\Delta i_B > 0$ and $\Delta i_C > 0$ because these quantities are less negative than before. The needles of the V_{BE}, I_B, and I_C meters, while still on the negative side of zero, have shifted toward the plus side. For V_{CE} the needle moves the opposite way, i.e., $\Delta V_{CE} < 0$ because a decreased collector current magnitude means less drop across R_2 so that V_{CE} is more nearly equal to $-V_{CC}$.

For the *npn* circuit on the other hand v_g aids V_{BB}, thereby increasing the forward bias on the emitter. This means V_{BE}, I_B, and I_C are increased in magnitude. Note that the corresponding needles in Fig. 8.23b have deflected further toward the plus side, thus ΔV_{BE}, Δi_B, and Δi_C are all positive. The increasing collector current means more drop across R_2. By Kirchhoff's voltage law this means V_{CE} must become smaller. The needle thus deflects toward zero and we have $\Delta V_{CE} < 0$.

Comparing results in the two circuits we see that directions of needle movement for corresponding meters are the same. In both circuits we have $\Delta V_{BE} > 0$, $\Delta i_B > 0$, $\Delta i_C > 0$, and $\Delta v_{CE} < 0$. Thus so far as small variations are concerned *pnp* circuits and *npn* circuits behave similarly and the hybrid-pi model represents both transistors with no modifications.

8.9   PRACTICAL TRANSISTOR CHARACTERISTICS

In previous sections we treat the current gain parameters α_F and β_F as constants. The only gain variations explicitly accounted for are those due to the avalanche multiplication factor M and are shown in (8.3), (8.15), (8.59), and (8.60). In the final stages of developing the hybrid-pi model we briefly alluded to the dependence of collector current upon base width which in turn varies with collector-base voltage. Let us now consider this and other effects in terms of their effects on α_F and β_F.

The variations of base width with V_{CB} (known as the Early effect, after J. Early who first proposed it as an explanation for the voltage dependence of alpha)[5] affect both the emitter efficiency γ_e and the base transport factor γ_b as seen in (8.6a) and (8.7a). As the collector-base reverse bias is increased, the base width decreases and both γ_e and γ_b move closer to unity. This means that α_F moves closer to unity and β_F increases significantly. Thus if I_C is measured with I_B held constant and collector voltage varied, $|I_C|$ shows a significant increase with increasing $|V_{CB}|$ and $|V_{CE}|$. The horizontal portions of the curves in Figs. 8.8 and 8.21 are replaced by tilted lines.

In addition to depending on collector voltage, alpha and beta depend on collector current at both very low and very high currents. The

5. J. M. Early, Effects of Space Charge Layer Widening in Junction Transistors, *Proc. IRE* 40(1952): 1401–6.

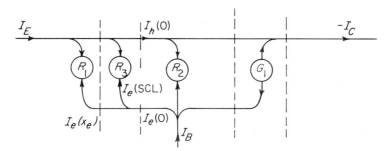

FIG. 8.24 Internal flow-generation-recombination diagram including the emitter junction space charge layer recombination in a *pnp* transistor.

low current behavior is explained as follows. In Fig. 8.3 the basic carrier flow and recombination and generation processes are depicted. The effect of recombination in the SCL of the base-emitter junction is neglected. If this is included the diagram takes the form shown in Fig. 8.24. This recombination process has the effect of adding a new component to I_E and I_B without changing I_C. This component is analogous to the $I'_s[\exp(qV/nkT) - 1]$ term discussed in Sec. 7.4. Thus, assuming $n = 2$ is appropriate, a term $I'_{ES}[\exp(qV_{EB}/2kT) - 1]$ should be added to the right side of (8.19a) to yield

$$I_E = I_{ES}[\exp(qV_{EB}/kT) - 1] - \alpha_R I_{CS}[\exp(qV_{CB}/kT) - 1]$$
$$+ I'_{ES}[\exp(qV_{EB}/2kT) - 1] \tag{8.63}$$

By similar reasoning an extra term should be added to (8.19b) to account for recombination in collector-base SCL when that junction is forward biased. However that is a refinement which is of less practical importance. Hence for I_C we simply write

$$I_C = - \alpha^i_F I_{ES}[\exp(qV_{EB}/kT) - 1] + I_{CS}[\exp(qV_{CB}/kT) - 1] \tag{8.64}$$

In this equation a superscript i is added to denote an idealized value of alpha, i.e., the alpha when emitter SCL recombination is not considered. The symbol α_F (no superscript) thus is available for representing the actual alpha. We define that alpha as follows:

$$\alpha_F = - \frac{I_C}{I_E}\bigg|_{V_{CB}=0} = \frac{\alpha^i_F I_{ES}[\exp(qV_{EB}/kT) - 1]}{I_{ES}[\exp(qV_{EB}/kT) - 1] + I'_{ES}[\exp(qV_{EB}/2kT) - 1]} \tag{8.65}$$

If the identity $(X^2 - 1) = (X - 1)(X + 1)$ where $X^2 = \exp(qV_{EB}/kT)$ is used this expression may be simplified to read

$$\alpha_F = \alpha^i_F \left[1 + \frac{I'_{ES}/I_{ES}}{\exp(qV_{EB}/2kT) + 1}\right]^{-1} \tag{8.66}$$

In silicon transistors one finds $I'_{ES} \gg I_{ES}$. Hence at small values of V_{EB} the actual alpha is much smaller than the ideal alpha. This in turn means that α_F is small when the collector current is small. On the other hand as V_{EB} is increased the collector current increases and α_F approaches α'_F.

It is often convenient to have the collector current expressed as a function of I_E and V_{CB} rather than V_{EB} and V_{CB}. This is the form of the relationship in (8.2). What we seek therefore is an updated version of (8.2). To obtain such an expression we must use (8.63) and (8.65) to eliminate V_{EB} from (8.64). Note that the denominator in (8.65) is identical with the sum of the first and third terms on the right side of (8.63). This fact is used to rewrite (8.63) as

$$I_E = (\alpha'_F/\alpha_F) I_{ES}[\exp(qV_{EB}/kT) - 1] - \alpha_R I_{CS}[\exp(qV_{CB}/kT) - 1]$$

$$(8.67)$$

If (8.67) is next solved for $\alpha'_F I_{ES}[\exp(qV_{EB}/kT) - 1]$ and this result is substituted into (8.64), the desired expression is obtained.

$$I_C = -\alpha_F I_E + (1 - \alpha_F \alpha_R) I_{CS}[\exp(qV_{CB}/kT) - 1] \qquad (8.68)$$

Then noting from (8.20) that $(1 - \alpha_F \alpha_R) I_{CS}$ is I_{CO} one obtains

$$I_C = -\alpha_F I_E + I_{CO}[\exp(qV_{CB}/kT) - 1] \qquad (8.69)$$

This expression is identical in appearance with (8.2). The only differences lie in the values of α_F and I_{CO}. In (8.2), α_F is the idealized alpha, now designated α'_F, and $I_{CO} = I_{CS}(1 - \alpha'_F \alpha_R)$. In (8.69) however α_F is the actual alpha and I_{CO} depends upon α_F via the expression $I_{CO} = I_{CS}(1 - \alpha_F \alpha_R)$. Hence in (8.69) the quantities α_F and I_{CO} are dependent on V_{EB} whereas in (8.2) they are constants.

The variation of α_F with V_{EB} implies corresponding variations of β_F with V_{EB}. Since (8.69) is identical in form with (8.2), it is clear that the actual beta may be calculated from the actual alpha in the usual way, i.e., $\beta_F = \alpha_F/(1 - \alpha_F)$, and (8.22a) applied directly but with β_F and I_{CO} understood to depend upon α_F and hence upon V_{EB}. Calculating β_F yields

$$\beta_F = \beta'_F \left[1 + (1 + \beta'_F) \frac{I'_{ES}/I_{ES}}{\exp(qV_{EB}/2kT) + 1} \right]^{-1} \qquad (8.70)$$

where $\beta'_F = \alpha'_F/(1 - \alpha'_F)$ is the idealized beta. Again for small V_{EB} the current gain (beta this time) is low but as V_{EB} (and hence I_C) is increased, it approaches the idealized beta β'_F. The above analysis is in terms of the *pnp* transistor. To use (8.66) and (8.70) for the *npn* case one only has to replace V_{EB} by V_{BE}. Also the *npn* collector current equations, (8.54), (8.56), (8.58), and (8.60), are appropriate when α_F, β_F, and I_{CO} are interpreted as depending upon V_{BE}.

Consider next the variations of alpha and beta at high collector currents. As I_C is increased from low to moderate currents, β_F approaches β_F'. However as I_C is increased further β_F decreases again. Similar remarks hold for the variation of α_F with I_C. The high current falloff of alpha and beta is due to a decrease in the emitter efficiency γ_e. At moderate and high currents the emitter efficiency is related to the properties of the base and emitter regions by

$$\gamma_e = (1 + D_e W n_n / D_h L_e p_p)^{-1} \tag{8.71}$$

This is the same as (8.6b) except that N_n/N_p in (8.6b) is replaced by a more general expression n_n/p_p. At low and moderate currents n_n and p_p are determined entirely by the impurity concentrations N_n and N_p, i.e., $n_n = N_n$ and $p_p = N_p$. In general $n_n = N_n + \Delta n_n$ and $p_p = N_p + \Delta p_p$. The quantities Δn_n and Δp_p are the excess majority carrier concentrations.

In Sec. 6.5 it is noted that the excess majority carrier concentration equals the excess minority concentration because of the need for vanishingly small space charge density everywhere except in the space charge layer of a *pn* junction. Now the carrier flows across the emitter-base junction cause the minority excesses to increase proportionally with the current which means that the majority excesses also increase proportionally with the current. In the emitter the impurity concentration N_p is so large that the majority excess Δp_p there is inconsequential. However the base is lightly doped, i.e., N_n is not very large. Hence Δn_n can become significant in comparison with N_n. Thus the variability of γ_e is emphasized by rewriting (8.71) as

$$\gamma_e = [1 + (D_e W N_n / D_h L_e N_p)(1 + \Delta n_n / N_n)]^{-1} \tag{8.72}$$

The behavior of γ_e, α_F, and β_F as I_C increases from moderate to large values can now be explained. At moderate collector currents Δn_n is negligible compared to N_n. Hence γ_e is very nearly unity as designed and α_F and β_F have their nearly ideal values. As I_C increases, the excess concentration Δn_n increases (because Δp_p must increase) to the point where Δn_n is no longer insignificant compared to N_n. Hence γ_e decreases slightly, α_F decreases slightly, and β_F decreases markedly.

The combination of the low current and high current effects described above leads to a composite dependence of β_F upon I_C as shown in Fig. 8.25. At $I_C = 10$ mA, beta attains a maximum value of 53. At lower currents beta drops due to the space charge layer recombination effects, and at higher currents it drops due to the emitter efficiency problem just discussed.

SUMMARY

- In a *pnp* transistor holes are injected from the p-type emitter into the n-type base. Most of these holes diffuse all the way across the base to be collected by the collector-base *pn* junction. The result is col-

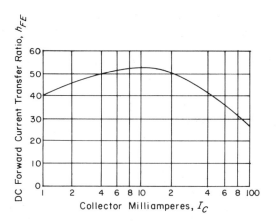

FIG. 8.25   Current dependence of h_{FE} (equal to
β_F) for a typical silicon transistor.

lector current given in part by $-\alpha_F I_E$. In addition there is a diode current due to the diode properties of the collector-base junction. The
complete collector current is given by (8.2).

● In an *npn* transistor, electrons are injected from the n-type emitter into the p-type base. Most of these electrons diffuse all the way
across the base to be collected by the base-collector *pn* junction. When
the base-collector diode effect is taken into account the resulting collector current is given by (8.54).

● In applications where emphasis is placed on the base current as
the input variable controlling the collector current, (8.14) and (8.58) for
pnp and *npn* transistors, respectively, are appropriate. These equations
express the collector current I_C in part as $\beta_F I_B$ where $\beta_F \equiv \alpha_F/(1 - \alpha_F)$.
Since α_F is close to unity, β_F is much larger than unity. Thus the current
gain from base to collector is large as contrasted with the current gain
from emitter to collector which is approximately unity.

● For a complete DC model of the junction transistor the Ebers-
Moll equations and various equations derived therefrom may be used.
These are (8.19 a,b) and (8.22 a,b) for *pnp* transistors and (8.55)–(8.58)
for *npn* transistors. Also, circuit models may be developed from these
equations as exemplified by Fig. 8.5 and the figure in Prob. 8.20.

● In applications calling for rapid changes in the collector current
the charge control model provides an appropriate characterization of
the junction transistor. In this model the collector current is shown to
be proportional to the base charge q_A which in turn is controlled by the
base current and by the base minority carrier lifetime. There is an additional component of charge called the saturation charge q_S. This exists
when the transistor is saturated, i.e., when the collector-base junction is
forward biased, and its existence limits the speed with which the tran-

sistor can come out of saturation. The saturation charge must be eliminated by reversed base current or by recombination before the transistor can desaturate and permit reduction in the collector current.

• In applications involving small changes in the transistor currents and voltages the hybrid-pi model of Fig. 8.19 is very useful. This model represents both *pnp* and *npn* transistors and involves elements with values readily determined from the transistor operating point and the transistor specification sheet.

• Ideally the current gain parameters α_F and β_F are independent of collector current and voltage. In fact however they are not. The transistor collector-base voltage influences α_F and β_F through its effect on the base width W. The collector current has both low current and high current effects on α_F and β_F. At low currents α_F and β_F are reduced because the recombination current in the SCL of the emitter-base junction is a major portion of the base current. At high currents α_F and β_F fall off because high level injection into the base region reduces emitter efficiency. The Ebers-Moll and other DC equations still apply if appropriate values of α_F and β_F are used.

PROBLEMS

8.1. Paralleling the logic in Sec. 8.2, develop for an *npn* transistor an equation analogous to (8.2). [Ans.: $I_C = -\alpha_F I_E - I_{CO}[\exp(qV_{BC}/kT) - 1]$, where α_F and I_{CO} are positive quantities]

8.2. A *pnp* transistor is operated in the following circuit.
    a) Calculate the collector current if $\alpha_F = 0.95$ and $I_{CO} = 10^{-6}$ A. [Ans.: -95 mA]
    b) Using Kirchhoff's current law calculate the base current. [Ans.: -5 mA]

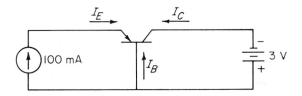

8.3. A *pnp* transistor has $1 - \alpha_F = 0.02$. Calculate α_F, $1 + \beta_F$, and β_F. [Ans.: $\beta_F = 49$]

8.4. We wish to estimate the amount by which γ_e differs from unity.
    a) Use the approximation $(1 + x)^{-1} \simeq 1 - x$, when $|x| \ll 1$, to put (8.6b) in a more convenient form for the desired estimate. [Ans.: $1 - \gamma_e = D_e n_{po} W / D_h p_{no} L_e$]
    b) Reexpress the minority carrier concentrations in the result of *a* in terms of n_i^2 and the doping densities in the emitter and base regions.
    c) What upper limit exists for doping densities if the emitter and base regions are to remain normal rather than becoming degenerate (as in a tunnel diode)?

    d)   What considerations determine the doping density lower limit?

    e)   Select reasonable values for doping densities, use typical values for D_e and D_h, and take $W = 10^{-4}$ cm and $L_e = 5 \times 10^{-4}$ cm. Calculate $1 - \gamma_e$.

8.5. We wish to estimate the amount by which γ_b differs from unity. Calculate γ_b for $W = 10^{-4}$ cm and $L_h = 10^{-3}$ cm.

8.6. We wish to calculate β_F as a function of collector voltage. Let $\beta_F = 100$ for $V_{CB} = 0$ and let the values of avalanche voltage and n be 80 V and 4, respectively.

    a)   Find V_{CB} for which the voltage-dependent current gain equals 200.

    b)   Find V_{CB} for which the voltage-dependent beta approaches infinity. (This is sometimes called "alpha equals one breakdown" since infinite beta corresponds to unity alpha.) The collector-emitter voltage corresponding to this condition is usually designated BV_{CEO}. [Ans.: 25.3 V]

8.7. Develop an expression for the emitter efficiency of a *pnp* transistor.

    a)   Refer to the definition for γ_e. The current $I_h(0)$ is simply the hole diffusion current at $x = 0$. Explain how one might justify approximating the current $I_e(0)$ by the electron diffusion current at $x = x_e$ (see Fig. 8.3). At what current levels would this be a poor approximation? (Recall the discussion in Secs. 7.4 and 8.9.)

    b)   Assuming the emitter region is much longer than the electron diffusion length, calculate $I_e(x_e)$ in terms of A (area), D_e, n_{po}, L_e, and V_{EB}.

    c)   Verify that the general expression for the base hole concentration is $p(x) = p_{no} + A_1 \exp(-x/L_h) + A_2 \exp(+x/L_h)$, i.e., show that this is the complete solution to the time-independent continuity equation when holes are minority carriers and the majority concentration is approximately constant.

    d)   Using appropriate references regarding hyperbolic functions, show that $p(x) = p_{no} + B_1 \cosh(x/L_h) + B_2 \sinh(x/L_h)$ is an equally acceptable complete solution. Find the equation relating A_1 and A_2 to B_1 and B_2 or vice versa.

    e)   Evaluate B_1 and B_2 by applying boundary conditions at $x = 0$ and $x = W$.

    f)   Assuming $\exp(qV_{EB}/kT) \gg 1$ and $\exp(qV_{CB}/kT \ll 1$, i.e., $V_{EB} > 0$ and $V_{CB} < 0$, calculate $I_h(0)$ in terms of A (area), D_h, p_{no}, W, and V_{EB}.

    g)   Evaluate γ_e and check against (8.6b).

8.8. Develop an expression for the base transport factor γ_b of a *pnp* transistor.

    a)   Refer to the definition for γ_b. Express γ_b in terms of derivatives of $p(x)$.

    b)   Assuming $V_{EB} > 0$, use the results of *d* and *e* of Prob. 8.7 to evaluate the required derivatives and calculate γ_b. The answer will be in terms of hyperbolic functions.

    c)   Assume $W/L_h \ll 1$ and expand γ_b in a second order polynomial in W/L_h. Compare with (8.7b).

8.9. Confirm the general nature of the characteristics plotted in Fig. 8.7.

    a)   Given $\beta_F = 20$, $\alpha_R = 0.9$, $I_{CO} = 10^{-13}$ A, and $kT/q = 26$ mV, find α_F, I_{ES}, and I_{CS}.

b) With the aid of Fig. 8.5 calculate and plot I_B vs V_{EB} for $V_{CB} = 0.5$, 0.6, 0.65 and compare with Fig. 8.7.

8.10. Confirm the general nature of characteristics plotted in Fig. 8.8. Using that figure and the values given in Prob. 8.9, calculate V_{EB} and V_{CB} for constant I_B and varying I_C and plot I_C vs V_{CE} using $V_{CE} = V_{CB} - V_{EB}$.

8.11. A *pnp* transistor has $\alpha_F = 0.98$, $I_{CO} = 1.5 \times 10^{-8}$A, and $I_{EO} = 0.8 \times 10^{-8}$ A. Calculate α_R and β_R.

8.12. A *pnp* transistor has $\alpha_F = 0.98$, $\alpha_R = 0.80$, and $I_{CO} = 10^{-8}$ A. We are concerned with the collector-emitter voltage drop when a transistor is in saturation, i.e., when both junctions are forward biased.

   a) Suppose $I_C = I_B = -1$ mA. Use the circuit of Fig. 8.6 to calculate V_{CB}, V_{EB}, and $V_{CE} = V_{CB} - V_{EB}$. (These conditions correspond to operation in the third quadrant, i.e., the normal or forward quadrant of the *pnp* collector characteristic.)

   b) Suppose the emitter and collector connections are interchanged so that $I_E = I_B = -1$ mA. Calculate V_{CB}, V_{EB}, and $V_{EC} = V_{EB} - V_{CB}$. How does V_{EC} is this case compare with V_{CE} in *a*? (These conditions correspond to operation in the first quadrant, i.e., the inverse or reverse quadrant of the *pnp* collector characteristic. The results show that in saturation a smaller collector-to-emitter voltage drop is realized by operating in the reverse mode. This is important in switching applications where the collector and emitter terminals simulate the contacts of a single pole single throw (SPST) relay and the base current simulates the current in the relay coil. An ideal switch has zero voltage drop when the contacts are closed. The transistor approaches this ideal best when inverted.)

8.13. a) Derive the equation for the i_C curve in Fig. 8.15a (partly solid, partly dashed).

   b) Verify that the two values labeled on the ordinate are appropriate.

   c) Solve for the risetime t_r.

8.14. A *pnp* transistor with $\tau_A = 0.5\ \mu s$, $\tau_S = 1.0\ \mu s$, and $\tau_F = 5$ ns is operating in steady-state saturation with $i_B = -1$ mA, $i_C = -10$ mA.

   a) Calculate q_A and q_S.

   b) Suppose that $-i_B$ is now changed suddenly to zero with i_C remaining constant at -10 mA. Calculate the time t_s required for q_S to reach zero.

8.15. Consider an *npn* transistor connected as shown below.

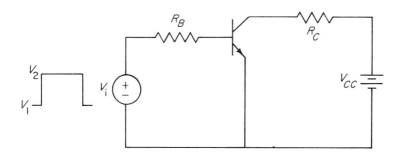

The circuit values are $V_1 = -2$ V, $V_2 = +12$ V, $V_{CC} = +12$ V, $R_B = 10$ kΩ, and $R_C = 1$ kΩ. The transistor is silicon with $\tau_A = 0.5$ μs, $\tau_S = 1.0$ μs, and $\tau_F = 5$ ns. The SCL capacitances vary as shown in the following graphs.

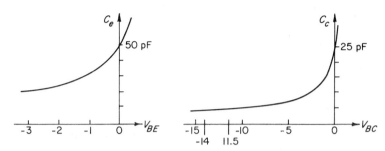

The objective is to determine the rapidity of response of the collector current to the rise and fall of the voltage V_i.

a) Assume v_i has been at the value $V_1 = -2$ V for a long time so that all transients have died out. Estimate the magnitudes of i_B and i_C and find values of v_{BE} and v_{BC}. [Ans.: -2 V and -14 V]

b) What are the approximate values of q_A and q_S for the condition described in a? [Ans.: zero]

c) Recognizing that q_A and q_S are not appreciable until forward bias of more than about 0.5 V is applied to the appropriate junction, simplify (8.35) to the form applying while $-2 < v_{BE} < +0.5$. [Ans.: $i_B = C_e(dv_{BE}/dt) + C_c(dv_{BC}/dt)$]

d) At $t = 0$, v_i changes to $V_2 = +12$ V. We are interested in the amount of time required for v_{BE} to change from -2 to $+0.5$ V since this is the time that must elapse before q_A (and hence i_C) starts increasing from zero. This time interval is called the delay time t_d. Straightforward solution of the differential equation in c is not possible because C_e and C_c vary with v_{BE} and v_{BC}, respectively. The way out is to integrate the above equation over the delay interval and we have

$$\int_0^{t_d} i_B\,dt = \int_0^{t_d} C_e \frac{dv_{BE}}{dt}\,dt + \int_0^{t_d} C_c \frac{dv_{BC}}{dt}\,dt$$

Canceling the dt in the integrals on the right side and converting the limits of integration into voltages we have

$$\int_0^{t_d} i_B\,dt = \int_{v_{BE}(0)}^{v_{BE}(t_d)} C_e\,dv_{BE} + \int_{v_{BC}(0)}^{v_{BC}(t_d)} C_v\,dv_{BC}$$

The integral on the left is simply the charge delivered through the base lead. The integrals on the right side are the charges acquired by the capacitances. Suppose one can estimate the average base current I_B during the delay interval. Then the left side can be replaced by $I_B t_d$ and we may solve for t_d to obtain $t_d = (\Delta q_{be} + \Delta q_{bc})/I_B$ where Δq_{be} and Δq_{bc} are abbreviations for the integrals on the right side of the previous equation. This equation says in effect that the time duration t_d is the charge that must be supplied divided by the average current causing the charge transfer.

e) Using Kirchhoff's voltage law calculate the voltage across resistor R_B at the beginning and end of the delay interval. From these estimate the average voltage during the interval and use Ohm's law to estimate the average base current. [Ans.: $I_B \simeq 1.3\,\text{mA}$]

f) Using the graph of C_e vs V_{BE} use graphic integration to find Δq_{be}. [Ans.: 95 pC]

g) Assume negligible current through R_C during the delay interval so that collector-emitter voltage remains constant at $+12$ V. Determine the voltage limits $v_{BC}(0)$ and $v_{BC}(t_d)$ and graphically find Δq_{bc}. [Ans.: -14 V, -11.5 V, 13 pC]

h) Calculate t_d. [Ans.: 83 ns]

i) At the end of the delay interval v_{BE} passes through $+0.5$ and q_A begins to be significant. This of course means i_C increases from zero and v_{CE} begins decreasing. As q_A and i_C increase finally v_{CE} is reduced to the point where $v_{BC} = +0.5$. This interval is the risetime and is of duration t_r. Since $-11.5 < v_{BC} < 0.5$ during this interval, q_S is still essentially zero. Write (8.35) for this interval.

j) Integrate the equation written in i and substitute $I_B t_r$ for the left side to obtain

$$I_B t_r = (1/\tau_A) \int_{t_d}^{t_d+t_r} q_A\,dt + \Delta q_A + \Delta q_{be} + \Delta q_{bc}$$

where Δq_A is the change in q_A during the interval and Δq_{be} and q_{bc} are again the charges supplied to C_e and C_c during the interval. Exact evaluation of the integral on the right requires knowledge of q_A as a function of time and this we do not know. Suppose we have reason to believe the variation is approximately linear. (This is the case whenever $I_B > \tau_F V_{CC}/\tau_A R_C = V_{CC}/\beta_F R_C$.) In that case Q_A, the average value of q_A, would be the average of the initial and final values and the integral could be replaced by $Q_A t_r$. Thus t_r may be found as

$$t_r = \frac{\Delta q_A + \Delta q_{be} + \Delta q_{bc}}{I_B - Q_A/\tau_A}$$

The physical interpretation is similar to that of the previous case. The charge to be transferred is divided by the average current available for accomplishing the transfer (the average base current minus the average recombination current Q_A/τ_A).

k) Find the values of v_{BC}, i_B, i_C, and q_A at the beginning and end of the risetime. Assume $v_{BE} = 0.6$ V and $v_{CE} = 0.1$ V at the end. [Hint: (8.36) simplifies at $t = t_d + t_r$ because dv_{BC}/dt becomes very small at that instant.]

l) Calculate Δq_A, Δq_{be}, Δq_{bc}, I_B, Q_A, and Q_A/τ_A. [Ans.: 60 pC, 7 pC, 120 pC, 1.1 mA, 30 pC, 60 μA]

m) Calculate the risetime t_r. [Ans.: 180 ns]

n) At the end of the rise interval v_{BC} passes through $+0.5$ V and q_S starts to build up. The variations in v_{BE} and v_{BC} now become small enough that the capacitance terms in (8.35) can be ignored. Also since i_C is now fixed at V_{CC}/R_C, q_A is constant and $dq_A/dt = 0$. The analysis thus becomes analogous to that conducted in conjunction with Fig. 8.16. Assuming v_i remains at the value V_2 long enough, calculate the steady-state value of q_S, designated as $q_S(\infty)$ in Fig. 8.16. [Ans.: 1000 pC]

o) Assume that the steady state described above has been attained and v_i now switches from V_2 back to V_1. For convenience let time be redefined so this instant is now called $t = 0$. What happens to i_C? It cannot change from V_{CC}/R_C until v_{CE} can rise from zero. This in turn requires v_{BC} to drop from $+0.6$ V to below 0.5 V to negative values. What does this decrease in v_{BC} imply about q_S? [Ans.: must decrease to zero]

p) The time interval during which q_S decreases to zero is called the storage time t_s. During this interval v_{BC} decreases from roughly $+0.6$ V to $+0.5$ V, and v_{BE} changes even less. This means Δq_{be} and Δq_{bc} can be ignored. Also q_A is again constant and (8.35) becomes a linear equation and may be solved analytically. Alternately one may use the integration method and obtain

$$t_s = \frac{\Delta q_S}{I_B - Q_A/\tau_A - Q_S/\tau_S}$$

where Δq_S is the required change in saturation charge (a negative number), Q_A is the constant value of q_A, Q_S is the average value of q_S during the interval, and I_B is the average base current during the interval (a negative number). Evaluate these quantities and find t_s. [Ans.: -1000 pC, $+60$ pC, $+500$ pC, -0.26 mA, 1.14 μs]

q) At the end of the storage interval, $q_S = 0$ and q_A starts to fall. The interval during which q_A and i_C fall to zero is the fall interval t_f. How does the situation during this interval compare with that during the rise? [Ans.: very similar; equations are the same but some numbers have different magnitude and/or sign.]

r) Calculate the fall time t_f. [Ans.: 584 ns]

8.16. Derive expressions for g_m, r_π, and C_π of the hybrid-pi circuit.

a) Show that $C_d = dq_A/dv_{EB} = (q/kT)q_A = (q/kT)\tau_F|I_c|$.

b) Calculate g_m in terms of q/kT and $|I_c|$. [Ans.: Eq. (8.50)]

c) Recalling that $\tau_A/\tau_F = \beta_F$, use the results of a and b to express r_π in terms of g_m. [Ans.: Eq. (8.51)]

d) Use the results of a and b to express C_d in terms of g_m. [Ans.: Eq. (8.52)]

8.17. A pnp transistor is operating with $I_C = -10$ mA.

a) Calculate g_m for this transistor. Assume $kT/q = .026$ V. [Ans.: 0.39 mho]

b) Calculate r_π if $\beta_F = 60$. [Ans.: 154 Ω]

c) Calculate the range over which r_π varies if β_F varies from 40 to 80.

8.18. Relate C_π of the hybrid-pi circuit to frequency response data commonly given on transistor data sheets.

a) Use the circuit of Fig. 8.19 omitting r_μ and r_o. Connect a sinusoidal current source of angular frequency ω from base to emitter and place a short circuit between collector and emitter to calculate the short-circuit current gain $\beta(j\omega) = i_c/i_b$ with $v_{ce} = 0$.

    b)   Analyze the circuit to find $\beta(j\omega)$.

    c)   Calculate the angular frequency ω_β at which $|\beta(j\omega)| = 0.707\,\beta_F$.

    d)   Assuming $\beta_F \gg 1$ calculate the angular frequency ω_T at which $|\beta(j\omega)| = 1.0$.

    e)   Data sheets commonly give values for β_F, C_μ, and $f_T \equiv \omega_T/2\pi$ though the names are often changed. In the case of β_F, the data sheet may list "h_{FE}" or "h_{fe} at 1 kHz." In the case of C_μ the data sheet may list "C_{ob}" standing for "output capacitance in the common base connection." Calculate C_π for a transistor with $h_{FE} = 50$, $C_{ob} = 10$ pF and $f_T = 100$ MHz if $|I_c| = 2$ mA. [Ans.: 117 pF]

    f)   It is frequently true that $C_e \ll C_d$ and $C_c \ll C_d$. Simplify the expressions for ω_β and ω_T for that case and show that $\omega_\beta = 1/\tau_A$ and $\omega_T = 1/\tau_F$.

    g)   Would the inequalities in f tend to be better satisfied at large or small collector currents?

8.19. A *pnp* transistor with $r_x = 100\,\Omega$, $\beta_F = 100$, $C_{ob} = 3$ pF, and $f_T = 700$ MHz is operating at $I_C = 5$ mA. Draw the hybrid-pi circuit and determine values for all elements. [Ans.: $r_\pi = 520\,\Omega$, $C_\pi = 41$ pF]

8.20. a)   Assign appropriate labels to the following circuit in order that it follow directly from (8.17a,b).

    b)   Repeat, using (8.19a,b).

    c)   Repeat, using various combinations from (8.17a,b), (8.19a,b), and (8.22a,b).

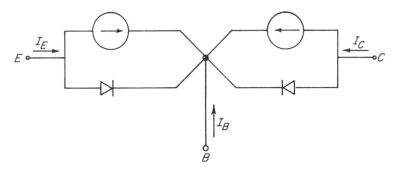

    d)   Develop the corresponding model for the *npn* transistor.

8.21. Develop a small signal circuit model for the *pn* junction diode.

    a)   Consider the low-frequency case where charge storage and SCL capacitance can be ignored. Denote the total diode voltage and current as $v_D = V_D + v_d$ and $i_D = I_D + i_d$, respectively, and rewrite the diode equation in these terms. Derive from the rewritten diode equation the equation relating v_d to i_d. Assume $|i_d| \ll I_D$ and $|v_d| \ll kT/q$. [Ans.: $v_d = R_p i_d + [kT/q(I_D + I_s)]i_d + R_n i_d$]

    b)   What are the dimensions of $kT/q(I_D + I_s)$? Draw a simple circuit model corresponding to the result obtained in a. [Ans.:

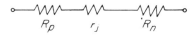

$$R_p \qquad r_j \qquad R_n$$

where $r_j = kT/q(I_D + I_s)$]

c) The effects of charge storage are described by a storage capacitance $C_S = (\tau_S q/2kT)(I_D + I_s)$ where τ_S is defined in Sec. 7.5. Consider the voltage which governs the stored charge and add a capacitance C_S into the circuit model developed above. Does your model behave reasonably when approaching the DC case as frequency becomes zero?

d) The SCL capacitance C also gives rise to a $C(dv/dt)$ current. Is v the junction voltage or the total voltage v_d? Add C to the circuit model. [Ans.:

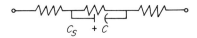

8.22. From the circuit of Fig. 8.5 derive an equation for I_B in terms of V_{EB} and V_{CE}. Plot I_B vs V_{EB} for $V_{CE} = -1, -0.5, 0 \text{ V}$.

8.23. Consider the following circuit.

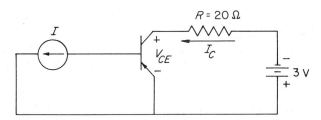

We wish to find I_C and V_{CE} for several given values of I. The transistor collector characteristics are those given in Fig. 8.8. The problem solution is the simultaneous solution of those characteristics with the I_C -V_{CE} characteristic of the external circuit.

a) Use Kirchhoff's voltage law to obtain the circuit I_C-V_{CE} equation. [Ans.: $I_C = -(3 + V_{CE})/20$]

b) This equation is a straight line. Evaluate its intercepts and graph the equation on a copy of Fig. 8.8. [Ans.: $V_{CE} = -3 \text{ V}$ when $I_C = 0$ and $I_C = -150 \text{ mA}$ when $V_{CE} = 0$]

c) Find I_C and V_{CE} for $I = 1 \text{ mA}$. [Ans.: $I_C = -50 \text{ mA}, V_{CE} = -2 \text{ V}$]

d) Repeat for $I = 0, +2 \text{ mA}$, and $+3 \text{ mA}$.

e) Estimate I_C and V_{CE} for $I = 4 \text{ mA}$.

CHAPTER 9

Fabrication Methods
for Semiconductor Devices

9.1 INTRODUCTION

To understand the behavior of semiconductor devices it is important to be aware of the processes by which they are fabricated. Their electrical characteristics are determined and often limited by these processes. For example, the frequency response of a transistor may be limited by the minimum base width obtainable by a given method of adding impurities to the semiconductor; or the number of devices per unit area in an integrated circuit chip can be limited by the minimum device sizes achievable by a certain fabrication procedure. The fabrication methods determine to a large extent the uniformity and stability of device characteristics. Underlying each of these factors is of course the economic one. Semiconductor devices are important today not just because of their unique mechanical and electrical properties, but because the device costs are low enough to make their use attractive in both routine and specialized applications. The cost of a device is mainly attributable to the methods used to make it, and semiconductor devices can be made with excellent electrical characteristics, long life, and astonishingly low costs. This unbeatable combination is responsible for the domination of semiconductor devices in today's electronics markets.

Here we examine the principal ways these results are achieved. Since the invention of the transistor in 1947 there has been a continuous evolution in manufacturing methods. These can be broadly distinguished by the way the rectifying junctions are formed. Some older methods are still in use today. We cannot look at each of these in detail but we will describe briefly several methods of junction formation and then concentrate on the most important method in today's technology: the so-called planar diffused silicon technology. Following the discus-

273

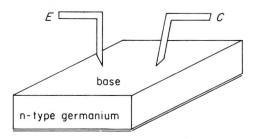

FIG. 9.1   Germanium point contact transistor.
Pointed metallic wires form the rectifying emitter and
collector contacts with the germanium base.

sion of junction formation an overview of the entire silicon planar
fabrication process is given and then some of the important processing
steps are examined in somewhat more detail.

9.2   JUNCTION FORMATION

A rectifying junction forms the heart of nearly all semiconductor
devices. We can trace the history of semiconductor devices largely
through the methods by which such junctions were formed.

9.2.1   Point Contact Junctions

The first practical transistor was a point contact device. The rectifying junctions were formed by placing suitable metallic wires in contact with a piece of germanium (see Fig. 9.1). One wire served as an
emitter, the other as a collector, and the piece of semiconductor as the
base. (The term "base" arose from the use of the semiconductor as a
mechanical base to support the emitter and collector wires.)

Rectification at a metal-semiconductor contact was not new in
1947. The earliest semiconductor devices, the crystal rectifiers in crystal
set radios, were formed in this way (though not with germanium). In
addition in the early 1930s the German physicist W. Schottky explored
the theoretical properties of similar junctions (see Sec. 9.2.6).

The point contact transistor set into motion the revolution brought
to electronics by semiconductor devices. They had several desirable
characteristics (such as good high-frequency properties) but they suffered from a serious flaw—their theoretical properties were so poorly
understood that a satisfactory design theory could not be developed.
For this reason research workers looked for other means to form rectifying junctions which would be amenable to analysis.

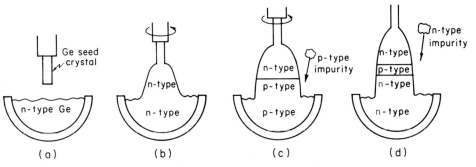

FIG. 9.2 Steps in the growth of a germanium crystal used to produce grown junction transistors.

9.2.2 Grown Junctions

In 1950 William Shockley, a physicist at Bell Telephone Laboratories, proposed and analyzed the electrical properties of a junction formed between p-type and n-type semiconductors called a *pn* junction. Shockley developed a theory of such structures allowing prediction of the way their properties depended on various physical and geometrical factors. (Shockley, along with Brattain and Bardeen, the inventors of the transistor, received the Nobel Prize in 1966 for this work.) It only remained to devise a method of forming a junction of this type.

The first such junction made was termed a grown junction. The sequence of steps by which it was made is sketched in Fig. 9.2. A crucible containing a doped semiconductor (assumed to be n-type germanium) is heated until molten. A germanium seed crystal is dipped into the molten material and withdrawn slowly. Surface tension causes the molten material to adhere to the seed. As it is withdrawn it freezes forming a single crystal of n-type germanium. The diameter of the crystal depends on the pull rate; about one inch per hour is typical. After growing a length of crystal, sufficient p-type dopant is dropped into the crucible to convert the molten material to p-type and the crystal growth is continued. Now the crystal is p-type and a crystal with a *pn* junction boundary is formed. Next n-type dopant is added reconverting the melt to n-type and causing an n-region to be formed. The final result is a crystal with two n-regions separated by a p-region as sketched in Fig. 9.2. Figure 9.3 is a photograph of a crystal of this type. This method of growing a crystal from a melt is termed the Czochralski process and is mentioned again in Sec. 9.3 as a method for growing crystals of silicon of a single conductivity type.

Grown junction transistors are formed from a Czochralski crystal by sawing it into rectangular parallelepipeds as shown in Fig. 9.4.

FIG. 9.3 Germanium crystal grown by the Czochralski process described in Fig. 9.2. At the top are the seed crystal and the chuck which supports the crystal during growth.

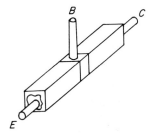

FIG. 9.4 Grown junction transistor.

Typically the devices might be 0.065 cm × 0.065 cm in cross section and 0.31 cm long. Thus a 1-in. diameter crystal could yield about 150 devices.

By today's standards grown junction devices are primitive. They had many faults, but the one that most stimulated efforts to look for improved methods was the poor frequency response resulting from the wide base regions achieved with this process. The minimum achievable base width was about 25 μm leading to a frequency cutoff of about 5 mHz.

9.2.3 Alloy Junctions

The next method of junction formation developed was the alloy process illustrated in Fig. 9.5. Again we shall assume germanium as the semiconductor (during early development germanium was the predominant semiconductor material). Suppose a crystal of germanium of a single conductivity type, say n-type, is grown for example by the Czochralski process, and cut into wafers or slices having the cross section of the crystal. The wafers are then cut into chips from which the individual devices are fabricated. The chips are typically 0.310 cm × 0.310 cm in cross section and 0.025 cm thick. A pellet of indium, a p-type dopant, is held in contact with the n-type germanium surface by suitable jigging and the system is heated to about 500°C in a nitrogen atmosphere. (Nitrogen is used to inhibit oxidation of the indium and

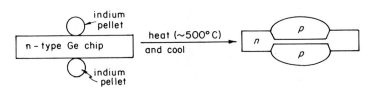

FIG. 9.5 Fabrication of a germanium *pnp* alloy junction transistor.

germanium.) The indium alloys with the germanium, dissolving an amount of germanium determined by the metallurgy of the two metals. The temperature is then lowered. As the indium-germanium system freezes some indium is incorporated into the germanium lattice resulting in p-type germanium and thereby forming a *pn* junction with the original n-type material. The upper part of the pellet is almost pure indium providing a metallic contact to the p-type region. This process is repeated on the opposite side of the wafer to yield a *pnp* transistor.

For a variety of electrical, mechanical, and economic reasons, devices of this type are vastly superior to grown junction devices. Many alloy junction devices, particularly germanium power transistors, are still made today. But again the frequency response was too low and the base width once more was the limiting feature. The base width in alloy devices can be made as small as a few micrometers leading to frequency cutoffs of the order of 200 mHz, but this is not high enough to meet many needs of the electronics industry.

9.2.4   Diffused Junctions

The next development brings us to the method which is the basis of today's technology—junction formation by *solid-state diffusion*. Since this process is described in more detail in the sections to follow, only the barest outline is sketched here. We have seen earlier that maintenance of a concentration gradient leads to a diffusion flux equal to the product of the diffusion constant and the gradient. While this has been applied only to the diffusion of holes and electrons it applies equally well to the diffusion of impurity atoms in a semiconductor.

The means of forming *pn* junctions by solid-state diffusion is sketched in Fig. 9.6. A wafer cut from an ingot of semiconductor (n-type silicon, for example) is placed in an atmosphere containing a p-type dopant (boron, for example). We see in a later section a way of doing this. The boron concentration at the silicon surface is larger than that in the bulk material and therefore the impurity diffuses toward the

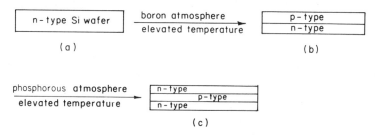

FIG. 9.6   Successive p- and n-type solid-state diffusion processes used to produce *npn* silicon wafer which is separated into individual transistors.

interior of the material. Because the boron atoms are massive their diffusion constant in silicon is very small. Appreciable diffusion will take place in a reasonable time only if the silicon is maintained at a high temperature. This causes the boron diffusion constant to increase (exponentially with temperature) and diffusion proceeds. Temperatures in the range 1000–1200°C are required.

The concentration of the boron is largest at the silicon surface and decreases with distance into the silicon. Where the boron concentration equals the concentration of the n-type background impurity the net impurity concentration is zero and a *pn* junction is formed. The depth of the junction depends upon the surface concentration N_s of the boron, the temperature T, the diffusion time, and the background impurity concentration N_B. With $N_B = 10^{16}$ cm^{-3}, $N_s = 10^{18}$ cm^{-3} and $T = 1200$°C a junction depth of about 3 μm is achieved in about 90 min. Even at elevated temperatures it is apparent that solid-state diffusion proceeds slowly.

The wafer containing the *pn* junction next is placed at an elevated temperature in an atmosphere of n-type impurity. The n-type impurity diffuses inward forming a *pn* junction where its concentration equals the net concentration in the p-layer. The result is shown in Fig. 9.6c. It is apparent that an *npn* structure has been formed. It is most important to recognize that the entire wafer (1–3 in. in diameter) is composed of this *npn* sandwich. If the wafer were divided into individual transistors (described in Sec. 9.3) then this one wafer could lead to several thousand transistors. Further, many wafers can be diffused at one time. The capability for batch processing inherent in the diffusion process leads to many unique properties of today's devices such as low cost and uniformity of characteristics.

It should be pointed out clearly that some very serious problems exist with making transistors as sketched in Fig. 9.6, although the first diffused devices were made this way. We see in the following section how this process has been modified to produce the highly successful silicon technology existing today.

The base widths produced in diffused devices are typically in the range 0.3–0.75 μm. The control attainable in solid-state diffusion makes it possible to produce base widths as small as 0.1 μm. It is possible with silicon transistors of this type to achieve amplification of signals up to a few tens of gigahertz (10^9 Hz). At these very high frequencies base width is not the only device property affecting frequency response; the emitter and collector depletion capacitances and the transit time of carriers through the collector depletion region become important.

9.2.5 Ion Implantation

In recent years solid-state diffusion has been the dominant means of forming *pn* junctions. It is a technologically sound process, as evidenced by the fact that the properties of discrete devices and integrated circuits fabricated using diffusion have characteristics (both electrical and economic) superior to those resulting from earlier processes. The dimensional control of such things as emitter area and base width leads to improved frequency response. The reproducibility inherent in the process and the batch processing afforded through the use of oxide masking lead to low cost and long-lived devices with superior electrical characteristics. The combination is hard to beat.

In spite of all this praise the diffusion process is not perfect. There are two principal sources of difficulty. First, the diffusion constants of the important impurities are generally so small that high temperature processing is required (for example 1000–1200°C in silicon). This is undesirable for several reasons. Where several diffusion steps are used in making a device or a circuit, the temperature involved in a given step influences all earlier steps, making overall control difficult. Also, at high temperatures the movement of any undesired impurities (contaminants) is enhanced; this can lead to a degradation in device characteristics. Second, the control over impurity concentration available for diffusion is not optimal. The control is obviously not really bad or the virtues of diffused devices described above would not be attainable, but an improvement in control could lead to a reduction in the spread in device parameters which in turn would mean improved devices and lower costs.

All of this discussion is a prelude to describing a process which provides a useful complement to solid-state diffusion, leading, in many cases, to better diodes, transistors, and integrated circuits. This process is termed *ion implantation*. It is carried out in the following way. Ions of the impurity atoms which are to be deposited are created by stripping away one or more electrons from the outer orbit. These ions are accelerated through potential differences of 20 000 V to 400 000 V and the beam of impurity ions is allowed to strike and penetrate the semiconductor surface. In penetrating the crystal the ions give up the kinetic energy they have acquired to the lattice atoms and come to rest. The impurity atoms are at this point present in the crystal primarily interstitially, i.e., in the spaces between the atoms which form the crystal. To be electrically active they must be present substitutionally, i.e., in lattice sites, where they can share electrons with the neighboring atoms. By heating the crystal to suitable elevated temperatures (in the range 300–900°C for silicon) the impurities take up lattice positions and behave as donors or acceptors, thus serving to dope the crystal. By controlling the rate of charge flow in the beam (*beam current*), layers of very uniform concentration can be deposited; by controlling the energy of the ions in the beam, the site of impurity deposit can be fixed; and finally by an appropriate annealing temperature virtually 100% of the impurities can be made electrically active. This is the process of ion implantation of impurities.

Ion implantation has several advantages. The most important is the precise control of the number of impurities deposited, achieved by regulating the beam current (the beam charge passing through unit cross section in unit time) and the deposition time. Controlled profiles of the impurities are attainable in principle by regulating the energy of the incident ions, but this feature is not often used in device technology. Low temperature processes are used, minimizing the problems mentioned in connection with diffusion. Finally, because the impurities appear precisely where deposited, smaller device dimensions are possible.

Ion implantation is not expected to replace diffusion as a means of junction formation. Rather, it will be used primarily to obtain precisely controlled numbers of impurity atoms which are then diffused into the host material. While ion implantation is becoming more widely used, its use at present is confined largely to specialized applications; most devices are made using conventional diffusion techniques.

9.2.6 Schottky Barrier Junctions

The final method of junction formation we consider is the Schottky barrier. This is simply a case of the old becoming new. If the metal is properly chosen, a metal-semiconductor interface forms a rectifying barrier referred to as a Schottky barrier. Gold on silicon falls into this category. These junctions are first cousins to the point contact junctions. Their current-voltage behavior is all but indistinguishable from that of a *pn* junction, and they have the advantage of no minority carrier storage and therefore no storage time, leading to diodes with fast switching characteristics. Schottky barriers are widely applied to high speed diodes and have also been used in some high-frequency field effect transistors.

The evolution of the methods used to form *pn* junctions has been sketched in this section. The methods, largely, are used to characterize the different types of devices manufactured; for example, one refers to alloy devices or diffused devices. Junction formation is only one aspect of device fabrication. Next we sketch the complete sequence of operations used to fabricate a particular type of device. Since the processes used depend strongly on the device type being made, we will select a particular type.

Let us describe a diffused silicon transistor. Silicon is chosen because it is by far the most commonly used semiconductor material; solid-state diffusion as the means of junction formation is also the most widely used. To be more specific we describe the fabrication of an *npn* diffused planar epitaxial silicon transistor. All the adjectives are self-evident except planar and *epitaxial* and these will be made clear in the description.

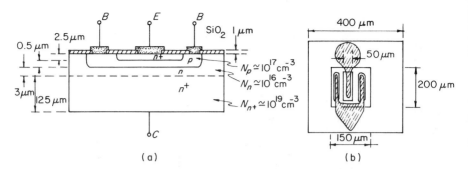

FIG. 9.7 (a) Cross-sectional and (b) top views of typical low power epitaxial diffused silicon *npn* planar transistor capable of handling a power of about 200 mW and signal frequencies of several hundred megahertz.

We first give an overview of the sequence of operations used in making the transistor of many adjectives. Then a few of the more significant aspects of the fabrication processes are discussed separately.

9.3 DIFFUSED SILICON TRANSISTOR FABRICATION

The specific device considered is a low power, medium-frequency transistor. A device of this type is sketched in Fig. 9.7 where typical doping levels and dimensions are shown. The symbol ν is used to designate a lightly doped n-type layer. A transistor of this sort might have a gain-bandwidth product of 500 mHz and handle power levels up to about 200 mW. A transistor with these capabilities is more or less the workhorse of the electronics industry since it meets the needs of the majority of circuit applications.

The flowchart in Fig. 9.8 shows the sequence of operations used to fabricate such a transistor. It is very important to recognize that batch processing is an essential feature of this technology; thus through most operations large numbers of potential devices are handled simultaneously. Some specific numbers make this point clear. The cross-sectional area of the device shown in Fig. 9.7 is 1.6×10^{-3} cm^2. The diameter of the silicon wafers from which these devices are fabricated is typically about 5.0 cm (about 2 in.). Thus each wafer potentially can yield about 12 000 transistors of this type. Two hundred wafers can be processed simultaneously through many of the fabrication steps described, particularly the diffusion and oxidation operations. Thus these processes permit about 2.4 million devices to be handled at one time!

The process begins with n-type silicon wafers prepared, for example, by sawing a Czochralski ingot into slices using a metal blade whose cutting edge has diamond dust imbedded in it. (Germanium and

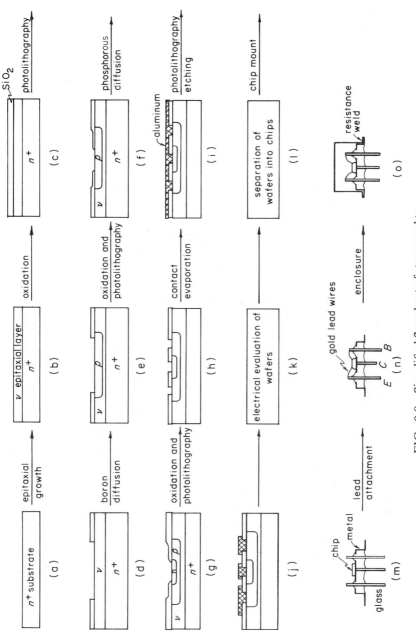

FIG. 9.8 Simplified flowchart of steps used to fabricate *npn* diffused silicon transistor of the sort in Fig. 9.7 (note gross distortion of vertical scale).

silicon have a diamondlike structure and are very hard.) The initial thickness of the sawed wafers depends on the final thickness required after the various processing steps. Assuming this final thickness to be nominally 125 μm, the wafers are cut to about 375 μm and are then lapped, using a fairly coarse abrasive, to about 250 μm. Following this the front surface of the wafer is polished to a mirror finish. Each lapping and polishing operation removes enough material to ensure that the crystalline damage introduced by the previous operation is removed. The result is a wafer 1–3 in. in diameter about 125 μm thick with one surface polished to a mirror finish.

The wafers thus produced serve either of two purposes: (1) diodes or transistors can be fabricated directly on them or (2) they can serve as substrates onto which epitaxial layers are deposited for device fabrication.

The term "epitaxial structure" in the present context refers to a thin, lightly doped n-type layer (referred to as the epitaxial layer) grown on a heavily doped substrate. The term epitaxial means "grown upon." The active portion of the transistor is formed in the epitaxial layer. This type of structure permits the simultaneous achievement of high collector-base voltage breakdown, low collector capacitance, low collector series resistance, and good high-frequency performance. The development of the epitaxial process was a significant milestone in the development of silicon device technology.

Since we are describing an epitaxial device, the wafers are assumed to serve as heavily doped substrates for epitaxial deposition as described in Sec. 9.5. The result is a deposited layer of silicon forming a single crystal with the substrate. The layer typically is thin (about 9 μm) and lightly doped (5×10^{16} cm^{-3}).

The first process step involves growing an oxide on the surface of each wafer. This oxidation step (described more completely in Sec. 9.6) is usually achieved by placing the wafers in steam at atmospheric pressure and a temperature of about 1200°C. Under these conditions a 1-μm layer of silicon dioxide (SiO_2) grows on the silicon surface in approximately 90 min. This oxide layer serves three valuable purposes: (1) it is used to define the regions of impurity diffusion, (2) it serves as an insulator isolating the silicon from the contact metals which may be deposited on the oxide, and (3) it helps to make the properties of the silicon surface independent of the ambient in which it exists. The unique properties of the oxide of silicon largely account for the wide use of silicon in the manufacture of semiconductor devices.

The first important use made of the oxide is that of a diffusion mask. Most Group III and Group V impurities diffuse much more slowly in SiO_2 than in Si. Thus a layer of SiO_2 on a Si surface can effectively mask the diffusant from the silicon. Photolithography is used to remove selected areas of the oxide in anticipation of the diffusion steps to follow. The principal steps in this process are:

1. A thin layer of a photographic emulsion called a photoresist is put on the wafer surface by depositing a few drops of the liquid, spinning the wafer, and allowing centrifugal force to provide a uniform, thin ($\simeq 1\,\mu$m) layer.
2. The layer is baked to drive off the solvents and enhance adherence between the oxide and the emulsion.
3. A thin glass plate with an array of precisely positioned opaque and transparent areas is placed on the emulsion and the surface is exposed to ultraviolet light which causes the exposed emulsion to polymerize.
4. The mask is removed and the wafer is put in a developing solution. There are two types of photoresists: a negative resist in which the developer removes the unexposed emulsion and a positive resist in which the developer removes the exposed emulsion. We shall assume a positive resist is being used. In either case over the surface of the wafer a very precisely positioned array of several thousand holes is opened in the photographic emulsion exposing the oxide.
5. The wafer is next put in a hydrofluoric acid (HF) solution which has the property of dissolving SiO_2 but not attacking either Si or the photoresist. The result is holes in the oxide corresponding to those in the photoresist.
6. Organic solvents are used to strip off the photoresist.

The result is sketched in Fig. 9.8d where only one of the several thousand (or tens of thousand) openings in the oxide is shown. From Fig. 9.8d onward only a single element of a wafer is shown. Remember, however, as each succeeding step is described that in fact complete wafers are being processed.

A wafer covered by a layer of silicon dioxide with several thousand openings has been produced. The wafer is next placed for approximately 20 min in a furnace at about 900°C in an atmosphere of boron. This results in a thin layer of boron deposited over the entire surface of the wafer. The wafer is then put in a boron-free furnace at high temperature ($\simeq 1200$°C) causing the boron in the windows to diffuse into the silicon while there is virtually no movement of the boron into the oxide (a more complete discussion of solid-state diffusion is given in Sec. 9.7). The result is the formation of a *pn* junction dividing the base and collector regions. This is shown in Fig. 9.8e. Note that the impurities have diffused away from the surface both vertically and laterally. The lateral diffusion has the very important effect of causing the *pn* junction at the surface to be formed under the silicon dioxide layer. The oxide thus shields the space charge layer of the silicon surface from contaminants in the atmosphere which can seriously degrade the junction properties (see Sec. 9.9).

The wafer is next oxidized again, growing an oxide of about 0.3 μm over the base region formed by boron diffusion (see Fig. 9.8f).

A photolithographic step opens another smaller window through which the emitter diffusion will take place (see Fig. 9.8g). It is important to appreciate certain implications of this step. It is apparent from Fig. 9.7a that the region in which the oxide is removed must be very carefully aligned within the diffused base region. The separation between the edges of the base and emitter junctions is small, typically only 25–50 μm. Further, recall that on a 2-in. wafer there may be potentially 12 000 transistors and this alignment condition must be met for every one! Requirements of this type are seen at many places in fabrication processes. They necessitate the use of sophisticated optical techniques in the manufacture of photolithographic masks but at the same time they also are responsible for the low cost of silicon devices since they make possible the simultaneous fabrication of many devices. The methods for making masks are discussed in Sec. 9.8.

The diffusion of the n-type emitter diffusant is carried out by placing the wafers in a furnace atmosphere containing phosphorus. The phosphorus is masked by the SiO_2 and diffuses only through the windows in the oxide. About 20 min at 1100°C results in a junction depth of about 2.5 μm. This in turn yields a base width of about 0.5 μm (see Fig. 9.7a). A heavily doped emitter region is produced to provide a high emitter efficiency and thereby a high current gain.

From Figs. 9.7a and 9.8g it is apparent that the principal portions of the collector-base and emitter-base junctions are coplanar leading to the term planar being attached to such devices. Actually the term carries with it the connotation of several other features including junctions formed by solid-state diffusion involving the use of oxide masking and photolithography with the surface space charge layers shielded by a protective layer.

Next, contacts must be made to the emitter, base, and collector regions. There are many ways of producing such contacts. A simple, widely used method is described here. To produce the emitter and base contacts the wafer is oxidized again and windows are cut into the oxide over the base and emitter regions. Then a layer of aluminum of about 3000 Å is deposited by evaporation. Photoresist is applied, exposed, developed, and left covering the metallic layer only where the metal is desired. The excess metal is etched away using an appropriate chemical, leaving the contact structure illustrated in Figs. 9.8j and 9.7b. The contact to the collector region (the back of the wafer) can be made by evaporating on the back of the wafer a very thin layer of titanium (a few hundred angstroms) and then a layer of gold of about 3000 Å. The titanium promotes adherence between the gold and the silicon.

Up to this point all processing has involved only wafers. In most processes, many wafers are processed simultaneously leading to inexpensive devices with uniform characteristics. Eventually the wafer must be separated into individual devices and handled separately. In this phase of manufacture the principal cost arises.

Prior to separating the wafer a sample of the units on the wafer is tested electrically to determine the percentage of devices having satisfactory characteristics. A set of needlelike metallic probes is placed on emitter and base contact areas while making electrical contact to the back (collector) of the wafer. Appropriate voltages and/or currents are applied to the device terminals and various device parameters judged to be most susceptible to failure are measured: voltage breakdowns, reverse currents, and current gain. If an insufficient percentage of the tested sample is good the wafer is discarded. Since the wafer at this point is relatively inexpensive, whereas the handling of individual units is costly, the percentage of good units must be high before it is profitable to continue the fabrication. From an economic point of view this step is critical. (Batch processing leads to an inexpensive wafer which can be discarded with relatively little loss.) Further, batch processing leads in general to wafers with uniform properties, and therefore testing a relatively small number of the devices gives an accurate picture of the properties of all the devices on a wafer.

The most common method of separating the wafer into individual chips is a "scribe-and-break" operation. A machine using a diamond-pointed tool scribes lines on the wafer between each row of devices. The wafer is then placed between two very thin plastic (mylar) sheets, laid on a moderately firm rubber surface, and a cylindrical rod is rolled over the wafer in the two (perpendicular) directions of the scribe lines. This (if all goes well) breaks apart individual chips. The process is similar to that used to break a thin glass plate into a set of rectangles. Silicon and germanium having the diamond crystal structure are brittle and such a technique can be used to break them into rectangular shapes.

The chips are next mounted on a suitable platform, for example, as illustrated in Fig. 9.9. Typically these structures are gold plated. The chip with a layer of gold on the back is placed in contact with the platform and heated to about 400°C causing the silicon and gold to alloy together, bonding the chip to its support.

Somehow electrical contacts to the emitter, base, and collector regions must be available to the external world. The most common method is to use the platform as the contact to the collector, and to bond fine gold wires to the emitter and base regions and attach these wires to the other segments of the platform. The process by which the leads are attached to the aluminum contacts (in our device) is termed thermocompression bonding. In this process the platform and wafer are heated to about 325°C. A thin gold wire (typically about 0.001 in. in diameter) is pressed down on the contact using a sharp hard metallic wedge. The pressure, temperature, and deformation of the wire lead to welding of the wire and contact metal. The other end of the wire is bonded in a similar fashion to leads through the platform but insulated from it which in turn permit external connection to the device.

The final fabrication operation is enclosure. Both for mechanical

FIG. 9.9   Two platforms to which a transistor chip
could be mounted.

and electrical protection it is desirable to isolate the semiconductor
chip from the environment. There are two basic ways to achieve this.
The chip-platform structure can be dipped in a suitable plastic which
is then molded and hardened in an appropriate shape. A second
method is to resistance-weld the platform to a metal can providing an
airtight structure referred to as a hermetically sealed unit.

Shown in Fig. 9.10 are a variety of completed transistors and
diodes. These range in size from a very large power diode structure to
the smaller power transistor structures to very small transistors and
diodes. Size is dictated by two considerations. Large enclosures are
needed in power devices to permit dissipation of heat generated. If
dissipation capabilities are not needed smaller enclosures are desirable
to minimize parasitic capacitances so the highest frequency device
capabilities can be used.

Encapsulation completes the device fabrication. Two important
operations then must be performed before the device is shipped to the

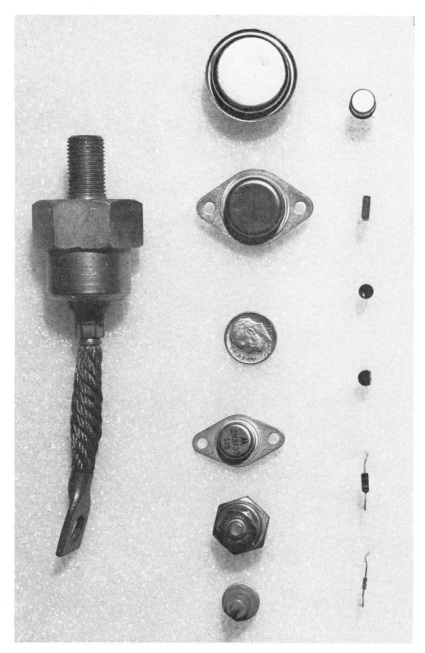

FIG. 9.10 Variety of diode and transistor structures illustrating packaging of devices for different uses.

customer. The important electrical characteristics must be measured and assured to be within the limits of the particular device code and the devices must meet the quality assurance standards. Many tests determine the quality of the finished product. Part of these are mechanical—for example, the strength and solderability of the external leads, resistance to mechanical shock, capability to withstand extremes in temperature, etc. Electrical tests ensure that electrical specifications have been met, and further tests are indicative of the long-term stability of electrical parameters. Once these conditions are satisfied the devices are ready for shipment.

Outlined here is a typical set of processes used to fabricate an *npn* diffused silicon planar transistor. Even in this outline form it is clear that many complicated steps are involved. This is true even though several processing steps are glossed over, leaving out numerous complex details, and certain operations are omitted entirely. In spite of the complexity the methods outlined lead to remarkably inexpensive devices with amazingly stable electrical characteristics. Transistors capable of amplifying frequencies up to 500 mHz and handling more than 100 mW of power with mean life under normal operating conditions upwards of 1000 years can be purchased for less than 50 cents! This is truly a tribute to the technology developed by the semiconductor device industry.

9.4 CLEANING PROCESSES IN SEMICONDUCTOR DEVICE TECHNOLOGY

The importance of cleanliness in semiconductor device manufacturing is difficult to overemphasize. We have seen the effect of very small amounts of impurities on the properties of semiconductor materials, and we know device characteristics may be very sensitive to the presence of impurities on the surface. Tremendous effort has gone into finding protective layers to isolate the active device from its environment. These considerations and more are responsible for nylon smocks and caps, clean rooms, etc., in the semiconductor industry. The semiconductor device industry undoubtedly represents the most refined large-scale technology in terms of cleanliness ever developed.

In this section one aspect of this cleanliness is discussed—the various chemical procedures used to produce clean semiconductor materials. We will not try to make the discussion quantitative; even to begin to do so would require discussion of sophisticated chemistry. Further, the theoretical justification for many procedures used is often not clear; the processes have been found effective through experience and are therefore continued.

Various cleaning procedures are appropriate to various steps in device fabrication. The process used depends on the environment the semiconductor has seen and what is to be done with it after cleaning.

No attempt is made to be exhaustive here; some typical situations are discussed.

The first thing to consider is the end result sought. We wish to remove all contamination (any unwanted matter) from the semi-conductor surface. Presumably the techniques used to prepare the material are responsible for the impurities within it. There are two broad classes of contaminants: mechanical and chemical.

Mechanical contamination consists of the surface damaged layer created by the sawing, lapping, and polishing operations plus bits and pieces of foreign matter which can be deposited on the surface. The surface damaged layer can be largely eliminated, beginning with the sawed wafer, by polishing with successively finer grit sizes. As a rule of thumb the depth of damage introduced by a polishing compound is three times the maximum grit size. In preparing a semiconductor wafer there is normally one lapping operation to get rid of most of the sawing damage followed by two polishing operations, the second with 0.3-μm polishing grit. The final damaged layer is removed using an acid mixture to dissolve a thin layer from the silicon surface. The physical contamination, foreign matter on the surface, is largely controlled by designing the wafer environment so as to make such matter non-existent through such methods as filtering the air in parts of the fabrication area, using so-called clean benches having a laminar flow of filtered air, using materials as lint free as possible, filtering the gases used in processing, requiring lint-free clothing in critical areas, etc. Contamination of this type is removed if it does occur by rinsing the wafers in ultrasonically agitated water. It is more important to get rid of the cause of such materials than to develop ways of removing them.

Many electrical parameters can be adversely affected by physical contaminants, often in subtle ways. Physical contamination on a surface can lead to epitaxial layers with excessive faults, erratic photoresist results due to surface irregularities, nonuniform diffusion, etc. A mechanically damaged surface can lead to voltage breakdown anomalies, high leakage currents, and low current gains.

The second broad class of contaminants is chemical in nature and more difficult to classify; their removal methods are more sophisticated. Chemical contaminants can be classified as organic, ionic, and atomic.

Organic contaminants are primarily greases, waxes, and oils. Waxes and oils may result from the mechanical preparation of the wafers. Grease can result from wafers or devices being handled or exposed to room air. Photoresist left on the wafer surface is an organic contaminant, as are residues from organic solvents and the solvents which can evaporate from plastic containers in which wafers or devices are sometimes stored. Organic contaminants are typically removed using organic solvents. Often solvents heated to boiling and ultrasonic agitation are used.

Ionic contaminants are primarily ions of the acids or bases used in cleaning the material and their effect on device behavior is particularly detrimental. They can result in high leakage currents, a variety of unstable device characteristics, and can cause the surface conductivity of the semiconductor to be substantially different from the bulk even to changing the conductivity type. Among the most prevalent ionic contaminants are the alkali ions, particularly sodium, which are especially harmful because they can diffuse rapidly through silicon dioxide. Ionic contaminants normally must be removed through chemical reactions. Nitric and sulfuric acids and their mixtures are commonly used for this purpose. Often the acid washes are hot and ultrasonic action is used in conjunction with them.

The atomic contaminants found on silicon surfaces are primarily the heavy metals such as copper and gold present in other chemicals used in processing. For this reason "Electronic Grade" acids and solvents, in which particular care has been taken to remove the heavy metals, are used.

One other feature of the cleaning processes merits attention. As noted, special grades of solvents and acids especially suited to device manufacture are used. Another widely used "chemical" of paramount importance is water. Water directly from the tap is normally loaded with organic and inorganic matter and is unsuitable for use in fabricating semiconductor devices, so specially treated water is used. Tap water is passed through a bed of chemicals which take out ionic materials and then through filters which remove most organic substances. The result is deionized water. The quality of such water is normally assessed by a conductivity measurement, a measure of the ion concentration. Where the conductivity of tap water might be 10^{-4} mho/cm the maximum conductivity of the water used in much of the device manufacture is 2.5×10^{-7} mho/cm.

By no means all considerations involved in cleaning are described or alluded to here, but we hope the nature of the problem and its solution are portrayed adequately.

9.5 EPITAXIAL GROWTH

In Sec. 9.3 the virtues of epitaxial material as applied to transistor properties are discussed. Assuming, as there, that we wish to make an *npn* transistor, the starting wafer should consist of a rather thin lightly doped n-type epitaxial region (the ν-layer) and a thick heavily doped n-type layer (the n^+-region or substrate). The initial thickness of the ν-layer should be such that after all the various heat treatments (principally diffusions and oxidations) the remaining high resistivity layer should be just sufficient to yield the desired collector breakdown voltage. (As a rule of thumb the breakdown field in silicon is about 30 V/μm.) Normally the initial thickness of the ν-layer is about three times the depth at which the collector-base junction is to be formed.

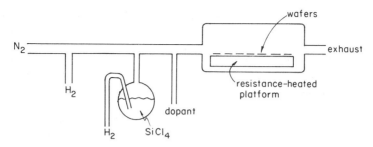

FIG. 9.11 Simplified version of an epitaxial deposition system.

An epitaxial layer can be deposited upon a silicon substrate in a number of ways. Here the one probably most commonly used is discussed. A simplified sketch of the apparatus used is shown in Fig. 9.11. Silicon tetrachloride and hydrogen (both gases) are combined at high temperature in the presence of the substrate to produce elemental silicon and gaseous hydrogen chloride. The silicon deposits on the substrates (as well as other parts of the deposition chamber) forming bonds with the silicon atoms at the surface to produce a single crystal of silicon. The chemical reaction used in producing the silicon is

$$SiCl_4(g) + 2H_2(g) \rightarrow Si(c) + 4HCl(g) \qquad (9.1)$$

(The letters g and c refer to gaseous and crystalline, respectively.) Most often a doped epitaxial layer is desired. It is achieved by bubbling hydrogen through a liquid containing a suitable impurity. Vapor containing the impurity is entrained in the hydrogen and deposited along with the epitaxial silicon, thus providing a doped layer.

The thickness of the epitaxial layer is controlled principally by deposition time, concentration of $SiCl_4$, temperature, and uniformity of gas flow. The deposition time is easy to control and therefore is not a great concern. The concentration of $SiCl_4$ in the deposition chamber is determined by the temperature at which the flask of $SiCl_4$ is maintained and the rate of H_2 flow through it. Both of these are readily measurable and, once fixed, they tend to be constant. The temperature at some point in the chamber is easy to measure, but it is difficult to ensure a uniform temperature for all the substrates. Moreover, it is difficult to be sure the temperature distribution does not vary from run to run. Nonuniform temperatures lead to variations in epitaxial layer thickness.

Thickness variations are also traceable to the gas flow through the deposition chamber. All substrates must see the same gaseous environment for uniform layer thicknesses. Ensuring this is very difficult. For example, if the H_2-$SiCl_4$ mixture enters at one end of the chamber it is reasonable to suppose that the $SiCl_4$ concentration seen by the first wafers is different from that seen by the last ones, introducing thereby a thickness variation. There is another more subtle problem associated with the gas flow. Gas flow in a tube with obstructions tends to be quite nonuniform; streamlines form around obstructions and the flow near the walls of the tube is normally different from that near the center. These considerations can affect the epitaxial thickness. To provide an adequately uniform gas flow giving sufficiently uniform and reproducible epitaxial layer thicknesses is a complex problem, solved in large part by empirical means. It is difficult to give typical values for the control of epitaxial thicknesses achievable. The thickness control within a run, the thickness control across a given substrate, and the control attainable from run to run depend on the system used and the nominal layer thickness. Reasonably typical values at a nominal 10-μm thickness are: control within a run and from run to run, 10 μm $\pm10\%$; control across a wafer, 10 μm $\pm2\%$. The range of layer thicknesses produced for various types of devices is 3–20 μm.

Finally, the resistivity of the deposited layer is affected by most conditions that affect the thickness—the temperature of the dopant liquid, the H_2 flow through it, and the uniformity of gas flow through the deposition chamber. The resistivity control attainable depends on the nominal value. Around 3 $\Omega \cdot$ cm a variation of $\pm25\%$ is probably reasonable.

9.6   OXIDATION

In Sec. 9.3 we noted the existence of a stable oxide of silicon probably provided the largest initial impetus to the use of silicon as the dominant semiconductor in device work. This oxide serves as a diffu-

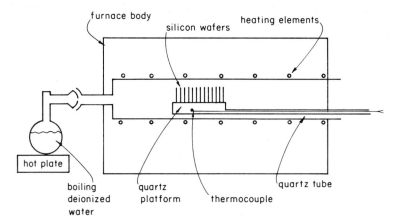

FIG. 9.12   System used to oxidize silicon wafers in steam at atmospheric pressure.

sion mask, as an insulator, and as a protectant to isolate the surface portions of the *pn* junction from the ambient.

A layer of silicon dioxide can be grown on a silicon surface in several ways. The oxidation of silicon in atmospheric steam is the method most commonly used. The silicon wafers to be oxidized are placed in a furnace maintained at a temperature high enough to grow an oxide layer of suitable thickness in a reasonable time. An atmosphere of steam is produced by boiling deionized water in a beaker connected to the tube (see Fig. 9.12). Because one end of the tube is open, the steam is at atmospheric pressure. The glassware used in the system is most often quartz since it has a very low coefficient of thermal expansion (so is less prone to fracture due to sudden temperature changes), it has a much higher melting point than most glasses, and it has fewer of those impurities affecting device properties than most glasses and ceramics.

The presence of water at the silicon surface results in a chemical reaction producing silicon dioxide. This reaction is

$$Si(s) + 2H_2O(g) \rightarrow SiO_2(s) + 2H_2(g) \tag{9.2}$$

The silicon dioxide produced is bonded to the silicon crystal but is not crystalline. Rather it is an amorphous (without structure) solid (s).

Oxide formation involves the diffusion of water (steam) molecules through any existing oxide to the silicon surface where the new oxide layer is formed. This is in contrast with materials where the new layer is formed at the oxide surface; an example is copper in which copper atoms diffuse to the copper oxide surface to promote growth.

The rate of oxide growth in atmospheric steam depends on oxide thickness, temperature, and time. Because water molecules must diffuse through the oxide layer for growth to occur, it is apparent that as the oxide thickness increases the rate at which water molecules arrive at the silicon–silicon dioxide interface decreases. Thus a thicker oxide grows more slowly than a thin one. The oxide grows rapidly initially, the rate of growth decreasing as the thickness increases. Temperature affects oxide growth in two ways. First, the diffusion constant of the water molecules increases as the temperature increases; hence more water molecules arrive at the silicon surface thus making possible a faster oxide growth. Second, chemical reactions normally proceed faster as the temperature increases (usually at an exponential rate) and therefore an increasing temperature permits the water molecules at the silicon–silicon dioxide interface to be used more rapidly in forming the oxide. Finally, the oxide layer increases in thickness as the oxidation is carried out for longer periods. Initially (for thin oxide layers) the rate of oxide growth is proportional to the time; for long times the rate of growth decreases and the square of the oxide thickness becomes proportional to the time. At 1100°C the transition occurs in about 25 min. At 1200°C the oxide growth is so rapid the linear rate hardly applies.

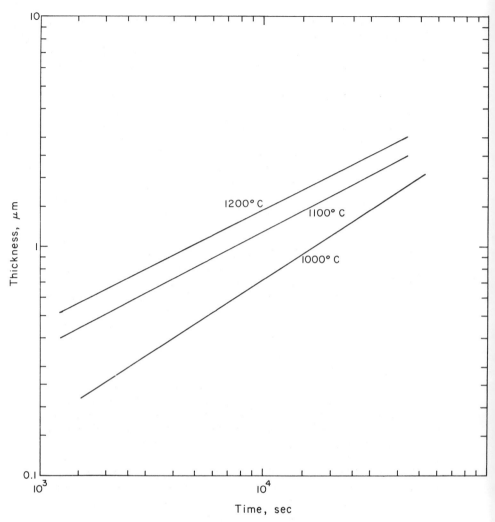

FIG. 9.13   Oxide thickness as a function of time for
silicon dioxide layers grown in steam at atmospheric
pressure.

The oxide thicknesses obtained in atmospheric steam for various
times and temperatures are shown in Fig. 9.13. The behavior alluded
to above is implicit in these curves. The reader might redraw one curve
to show thickness versus time on a linear scale (rather than the logarithmic scales of Fig. 9.13). In the earlier discussion it was seen that an
initial oxide thickness of about 1 μm (10 000 Å) was used. Figure 9.13

shows that a layer of this thickness could be grown in about 120 min at 1100°C or 80 min at 1200°C.

An important question is what conditions might result in a faulty oxide layer? The answer is that very few things damage the oxide itself. The oxide is easy to grow reproducibly. If there were particles on the surface prior to oxide growth t..en flaws, probably pinholes, could be introduced into the oxide layer, but there is no reason for this difficulty to occur. The oxide will trap any impurities on the original surface, so it must be carefully cleaned before oxidation is started. This is not because of the integrity of the oxide, but rather the sensitivity of silicon devices to contaminants on the surface or in the oxide.

It is thus relatively easy to grow high quality layers of silicon dioxide in atmospheric steam. Other methods of growing SiO_2 are used in special cases but steam grown oxides are most common.

9.7 DIFFUSION OF IMPURITIES IN SILICON

The great majority of semiconductor devices manufactured today, whether discrete devices or integrated circuits, use diffusion of impurities to produce impurity distributions needed for the desired device characteristics. Solid-state diffusion as a means of control of impurity concentrations has many virtues. It is a batch process with many wafers processed in a single step, thus introducing important economies (about two hundred wafers can be diffused in a single operation). The use of oxide masking permits accurate delineation of the regions in which impurities are to be added. This feature and the control of junction depths attainable are mainly responsible for the very high-frequency transistors in use today. For reasons mentioned previously, the information here is confined to solid-state diffusion as applied to silicon devices even though some diffused devices are made with other semiconductor materials.

The general features of diffusion are introduced in Chap. 5 where the diffusion of holes and electrons are considered. There we noted that an essential feature of diffusion is a concentration gradient. For example, a concentration gradient in the impurity concentration $N(x)$ leads to a diffusion flux F given by

$$F = -D \frac{dN}{dx} \tag{9.3}$$

where D is the diffusion constant of the impurity and F is the number of impurity atoms crossing a unit cross section in unit time. If D is measured in cm^2/s and N in cm^{-3}, then F has the units of $cm^{-2} \cdot s^{-1}$.

Impurities diffuse in solids by either of two mechanisms (see Sec. 9.2.5). They can move through vacant spaces in the crystal (interstitial diffusion) or they can move from one crystal lattice site to another (sub-

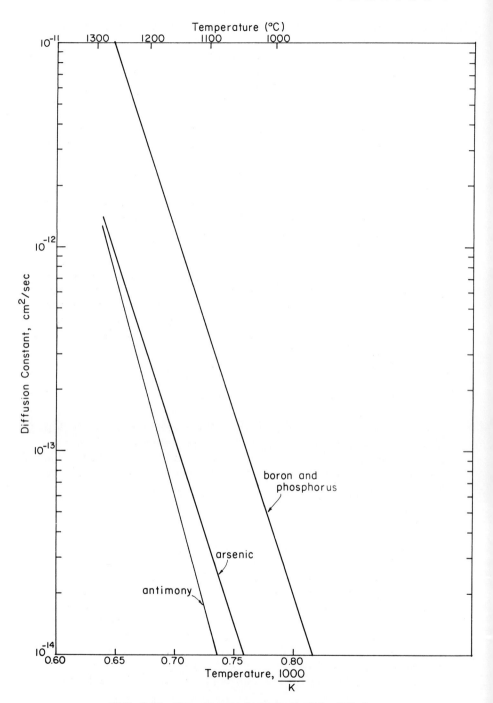

FIG. 9.14   Temperature dependence of the diffusion
constants of several impurity atoms in silicon.

stitutional diffusion). Interstitial diffusion is not very common, primarily because most impurity atoms are too large to move in the interstices of the crystal. Where it does occur it leads, as might be imagined, to very rapid diffusion. The important acceptor and donor atoms in silicon (Groups III and V) diffuse substitutionally for the most part. A relatively large amount of energy is required for this process to take place; enough energy must be available to move the host atom (silicon, in this case) out of the lattice site and to move the impurity in. The most common source of this energy is heat. Figure 9.14 shows the diffusion constants for several impurities in silicon. It is apparent that the diffusion constants are quite small even at high temperatures. It is this fact that leads to silicon diffusion processes being carried out at temperatures typically in the range 1000–1200°C. Note that the straight-line plot of ln D vs $1/T$ implies that D depends exponentially on $1/T$. For Groups III and V impurities in silicon, D decreases by a factor of about ten for each 100°C decrease in T.

Qualitatively the solid-state diffusion process is easy to describe. The impurity concentration at a silicon surface is maintained higher than that in the interior (how this is done is described later); consequently there is a movement of impurity atoms away from the surface into the bulk. If devices are to be designed using this process a precise description of impurity distribution is needed. The differential equation describing the diffusive motion of impurity atoms is obtained by substituting (9.3) into the continuity equation (5.31), giving

$$\frac{\partial N}{\partial t} = -\frac{\partial}{\partial x}\left(\mu N \varepsilon - D\frac{\partial N}{\partial x}\right) + G - R \tag{9.4}$$

where N is the impurity concentration. (We assume for simplicity that N is spatially dependent only on x.) Since there is no generation or recombination of impurities, G and R are both zero. We assume there is no electric field in the semiconductor so the drift component vanishes. Equation (9.4) then reduces to

$$\frac{\partial N}{\partial t} = D\frac{\partial^2 N}{\partial x^2} \tag{9.5}$$

This differential equation describes the temporal and spatial behavior of the impurity concentration $N(x, t)$.

The exact form of the solution to (9.5) depends on the boundary conditions or initial conditions describing the particular diffusion process being used. From an infinity of possibilities, fortunately two cases describe satisfactorily most situations met in practice. The first is the infinite source case in which a constant surface concentration of impurities is maintained during diffusion. The second case is a limited source diffusion in which a fixed number of impurities is deposited in a very thin layer at the semiconductor surface and allowed to diffuse into the material. In this case the surface concentration is a decreasing function of time. Only one condition has been given for both the infinite and limited source diffusions and since (9.5) is a second order differential equation a second condition must be specified. It is the same for both, namely that $N(\infty, t) = 0$ (the impurity concentration at $x = \infty$ is zero).

We will not solve (9.5) for either case; in both instances the solution is deceptively difficult. Here we simply state that both diffusion processes lead to similar impurity distributions (for a given surface concentration) and both closely resemble a decreasing exponential function with a characteristic (diffusion) length $2\sqrt{Dt}$. A typical diffusion length is 10^{-4} cm.

Let us now look specifically at the diffusion apparatus. Diffusion systems consist basically of a high temperature furnace, equipment which accurately controls furnace temperature, and a suitable impurity source. These systems are identical (except for the impurity source) to those used to grow thermal oxide layers. An example is sketched in Fig. 9.15 using an impurity source described later in this section.

The furnaces used in solid-state diffusion are resistance heated. Current is caused to flow through coils of a material (most commonly a special alloy of steel) having the proper resistance and metallurgical characteristics to permit achieving high temperature; the material must, of course, be stable at the high temperatures. The heating coils surround the diffusion tube so as to provide uniform heating. Since the device manufacturer wishes to diffuse as many slices as possible in a single run, diffusion furnaces are designed to provide a zone of uniform temperature which is as long as possible. Furnaces presently made can provide lengths of up to 36 in. with a temperature variation of $\pm 0.5°$C.

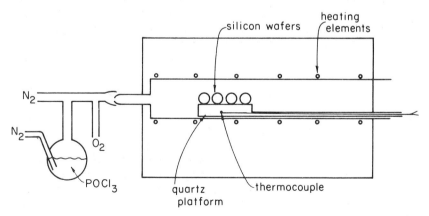

FIG. 9.15   Solid-state diffusion system using phosphorus oxychloride as a source of phosphorus.

Another trend is to use wafers of larger diameter. For many years the 1.25-in. wafer was a standard, limited by the inability to grow larger crystals with adequate resistivity uniformity and crystalline perfection. Recent improvements in crystal growing have resulted in the use of 2- to 3-in. wafers. As a consequence the diffusion furnace manufacturer has had to provide furnaces with the same temperature control in diffusion tubes capable of accommodating the larger wafers.

Temperature uniformity is achieved through sophisticated control circuitry to supply power to the heating coils when needed to maintain temperatures as nearly constant as possible. An outline can be given of the way in which this control is achieved. The furnaces have separate heating coils for each of the two ends and the center of the furnace. Power can be supplied to each element independently. Thermocouples sense the temperature in each of the three zones. (For reasons which will be made clear in a moment there are usually three thermocouples in the center zone and one each in the end zones.) The voltage generated by one of the center thermocouples is compared with a reference voltage which can be externally adjusted and the difference between the two determines whether power is supplied to the center zone. If the temperature there is too low, the voltage difference can be used to turn on an SCR (see Chap. 10 for a description of this device) which allows current to flow into the center coil. Since it is necessary to maintain the temperature throughout the furnace as uniform as possible, this calls for controlling also the temperatures of the end zones. To do so, the voltage from a second of the center zone thermocouples is compared with that in the nearest end zone. The difference between these is initially adjusted to zero. Then whenever the temperature in the center zone rises, a voltage difference appears between these two thermocouples and this turns on an SCR which causes power to be supplied to the end zone. Thus a sufficiently uniform temperature throughout a diffusion furnace can be maintained to produce the precise diffusion profiles needed in today's high performance silicon devices. Figure 9.16 shows a set of four furnaces suitable for diffusion or oxidation built into a single cabinet. The cabinet is open to show the control circuitry and the external connections to the thermocouples in each of the three zones of the furnaces. Also shown are flow meters used to control the gas flows which may be needed in a specific process. Not shown are the quartz tubes (they would fit into the four openings into the furnaces) and the diffusant sources.

Let us next look at the process by which impurity atoms are introduced into the furnace. The diffusant source can be liquid, solid, or gaseous. And within each class are many variations in the way the impurity is supplied. Since it is unreasonable to take a comprehensive view of diffusion sources, we shall look at a widely used representative method involving a liquid source.

Let us consider the use of $POCl_3$, phosphorus oxychloride, as a

FIG. 9.16 Set of four furnaces suitable for diffusion or oxidation. (Courtesy of the Lindberg Co., Chicago)

source of phosphorous impurity. A system using $POCl_3$ is illustrated in Fig. 9.15. A flask of $POCl_3$ is maintained near room temperature, most often using a water bath. Nitrogen gas is bubbled through the liquid entraining some $POCl_3$ which is mixed with O_2 and more N_2 prior to entering the diffusion tube. In the furnace the $POCl_3$ and oxygen react to form P_2O_5, phosphorus pentoxide. The P_2O_5 reacts in turn with the silicon to produce elemental phosphorus and silicon dioxide. The chemical reaction is

$$2P_2O_5 + 5Si \rightarrow 4P + 5SiO_2 \tag{9.6}$$

The combination of phosphorus and silicon dioxide at the silicon surface produces a glasslike phase which is liquid at diffusion temperatures. This material provides a high surface concentration of phosphorus (approximately 10^{21} cm^{-3}, depending on the diffusion temperature) leading to phosphorous diffusion into the silicon.

Phosphorus oxychloride, POCl$_3$, is a particularly useful source. The concentration of phosphorus can be varied widely and controlled closely by the source temperature and nitrogen flow. Because very little POCl$_3$ is used in a given run the source needs to be replenished only infrequently.

If an infinite source diffusion is desired, the silicon is left in the furnace throughout the diffusion time. If a finite source diffusion is wanted, the semiconductor material is left in the furnace containing phosphorus only for a limited time, after which it is transferred to a second source-free furnace for the remainder of the diffusion period.

Other liquid diffusion sources are used in much the same way. Examples are PBr$_3$ and BBr$_3$ as sources of phosphorus and boron, respectively. There are in addition several solid sources. A solid is most often placed in the high temperature zone of the furnace where its vapor pressure is sufficiently high to produce the desired impurity concentration.

The typical junction depths produced by diffusion are in the range 1–5 μm. There are trade-offs among time, temperature, surface concentration N_s, and background concentration N_B in attaining these junction depths. A typical set of conditions for phosphorous diffusion in silicon is $N_s = 5 \times 10^{20}$ cm^{-3}, $N_B = 5 \times 10^{15}$ cm^{-3}, $T = 1200°$C, and $t = 60$ min, giving a junction depth of about 4 μm. Lowering the temperature to 1100°C causes the diffusion constant of phosphorus to decrease by almost a factor of ten and about 600 min is required to achieve the same junction depth. It is apparent why temperatures as high as possible are used.

Several factors limit maximum usable diffusion temperature. First, while silicon melts at 1415°C, it begins to soften at significantly lower temperatures. Silicon wafers may warp appreciably at 1300°C. Second, some diffusants react with silicon at very high temperatures to produce compounds that are difficult to remove and that may interfere with later processing; for example, photoresist adherence may be adversely affected. And finally, higher temperatures cause the heating elements in furnaces to degrade faster. These considerations lead to 1250°C being the maximum temperature used in diffusion processes with silicon.

9.8 FABRICATION OF PHOTOMASKS

Photolithographic processes mainly determine the geometry of silicon devices: bipolar devices, unipolar devices, and integrated circuits. This is evident from the flowchart illustrated in Fig. 9.8. Photolithography is important in the high-frequency performance of devices since it provides fundamental limits on electrode size and spacing and thereby affects the junction and parasitic capacitances and base resistance. Further the density of elements on integrated circuits can be limited by capabilities of photolithography. This is important in both the performance and economics of integrated circuits.

The two most important constituents of the photolithographic process are the photoresist itself and the masks through which the exposures are made. Commercial photoresists are multicomponent mixtures, polymers dissolved in organic solvent solutions with photosensitizers added. (Their exact composition is proprietary information of the manufacturer.) Basically they are photographic emulsions which polymerize when exposed to light. Most resists are particularly sensitive to blue light. Because of their spectral sensitivity, photoresists can be safely handled under safelights. Gold fluorescent tubes are commonly used.

The limitations on the line widths attainable with commercially available photoresists is less a function of the resist than of the associated apparatus and processing. There is a grain size in the resist and the light used to expose it is diffused in the resist, and both influence the minimum line width. But other factors are normally more important: diffraction and edge effects in the photomasks, imperfect adherence of the resist to the substrate (leading to etching under the resist), imperfect collimation of the light source (leading to exposure in the opaque regions of the masks), etc. Resolution of these problems is in part an art (often a large part) and in part science.

Having mentioned some problems encountered we shall discuss only one of them: the photomasks, particularly crucial in the fabrication process. They affect in a critical way both the electrical performance and cost of the devices. Geometrical limitations of the masks place an upper bound on device performance; imperfections in the masks can lead to poor device characteristics and therefore higher costs.

Several different masks are required in the fabrication of a given device. The transistor sketched in Fig. 9.7 requires four masks; more complicated structures or integrated circuits may require up to ten masks. It is most important to recognize that these masks are used in sequence and therefore each mask must register with the previous masks. This must be true not only within a given device but for all the devices on the wafer. It cannot be true only for a particular set of masks—a matched set, so to speak. The masks must be completely interchangeable: for example, any emitter diffusion mask must register with any base diffusion mask. The number of patterns on the masks depends on wafer size and the individual device dimensions. About 12 000 patterns of the sort shown in Fig. 9.7 can be put on a 2-in. wafer; on the other hand, possibly only a few hundred patterns of a complicated integrated circuit could fit on the same wafer. But in all cases there must be registration among all the patterns if the yield of good devices is to be high, and this becomes more and more difficult to achieve as the elements on the chips are made smaller and placed more closely together.

The upshot is that sophisticated optical techniques have been developed to produce photomasks of high integrity. The remainder of this section describes briefly the way in which such masks are made. Basically the process is to produce a large replica of the pattern to be formed on an individual chip; this pattern is then reduced photographically and printed in a precise array on a photographic glass plate.

9.8.1   Original Artwork

The initial artwork is a high contrast image of the final mask element, commonly produced by using a composite mylar film consisting of red mylar about 30 μm thick and a transparent layer about 125 μm thick. The desired pattern is cut into the red film only, which is then peeled away leaving a transparent image of the mask element. The cutting can be done by hand using a special knife but this is not very satisfactory for a variety of reasons. The principal problem is that of error; transcribing the drawing of the pattern to the mylar film without error is difficult. More and more mask manufacturers feed the data describing the pattern into a computer by punched cards and the computer then drives the cutting machine.

The size of the initial artwork depends upon the semiconductor chip size, the dimensions of the smallest element, the allowable tolerance in the pattern, and how large a pattern the reducing camera can handle. Let us look at a numerical example. Suppose the overall reduction from original artwork to final chip pattern is 250X. An error of 25.4 μm (0.001 in.) on the artwork leads to an error of 0.1 μm on the final mask. For devices of the type illustrated in Fig. 9.7, the tolerance on various spacings is about 2.5 μm; thus the 0.1 μm error is insignificant. On the other hand, in very high-frequency devices such an error might not be tolerable in which case a larger reduction, maybe 1000X, would be required.

With a chip size of 0.040 $\times$ 0.040 cm^2 a reduction of 250X implies the original pattern should be 10.3 $\times$ 10.3 cm^2. For an integrated circuit chip 0.4 cm on a side requiring a 1000X reduction the initial pattern would be 400 $\times$ 400 cm^2. An original of this size is difficult to handle both photographically and physically. Typically the originals are about 1 m^2.

The first reduction is normally in the range 10–500X. The camera used for the reduction consists of a lens, film holder, and platform to hold the artwork. Because of the large size of the original pattern and the substantial reductions often required, the lens and pattern are separated by several feet. A reduction of 100X would call for a separation of about 30 ft.

This imposes some serious constraints on the construction of the camera. The lens, film, and pattern must be mounted on a precisely made platform to allow their relative positions to be set accurately. Moreover, because even very small errors in the original can lead to intolerable errors in the final mask, the whole camera structure must be isolated as much as possible from all vibration. All sorts of sophisticated isolation techniques are employed. Some companies have drilled down to bedrock and mounted their cameras on this firm foundation. The temperature and humidity in the camera room must be carefully controlled since variations in either can lead to unpredictable or uncontrolled dimensional changes in the mylar films and the camera structure. Obviously such a system can be very costly; its use points out how important good masks are in the production of silicon discrete devices and integrated circuits.

The artwork is mounted vertically on a ground glass plate which serves to diffuse the illumination of the pattern. Transmitted illumination is used since it permits much greater contrast than frontal illumination. The illuminating light is that for which the photographic emulsion used is most sensitive. The pattern is photographed on a high resolution photographic plate and developed and processed in a conventional way.

9.8.2   Step and Repeat Camera

The next reduction produces the final size of the mask element, either discrete device or integrated circuit. The camera used is essentially a microscope in reverse; the reductions obtained are typically 20–50X. The image of the pattern obtained in the first reduction is projected on a photographic plate where a copy of it is exposed; using a precisely controlled movement the plate is transported to a new position and another exposure is made. This process is repeated until a complete mask, somewhat larger than the wafer to be exposed, is obtained. For obvious reasons this system is referred to as a step and repeat camera.

Because of the small dimensions involved in this final reduction, dust, dirt, or any foreign particles can lead to unusable masks. Thus the final reduction should be carried out in clean rooms as nearly dust free as possible.

9.8.3   Contact Printing

The mask obtained by this final reduction serves as a master; it is not used directly to prepare the masks used in device production. Instead contact printing is used to prepare copies of the master and these copies or submasters are actually used to produce the masks used on the production line. Once again conditions of utmost cleanliness are maintained during preparation of the working masks.

The masks described above are termed emulsion masks because the opaque and transparent areas on them are formed by photographic emulsion. Since the emulsion is soft such masks are easily damaged by scratching and it is virtually impossible to clean them. It is possible to make masks which can be cleaned. Glass slides covered with a thin layer of chromium are in turn covered with a photoresist film. This film is exposed by a submaster and then developed, allowing the underlying chromium to be etched to produce the mask pattern. Masks of this type are durable but more expensive than emulsion masks; they have not been widely adopted. Other more exotic mask materials have also been used. There are masks transparent to visible light but opaque to ultra-violet light. The development of more complicated integrated circuits has kept the mask designers constantly trying to produce improved masks with respect to definition, cleanability, cost, etc.

9.9   DEVICE RELIABILITY

There are several characteristics of semiconductor devices which have led to the phenomenal impact which they have had on the electronics industry; these are electrical characteristics, size, cost, and life. In many ways the electrical characteristics per se are not so significant; there are not really so many things electronic which can be done with semiconductor devices which cannot be achieved with vacuum tubes. Rather the size, cost, and life—coupled with good electrical performance—provide the unique set of properties. There is a relation between size and life which may not be obvious. The small size of semiconductor devices allows miniaturization of circuitry and this is certainly important. The small size of such devices makes feasible the construction of equipment that uses large numbers of devices. The most notable example is the digital computer which uses large numbers of transistors and diodes, whether as discrete devices or integrated circuits. The use of such large numbers of devices only becomes practical when at least two conditions are met: the devices must be small, and their operating life must be long enough so that the equipment does not frequently malfunction. It is of no value to be able to pack a hundred thousand devices into a couple of relay racks if the resulting piece of equipment is constantly inoperative. To utilize fully the capabilities of semiconductor devices they must be long-lived.

The degree to which this condition has been met is astounding. The failure rate of the ordinary commercial silicon devices under normal operating conditions is about 0.01% per year (thus out of 10 000 devices we might expect to have one failure per year). But this is only part of the story. Failure rates as described above, as good as they are,

are not adequate for critical applications such as computers, telephone central offices, space applications, etc. By exercising care in packaging and testing, failure rates of about 0.00001% per year appear to be achievable where the device is operated at junction temperature of 80°C. Thus if one million devices were operated in this way for a year one failure would be expected. It might seem that this is an idle achievement since it is not obvious that any system can really take advantage of this performance. But this is not true. The very low failure rates simplify system design by reducing maintenance and operating costs and the need for redundancy in circuitry.

Let us look at some sources of failures and how to minimize their effect in silicon devices. Electrical characteristics of silicon devices are sensitive to the presence of unwanted impurities in or near the region where the space charge fields intersect the silicon surface. Such contaminants can lead to bad initial characteristics (especially reverse currents, voltage breakdowns, and current gain) and degradation of these characteristics over time. A major reason for the strict cleanliness in device manufacture is to minimize these contaminants which result from improper handling of devices during fabrication, impure chemicals or gases, impurities in the ambient in which the devices are made, and impurities emitted during operation by the structure in which the device is enclosed.

It is most important not only to reduce to a minimum the contaminants introduced during fabrication but also the device must be protected from its environment after completion. More research has gone into achieving this goal, probably, than any other aspect of silicon device design. In the beginning silicon dioxide was recognized as serving as a quite effective barrier to the diffusion of contaminants from the ambient to the silicon surface. Although the reason was not understood for several years, a layer of phosphorus on the oxide surface was found to improve the protective properties of silicon dioxide. While the diffusion constant of most impurities in silicon dioxide is very low, there are some exceptions, notably the alkali metals of which sodium is the most important. Sodium is amazingly prevalent. It exists in chemicals, body oils, sweat, combustion products, etc. Sodium exists as a mobile positive ion in SiO_2 and can therefore induce negative charges in the silicon surface, thus altering surface properties of the material and thereby the electrical properties of the devices.

While every effort was made to eliminate sodium, parallel studies were made to find a protective layer with the insulating properties of SiO_2 but in which the diffusion of Na was slow. The most successful of these is dielectric silicon nitride (Si_3N_4). No attempt will be made to describe the method of putting down the Si_3N_4 layer. It will simply be stated that after the emitter diffusion a $0.5\,\mu m$ layer of Si_3N_4 is deposited over the silicon dioxide. The remainder of the fabrication then continues as shown in Fig. 9.8. Undoubtedly the largest single factor leading to the long life of silicon devices is the presence of a protective layer of this type. Silicon dioxide (together with the phosphorus layer) functioned well, but silicon nitride is even more effective.

Other factors can also cause device failures. And with Si_3N_4 protecting the surface so admirably these other things become much more important. A principal failure source is a break in the wire bond to the emitter or base regions or to the leads of the enclosure. These faults are due in part to improper bonding. They can also result from a metallurgical reaction between the Au wire and the Al contact area leading to embrittlement and breakage. Either the Au or Al (or both) might be replaced by other materials, but it is difficult to find an adequate substitute. And the Au-Al system does have the practical advantages of being simple, readily implemented, and inexpensive. It is still widely used. Efforts to develop other contacting processes have continued and several alternative schemes have been devised. The longest-lived discrete silicon devices made today have a rather complicated multicomponent contact material with a top layer of gold; thus the finished device has gold-to-gold bonding eliminating the embrittlement problem.

It is interesting to consider the reliability of integrated circuits. Because there can be many devices on an integrated circuit chip one might expect its failure rate to be exceedingly high. Fortunately, this is not correct. The life of integrated circuits is just about equal to that of discrete devices of comparable size.

SUMMARY

- The technology associated with the fabrication of diffused silicon devices is of particular importance since the great majority of semiconductor devices used today—discrete or integrated, diodes, field effect transistors, and bipolar transistors—fall into this category. It is this technology, to a large extent, which has made possible the inexpensive, high performance, long-lived devices which have had such an impact on the technological world.

- 1. Photolithography is used to form the horizontal geometry, thus permitting precisely dimensioned structures to be obtained.

- 2. Silicon dioxide grown on the silicon surface provides a diffusion mask, allowing precise location of where dopant is added. Silicon dioxide is also used as an insulator allowing contacts to overlay the active device areas, thus permitting very small devices to be formed. Finally silicon dioxide is effective in isolating the sensitive device surface from contaminants in the ambient.

- 3. Solid-state diffusion is used to add dopants, thereby providing much greater control over impurity concentrations than earlier doping methods.

● 4. Batch processing is used through much of the process, permitting large numbers of potential devices to be handled simultaneously leading to low cost devices with uniform characteristics.

● 5. The use of protective layers over the device surfaces leads to very long-lived devices. Silicon dioxide originally used to provide this capability has been superseded by silicon nitride which gives superior performance.

● Note one other special feature. The processes involved in making silicon devices encompass many different disciplines. Essential parts involve physics, chemistry, and metallurgy as well as, implicitly, electrical engineering. The semiconductor device designer has to have more than a passing knowledge of each of these subjects to do the job well. And with the development of integrated circuits, the design of the electronic circuit can no longer be separated from that of the device. It is a challenging field.

CHAPTER 10

Other Semiconductor Devices

10.1 INTRODUCTION

In earlier chapters we discuss in detail the conduction processes in semiconductor materials and in two of the most important semiconductor devices—the junction diode and the junction transistor. We also discuss the fabrication of these devices.

Now consider the physical operation and electrical characteristics of a number of other important semiconductor devices that can be made by these and related processes. We often draw heavily on our studies of the junction diode and the bipolar junction transistor (BJT) because the operation of most devices we discuss here involves the same physical principles and phenomena.

10.2 JUNCTION FIELD EFFECT TRANSISTOR (JFET)

The field effect transistor (FET) is a semiconductor device in which current flow is controlled by electrically varying the resistance of the "channel" through which it flows. The JFET uses the fact that the depletion layer (space charge layer) width of a *pn* junction varies with voltage. By designing the device so that increases in SCL width occur at the expense of the effective cross section of the current-carrying resistor, the desired variation in resistance can be obtained. Figure 10.1 shows perspective and cross-sectional views of a particular JFET configuration termed an n-channel device for reasons which will become clear. (Because of structural symmetry only half the device is shown in the cross-sectional view.)

Structurally the n-channel JFET is formed on a layer of heavily doped p-type material known as the substrate. A lightly doped n-type layer is formed on the substrate using epitaxial or diffusion processes.

311

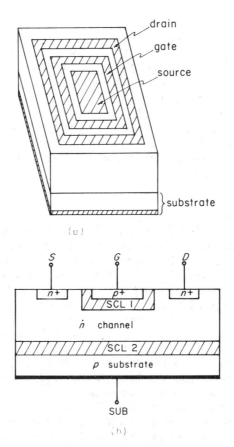

FIG. 10.1   (a) Perspective and (b) cross-sectional views of general structure of junction field effect transistor.

The current in the device will flow in this n-layer. A region of p-type material is then produced in the n-layer using oxide masking (assuming a silicon device), photolithography, and solid-state diffusion. Metallic contacts are applied as shown in Fig. 10.1: (1) a large area contact to the substrate; (2) a contact to the p-region, known as the gate G; and (3) two contacts to the n-layer, one designated as the source S and the other as the drain D. Majority carriers normally enter the n-material by the source, flow through the n-type channel, and leave via the drain. By controlling the dimensions of the channel the gate determines the numbers of carriers available to carry current in the channel.

The electrical characteristic of prime interest is the drain current I_D as a function of drain-to-source voltage V_{DS} with the gate-to-source voltage V_{GS} as a control parameter. These two quantities are related by the drain-source resistance R_{DS}, consisting mainly of the resistance of the long thin channel shown in Fig. 10.1b. This resistance is proportional to the channel length and resistivity and inversely proportional to the area perpendicular to the current flow. This area is proportional to the thickness of the channel, i.e., the distance from the upper edge of SCL 1 to the lower edge of SCL 2. As the junction voltage across various portions of the SCLs is varied, the SCL widths vary so that the channel thickness changes and the resistance of the channel varies. Let us examine these variations by beginning with the simplest case, diode operation of the FET.

Diode Operation

To operate the JFET as a diode (i.e., as a two-terminal device) we tie the gate and substrate to the source as shown in Fig. 10.2. Consider how I_D varies with V_{DS}. When the voltage V_{DS} is small enough, the SCL boundaries are essentially in their thermal equilibrium locations and the width of the channel is independent of V_{DS}. Under those circumstances $I_D = V_{DS}G_{DS}(0)$, where $G_{DS}(0)$ is the drain-source conductance (reciprocal of the resistance) computed from geometrical considerations when $V_{DS} = 0$. Thus for small V_{DS}, say $|V_{DS}| \leq 0.1$ V, the I_D-V_{DS} graph is a straight line through the origin. For larger V_{DS} there is a significant potential variation along the channel and the SCL boundaries are displaced from their original positions. Suppose $V_{DS} = +1$ V. Designating the source terminal as the reference point, i.e., as the point of zero potential, the SCL boundaries and the potentials at various locations in a JFET might be as shown in Fig. 10.2. The source, gate, and substrate are at zero potential whereas the drain has a potential of $+1$ V. The potential along the channel thus varies from zero to $+1$ V. As a re-

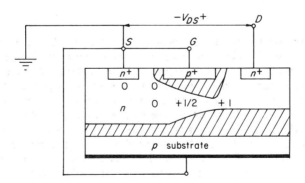

FIG. 10.2   Diode connection of JFET. The SCL boundaries and potentials are shown for $V_{DS} = +1$ V.

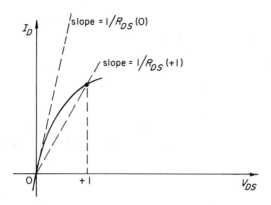

FIG. 10.3   Portion of the *I-V* characteristic of JFET operated as a diode.

sult there is zero bias across those portions of the *pn* junctions near the source, 1 V of reverse bias across those portions near the drain, and intermediate amounts of reverse bias across the intermediate portions. Thus near the drain the SCLs are appreciably wider than in thermal equilibrium and the channel is correspondingly thinner there. As a result the drain-source conductance is decreased, i.e., $G_{DS}(+1) < G_{DS}(0)$, and the drain current $I_D < (+1)G_{DS}(0)$. Hence the characteristic must now fall below an extrapolation of the initial linear variation (see Fig. 10.3). As V_{DS} is increased further the channel is squeezed thinner yet until the two SCLs reach one another at some point and the channel is said to be "pinched off." The required value of V_{DS} is designated as the "pinchoff voltage" V_P. What happens to the current when pinchoff occurs? Our first guess might be that the current becomes zero. This cannot be true; if the current were zero there would be no voltage drop along the channel and therefore no pinchoff. At the point of contact there is a large electric field due to V_{DS}, and the conductivity is not actually zero. An exact analysis of the pinchoff region is quite complex. In a qualitative way the following situation applies. The pinched-off portion of the channel is a relatively thin region, largely depleted of mobile carriers and with a large electric field that sweeps the electrons (in the n-channel device we are considering) toward the drain. The current then is held nearly constant at the value it had when pinchoff occurred. If V_{DS} is increased further, the width of the pinchoff region widens slightly to support the increased voltage. The gate-to-channel voltage at the left edge of the region is still V_p. Because the nonpinched-off portion of the channel has been shortened slightly, there is a small increase in I_D. This dependence of I_D on V_{DS} beyond pinchoff accounts for the output impedance of the JFET. The matters described here are summarized in Fig. 10.4. From this figure and the above discussion we

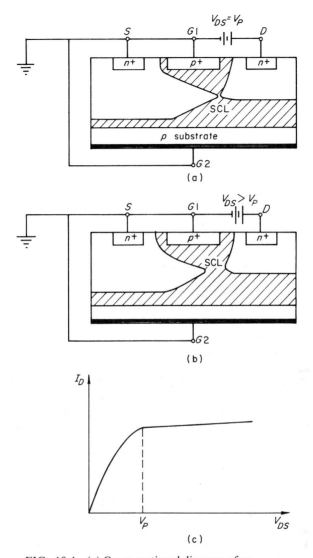

FIG. 10.4   (a) Cross-sectional diagram of an
n-channel JFET for V_{DS} equal to the pinchoff voltage
V_p. (b) Cross-sectional diagram for $V_{DS} > V_p$. The
potential difference between the gate and the channel
at the left edge of the pinchoff region is V_p. Thus the
channel is shorter than for the case where $V_{DS} = V_p$.
(c) Current-voltage characteristic for a diode connected JFET. Beyond pinchoff I_D increases slightly due
to the shortening of the channel as illustrated in (b).

see that the field effect diode, i.e., the FET connected as a diode, acts approximately as a resistor for $V_{DS} < V_p$ and as a constant current device if $V_{DS} \geq V_p$.

Triode Operation

To operate the FET as a triode we again tie the substrate to the source but leave the gate free as an independent terminal. This gives four variables of interest: I_D, V_{DS}, I_G (the current flowing into the gate terminal), and V_{GS}. The characteristic of prime interest is again I_D vs V_{DS}. However we now have the possibility of a family of I_D-V_{DS} curves, one curve for each value of V_{GS} or I_G we wish to consider.

Suppose $V_{GS} = 0$, for example, the case just discussed in diode operation. To obtain $V_{GS} = 0$ we connect a short circuit from gate to source. Thus the diode characteristic of Fig. 10.4c is also the triode I_D-V_{DS} curve for $V_{GS} = 0$.

Next consider positive V_{GS}. Two things happen in this case: (1) the SCL of the gate pn junction narrows to slightly widen the channel everywhere, and (2) substantial gate current flows because the pn junction is forward biased. This gate current simply flows from gate to source. There is no current gain mechanism; the existence of I_G does not significantly change I_D. Any significant change in the I_D-V_{DS} characteristic is a minor change due solely to changes in channel thickness. The conclusion then is that positive V_{GS} is not particularly useful. We are required to supply gate current (and hence power) and get little in return. Thus JFETs are seldom operated with positive V_{GS} and we shall not consider it further.

For negative V_{GS} we find a much more attractive situation. The gate current is microscopic (assuming we avoid voltage breakdown), and, whereas the practical range of positive voltage is limited by the forward conduction of a pn junction, the practical negative range is from zero to the avalanche voltage. This means that significant shifting of the SCL boundary is possible and hence the I_D-V_{DS} characteristic is subject to substantial control by V_{GS}.

To see this more specifically let us again develop I_D vs V_{DS}, this time for V_{GS} equal to a constant negative value. At $V_{DS} = 0$ there exists a uniform reverse bias across the gate pn junction and zero bias on the substrate pn junction. Hence the substrate SCL is in its thermal equilibrium condition but the gate SCL is wider everywhere. This means the channel is thinner everywhere, thereby decreasing the drain-source conductance at $V_{DS} = 0$. The initial slope of the I_D-V_{DS} characteristic is thus less than for the $V_{GS} = 0$ case and the entire curve lies below the one for that case. In addition pinchoff occurs sooner. In effect the negative voltage on the gate gives us a head start in attaining pinchoff, which occurs when the reverse bias near the drain equals V_p. Thus the pinchoff

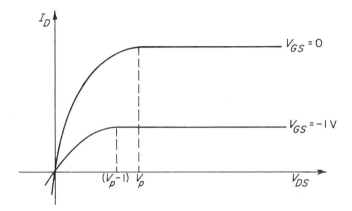

FIG. 10.5   Drain characteristics for a JFET operated as a triode.

condition is

$$V_p \simeq V_{DS} - V_{GS} \equiv V_{DG} \tag{10.1}$$

For $V_{GS} = -1$ V, for example, see Fig. 10.5.

If V_{GS} is more negative yet, the pinchoff current is further reduced. Finally, for $V_{GS} \leq -V_P$ the channel is pinched off along its entire length when $V_{DS} = 0$. Thus the channel resistance is considered infinite for practical purposes and $I_D = 0$ for all V_{DS}.

A detailed physical analysis of the JFET is rather complicated. Here we simply present an approximate derivation based on that of Middlebrook.[1] Although the derivation is not at all rigorous it yields results that agree quite well with experiment.

Assume the channel is not pinched off. Within the channel there is a total mobile charge with magnitude Q. If T is the carrier transit time, i.e., the amount of time required for a carrier to traverse the channel length L, then the drain current I_D is simply the charge Q divided by the transit time T, i.e.,

$$I_D = Q/T \tag{10.2}$$

The transit time T is approximated as follows. The average electric field in the channel is $\mathcal{E}_{av} = V_{DS}/L$. This field times mobility μ gives the average carrier velocity $v_{av} = \mu V_{DS}/L$; this is a space average. The time average of the carrier velocity is simply $\bar{v} = L/T$. Making the assumption these two averages are approximately equal yields transit time

1. Middlebrook, Field-Effect Transistor Characteristics, pp. 1146–47.

$T = L^2/\mu V_{DS}$. Combining this with (10.2) gives

$$I_D = (\mu V_{DS}/L^2)Q \tag{10.3}$$

Next consider how the charge Q depends on the impurity distribution within the channel and the length and average cross-sectional area of the channel. The average cross-sectional area varies with V_{GS} and V_{DS}. If the potential difference between gate and channel is made equal to $-V_p$ the average cross-sectional area and Q both become zero. For less negative values of this gate-channel potential difference the channel cross section and Q are greater than zero.

We now postulate that Q depends linearly on the difference between V_{GC} (the average potential difference between the gate and channel) and the pinchoff voltage,

$$Q = C[V_{GC} - (-V_p)]$$

where C is a constant having the units of capacitance. Taking the source as a reference point, the gate potential is V_{GS}. The channel potential varies from zero at the source end to V_{DS} at the drain end; we shall estimate the average value as $V_{DS}/2$. Thus

$$V_{GC} = V_{GS} - (V_{DS}/2) \tag{10.4}$$

$$Q = C[V_{GS} + V_p - (V_{DS}/2)] \tag{10.5}$$

If (10.5) is now combined with (10.3) the drain current is given by

$$\begin{aligned} I_D &= (\mu V_{DS}/L^2)C[V_{GS} + V_p - (V_{DS}/2)] \\ &= (\mu C/2L^2)[2(V_{GS} + V_p)V_{DS} - V_{DS}^2] \end{aligned} \tag{10.6}$$

This expression holds up to the onset of pinchoff. To detect the onset of pinchoff we may look at the slope of I_D vs V_{DS}, i.e., at

$$\frac{\partial I_D}{\partial V_{DS}} = (\mu C/2L^2)[2(V_{GS} + V_p) - 2V_{DS}] \tag{10.7}$$

We see that $\partial I_D/\partial V_{DS} \to 0$ as $V_{DS} \to V_{GS} + V_p$. This is consistent with the original definition of V_p in Fig. 10.5, namely, that for $V_{GS} = 0$, pinchoff occurs when $V_{DS} = V_p$. Since as V_{DS} approaches $V_{GS} + V_p$ the slope approaches zero, the current must approach a constant. This constant current may be found from (10.6) by letting $V_{DS} = V_{GS} + V_p$, thereby obtaining

$$I_D = (\mu C/2L^2)[2(V_{GS} + V_p)^2 - (V_{GS} + V_p)^2] = K(V_{GS} + V_p)^2 \tag{10.8}$$

where $K \equiv \mu C/2L^2$.

Two operating conditions, *cutoff* and *breakdown*, are not covered by (10.6) and (10.8). If V_{GS} is more negative than $-V_p$ then cutoff is said to occur because $I_D = 0$. If the reverse voltage across the gate-channel junction becomes too large avalanche breakdown occurs and large drain and gate currents can flow. Assuming V_{DS} is positive the greatest amount of gate-channel reverse bias occurs at the drain end of the channel. Thus the drain-gate voltage V_{DG} directly determines whether breakdown occurs. Denoting the junction avalanche voltage as V_A the current-voltage equations for the JFET become:

cutoff region $\qquad I_D = 0 \qquad V_{GS} \leq -V_p \qquad 0 \leq V_{DG} < V_A$ $\qquad$ (10.9)

nonpinchoff region $\qquad I_D = K[2(V_{GS} + V_p)V_{DS} - V_{DS}^2]$ $\qquad$ (10.10)

$$-V_p \leq V_{GS} \leq 0 \qquad 0 \leq V_{DG} < V_p < V_A$$

pinchoff region $\qquad I_D = K(V_{GS} + V_p)^2$ $\qquad$ (10.11)

$$V_p \leq V_{DG} < V_A \qquad -V_p \leq V_{GS} \leq 0$$

Note that the distinction between nonpinchoff and pinchoff is stated in terms of $V_{DG} \lessgtr V_p$. Since $V_{DG} = V_{DS} - V_{GS}$, the condition $V_{DS} < V_{GS} + V_p$ is identical with $V_{DG} < V_p$, etc.

The constant K is often not listed on a manufacturer's device specification sheet. Instead it is implicitly given via a current parameter I_{DSS}, the current that flows from drain to source when the gate is shorted to the source, i.e., when $V_{GS} = 0$. (It is understood that the operation is in the pinchoff region.) To obtain the relationship between K and I_{DSS}, let $V_{GS} = 0$ in (10.11) and thereby obtain

$$I_D \bigg|_{V_{GS} = 0, V_{DS} \geq V_p} = K V_p^2 \equiv I_{DSS} \qquad (10.12)$$

Given this expression, K may be calculated from the manufacturer's specifications of I_{DSS} and V_p. Moreover, (10.11) may be rewritten in terms of I_{DSS}. If the right side of that equation is multiplied and divided by V_p^2 and (10.12) is used, then (10.11) becomes

$$I_D = I_{DSS}(V_{GS}/V_p + 1)^2 \qquad (10.13)$$

The device discussed above is an n-channel JFET. Interchanging the types of impurities used in the three regions, we would have a p-channel JFET with current carried by holes rather than electrons but with the same physical principles applying. The difference lies only in the polarities of the charges, currents, and voltages—all are reversed. Thus in the p-channel JFET the normal values of V_{GS} are positive whereas V_{DS} and I_D are negative, as are parameters V_p, K, and I_{DSS}.

The circuit symbols for the JFET are shown in Fig. 10.6. Notice that the gate arrow direction corresponds to the forward current direction for the gate-source pn junction.

10.3 METAL-OXIDE-SEMICONDUCTOR FET (MOSFET)

A second category of field effect transistor is the metal-oxide-semiconductor FET of which there are two types, depletion and enhancement. In the depletion type the SCL of a pn junction is replaced

FIG. 10.6   Circuit symbols for JFETs.

by the SCL associated with a capacitance made up of a metal film, an oxide dielectric, and a semiconductor (see Fig. 10.7a). Application of an external voltage from gate to source varies the thickness of this SCL and thereby the thickness of the channel. The I_D-V_{DS} characteristics are similar to those in Fig. 10.5 with one significant difference. Because of the insulator no gate current flows in the MOS device, which means that positive values of V_{GS} can be usefully employed. Equations (10.9)– (10.13) again apply, except that V_{GS} can be positive and V_{DG} can be negative.

The MOSFET described above is a depletion FET because the depletion of charge by the advancing SCL controls the properties of the channel. By contrast, the channel of an enhancement MOSFET is an enhanced region with carrier concentration increased above the thermal equilibrium value. The structure of this device is shown in Fig. 10.7b. In this figure we find no visible n-type channel from drain to source, but in spite of what we see this is an n-channel device! Applying $V_{GS} > 0$ causes a positive charge to appear on the gate electrode that induces an equal and opposite negative charge at the semiconductor surface. For small values of V_{GS} the surface layer is depleted of holes (the ma-

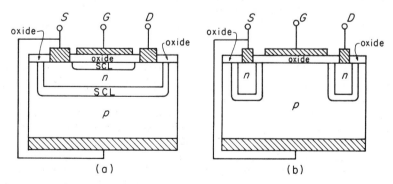

FIG. 10.7   Cross-sectional views of (a) depletion MOSFET and (b) enhancement MOSFET.

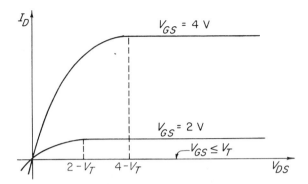

FIG. 10.8   Drain characteristics of enhancement
MOSFET.

jority carrier in the p-type material), and the negative charge is due to
the ionized acceptors in this depletion layer. When V_{GS} becomes large
enough, however, the large electric field in the depletion region induces
a concentration of electrons at the surface sufficient to produce a thin
n-type layer. This region is referred to as an inversion layer since it has
a conductivity type opposite to that of the substrate. The voltage at
which the carrier concentration in the inversion layer is equal to that in
the substrate is called the threshold voltage V_T. As V_{GS} increases above
V_T the conductivity of the inversion layer increases.

It is apparent that the inversion layer provides a conducting path
between the source and drain regions. The amount of drain current that
flows for a given V_{DS} increases as V_{GS} increases above V_T. The concept
of pinchoff still applies in the sense that when a drain current flows in
an inversion layer the channel thins out near the drain, and when V_{DS}
becomes large enough there is insufficient voltage to produce inversion
and a pinchoff condition results. This occurs when $V_{GS} - V_{DS} < V_T$.
Figure 10.8 gives the drain characteristics of a typical enhancement
MOSFET.

The equations for the enhancement MOSFET are the same as
(10.9) and (10.11), but with V_p replaced by $-V_T$. However, (10.12)
and (10.13) do not apply since I_{DSS} is zero; hence I_{DSS} is not useful in
characterizing the enhancement MOSFET.

Field effect devices can be fabricated in smaller areas than can
comparable bipolar transistors. For this reason and because $I_D = 0$ for
$V_{GS} = 0$ the enhancement type MOSFET is widely used in digital integrated circuits where large numbers of devices per chip are often desirable, such as in memory circuits in digital computers. The MOS devices illustrated in Fig. 10.7 are n-channel. The corresponding
p-channel devices are formed by interchanging p- and n-type materials.

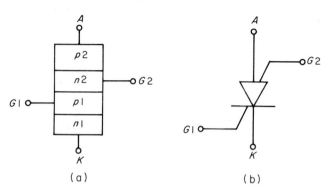

FIG. 10.9 (a) Schematic representation of a four-terminal *pnpn* device and (b) its circuit symbol.

10.4 *pnpn* DEVICES

The *pnpn*s are a class of switching devices used extensively in power control applications. The designation *pnpn* refers to the four layers of semiconductor material that make up the devices, as shown in Fig. 10.9. For generality the figure shows a four-terminal device, the silicon controlled switch (SCS). Most commonly only three terminals are externally available—A, K, and $G1$ in the case of the silicon controlled rectifier (SCR) or A, K, and $G2$ in the case of the complementary SCR.[2]

The physical operation of these devices is closely related to that of the bipolar junction transistor. With the potential of terminal A positive with respect to terminal K, region $p2$ in Fig. 10.9 emits holes into $n2$ where some recombine and the others are collected by the reverse bias of the space charge layer between $n2$ and $p1$. Similarly, region $n1$ injects electrons into $p1$ where some recombine and the others are collected in $n2$. The physical details of these emitting, recombining, and collecting events are discussed by Muss and Goldberg.[3] For our purposes the operation of *pnpn* devices can be obtained more easily by use of the now classic two-transistor analog.[4,5,6]

In this analog we note that regions $p2$, $n2$, and $p1$ in Fig. 10.9 can be considered to make up a *pnp* transistor with $p2$ as the emitter, while regions $n2$, $p1$, and $n1$ make up an *npn* transistor with $n1$ as the emitter. Since $n2$ and $p1$ simultaneously perform two functions each, we have the *pnp* collector tied to the *npn* base, and vice versa. For illustrative

2. Grafham and Hey, *SCR Manual*, p. 1.
3. D. Muss, and C. Goldberg, Switching Mechanisms in the *n-p-n-p* Silicon Controlled Rectifier, *IEEE Trans. Electron Devices*, Vol. ED-10, 1973.
4. Grafham and Hey, *SCR Manual*, pp. 1–4.
5. Murray, *SCR Designers' Handbook*, pp. 1.3–1.11.
6. RCA, *Solid-State Power Circuits*, pp. 195–97.

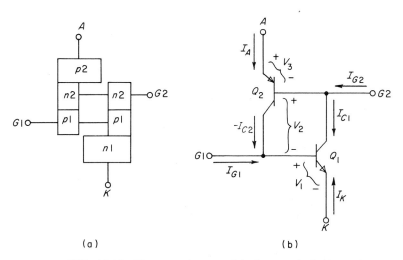

FIG. 10.10   Two-transistor model of a *pnpn* device in
(a) pictorial form and (b) circuit form.

purposes we bisect $n2$ and $p1$ as shown in Fig. 10.10a and this leads to
the two-transistor circuit model in (b).

Suppose a positive voltage is applied between terminals A and K in
Fig. 10.10b, i.e., V_{AK} is positive, and suppose for initial discussion that
terminals $G1$ and $G2$ are left open circuited so that I_{G1} and I_{G2} are zero.
With $V_{AK} > 0$, then initially $V_3 > 0$, $V_2 > 0$, and $V_1 > 0$. The collector-
base junctions of Q_1 and Q_2 are thus reverse biased so that I_A equals at
least the sum of I_{C01} and I_{C02}. We say "at least" for the following reason. The current coming out of the collector of Q_2 flows into the base of
Q_1. This base current times β_F of Q_1 adds to the collector current of
Q_1. This in turn gives Q_2 a negative base current. This base current
times β_F of Q_2 further increases the current coming out of the collector
of Q_2 that flows into the base of Q_1, etc.! Thus it is possible to find substantial collector and emitter currents flowing in Q_1 and Q_2.

To characterize this situation quantitatively we use the DC equations (8.3) and (8.59) for Q_1 and Q_2. These equations include the avalanche multiplication factor M and are understood to contain alphas
that are small when $|I_C|$ is small and approach unity when $|I_C|$ is large.
Writing those equations in terms of the variables in Fig. 10.9b we obtain

$$I_{C2} = -M\alpha_2 I_A + MI_{C02}[\exp(-qV_2/kT) - 1] \qquad (10.14)$$
$$I_{C1} = -M\alpha_1 I_K - MI_{C01}[\exp(-qV_2/kT) - 1] \qquad (10.15)$$

From the circuit connections in Fig. 10.10b we have the following two
Kirchhoff current equations.

$$I_A + I_{G2} = I_{C1} - I_{C2} \qquad\qquad (10.16)$$

$$I_A + I_{G1} + I_{G2} + I_K = 0 \qquad\qquad (10.17)$$

Using (10.14–10.17), we can solve for the anode current I_A in terms of the center junction voltage V_2 and the gate currents I_{G1} and I_{G2}. Thus after a certain amount of algebraic manipulation we obtain

$$I_A = \frac{M\alpha_1 I_{G1} - (1 - M\alpha_1)I_{G2} + MI_S[1 - \exp(-qV_2/kT)]}{1 - (\alpha_1 + \alpha_2)M} \qquad (10.18)$$

where $I_S = I_{C01} + I_{C02}$. This equation characterizes the general four-terminal device. Consider now its application to the two-terminal device (the Shockley diode) for which $I_{G1} = I_{G2} = 0$. Equation (10.18) then simplifies to

$$I_A = MI_S[1 - \exp(-qV_2/kT)]/[1 - (\alpha_1 + \alpha_2)M] \qquad (10.19)$$

If V_{AK} is initially zero and gradually raised to positive values the following is observed. At $V_{AK} = 0$, obviously $I_A = 0$; there is no energy source to cause a current. As V_{AK} is made slightly positive the junction voltages V_1, V_2, and V_3 become positive so that the transistor emitters are slightly forward biased and the collectors are reverse biased. In general, because the collectors are reverse biased, V_2 will constitute much more than one-third of V_{AK}. Suppose $V_{AK} = 1$ V and $V_2 > 0.8$ V while $V_1 = V_3 <$ 0.1 V. What value of I_A is predicted by (10.19)? At $V_3 > 0.8$ V the exponential is negligible and the factor M is unity. What about the alphas? Recall that in Sec. 8.9 the dependence of alpha upon base-emitter voltage is discussed. With base-emitter voltages of less than 0.1 V, the alphas are not close to unity; in fact their sum is much less than unity. Thus (10.19) predicts simply $I_A = I_S$.

If V_{AK} is now increased from 1 to 2 V, V_2 increases by 1 V while V_1 and V_3 remain at their previous values and I_A remains at I_S. The voltages V_1 and V_3 do not change because I_A does not change, and vice versa. Now let V_{AK} be raised to the point where V_2 is near the avalanche breakdown voltage of the center junction. In that case M increases from unity, thus initiating an increase in I_A. This increased I_A flows through the emitter junctions of Q_1 and Q_2 and causes V_1 and V_3 to increase. These emitter-base voltage increases in turn increase the transistor alphas, and this is the key to the device operation. The alpha increase causes $1 - (\alpha_1 + \alpha_2)M \to 0$. Equation (10.19) demands that V_2 be reduced so the numerator also approaches zero, predicting an indeterminant rather than an impossible situation ($I_A \to \infty$). At the exact point where the denominator of (10.19) vanishes, then, the voltage V_2 is exactly zero. The voltage V_{AK} at that point will equal $V_1 + V_3$ or approximately 1.4 V since the transistors now have base-emitter voltages of about 0.7 V to carry the current I_A. (We are assuming silicon devices carrying currents in the range 10–100 mA.)

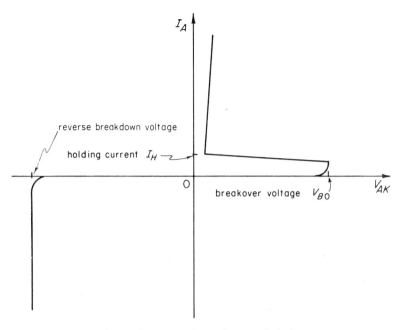

FIG. 10.11   Current-voltage characteristic for a *pnpn* diode, i.e., the Shockley diode.

What happens if the voltage V_T of the external generator is increased so that I_A rises further? In that case $\alpha_1 + \alpha_2$ exceeds unity, the denominator in (10.19) is negative, and V_2 is positive so that the numerator of (10.19) is negative. What does V_2 positive mean? It means that the center junction of the device, i.e., the collector-base junctions of the analog transistors, is forward biased. Hence the analog transistors are saturated. It also means that $V_{AK} < V_1 + V_3$. If at this current level V_1 and V_3 are, say, 0.8 V and V_2 is 0.6 V, then the net terminal voltage V_{AK} will be only $0.8 - 0.6 + 0.8 = 1.0$ V.

The overall current-voltage characteristic of this two-terminal *pnpn* device is shown in Fig. 10.11. As described previously, a current of the order of I_S (negligible on the scale in Fig. 10.11) flows until V_{AK} is such that avalanche multiplication becomes important. This is near the *breakover voltage* V_{BO}, the point where $\partial I_A / \partial V_{AK}$ becomes infinite. Then as I_A is increased beyond the breakover point, V_{AK} rapidly falls to a value of approximately 1 V. The current at this point is called the *holding current* I_H because the external circuit must supply at least this much current to hold the device in the low voltage–high current state. The reverse characteristic is also shown. For negative V_{AK} the current is negligible until V_{AK} reaches the reverse breakdown voltage, the voltage at which both emitter-base junctions are in avalanche breakdown.

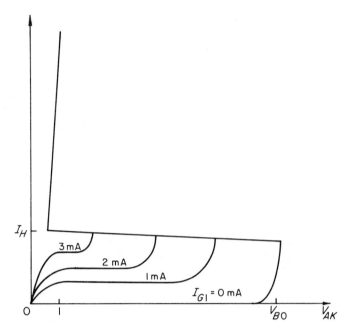

FIG. 10.12   Current-voltage characteristics of an
SCR, i.e., *pnpn* triode with p-type gate.

Consider next the silicon controlled rectifier (SCR), in which current supplied via gate terminal $G1$ is used to increase I_A to the point where $\alpha_1 + \alpha_2 \longrightarrow 1$. Assuming typical values for the current gains of Q_1 and Q_2, a fraction of a milliampere of I_{G1} raises the current level in transistor Q_1 to the point where α_1 is not small. According to (10.18), then, I_A is at least a few milliamperes which in turn means that α_2 is also no longer small. Then only a little avalanche multiplication is required for I_A to reach the point where regeneration occurs and the sum of the alphas exceeds unity. Hence breakover, or "firing" as it is commonly called, occurs at a value of V_{AK} less than the breakover voltage of the Shockley diode. Each value of I_{G1} has a corresponding value of firing voltage, i.e., a value of V_{AK} at which regeneration occurs. Clearly if I_{G1} is larger, then a smaller V_{AK} is required for firing to occur. The *I-V* graph analogous to Fig. 10.11 thus becomes a family of curves (see Fig. 10.12; the third quadrant is identical with that in Fig. 10.11 and hence is not shown).

This completes our introductory examination of the physical principles and characteristics of *pnpn* devices. Further information may be found in the references cited at the end of the chapter.

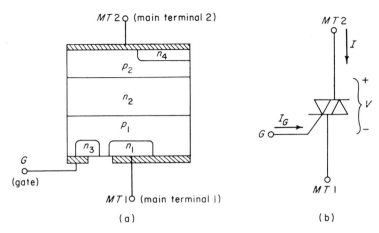

FIG. 10.13 (a) Schematic representation of a triac and (b) its circuit symbol. ([a] Grafham and Hey, *SCR Manual*, p. 182)

10.5 TRIAC: A MODIFIED *pnpn* DEVICE

The triac is a *pnpn*-type device that conducts bidirectionally and is triggerable by both negative and positive gate signals. The physical structure is represented schematically in Fig. 10.13a.[7] The main terminal (MT) characteristics of the device are shown in Fig. 10.14. This figure portrays the bidirectional characteristics noted earlier; the device operates in the first and third quadrants.

Consider the triggering of this device. As stated earlier the device

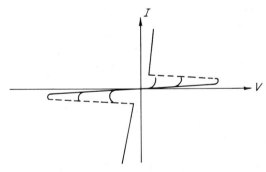

FIG. 10.14 Main terminal characteristics of the triac.

7. Grafham and Hey, *SCR Manual*, p. 182.

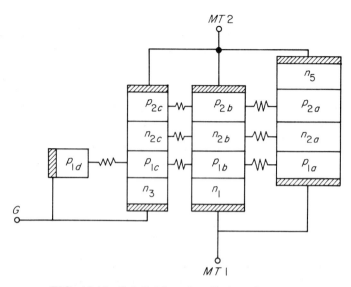

FIG. 10.15   Subdivision of a triac into three *pnpn* devices.

can be triggered by a gate signal of either polarity. Because of this versatility there are four possible operating modes:

1+: first quadrant with I_G positive
1−: first quadrant with I_G negative
3−: third quadrant with I_G negative
3+: third quadrant with I_G positive

The discussion of these modes is facilitated by subdividing the device into several interconnected *pnpn* devices, much as the *pnpn* was subdivided into a pair of transistors. With the aid of Fig. 10.15 the triggering and conduction processes are discussed for each mode.

Mode 1+

In this mode $MT2$ and the gate are driven positive with respect to $MT1$. This places the opposite ends of p_1 at different potentials. More specifically, using the notation in Fig. 10.15, the potentials measured relative to $MT1$ in the four sections of p_1 are

$$V(p_{1d}) > V(p_{1c}) > V(p_{1b}) > V(p_{1a}) \qquad (10.20)$$

Thus the p_{1b}-n_1 junction experiences a forward bias. As a result the SCR made up of $p_{2b} n_{2b} p_{1b} n_1$ turns on in conventional fashion and conducts current from $MT2$ to $MT1$.

Mode 1 −

In this mode $MT2$ is still positive but the gate now is driven negative with respect to $MT1$. Hence the p_1 potential relationships now become

$$V(p_{1d}) < V(p_{1c}) < V(p_{1b}) < V(p_{1a}) \tag{10.21}$$

These relationships mean that the p_{1c}-n_3 junction experiences a forward bias and the SCR made up of $p_{2c}n_{2c}p_{1c}n_3$ turns on. This turn-on causes $V(p_{1c})$ to rise toward the potential of $MT2$. Current flows from p_{1c} into p_{1b} thereby providing a turn-on gate current for the $p_{2b}n_{2b}p_{1b}n_1$ SCR which again conducts current from $MT2$ to $MT1$.

Mode 3 −

In this mode $MT2$ and the gate are both negative with respect to $MT1$. Inequality (10.21) still characterizes the potentials in p_1 and the p_{1c}-n_3 junction still experiences a forward bias. However the $p_{2c}n_{2c}$ $p_{1c}n_3$ SCR now has a negative anode-cathode voltage and does not turn on. Instead electrons are injected from n_3 across p_{1c} and into n_{2c}. This electron flow continues through n_{2b} to n_{2a} where it acts as a negative gate current for an SCR with n-type gate. Hence the SCR made up of $p_{1a}n_{2a}p_{2a}n_5$ turns on and conducts current from $MT1$ to $MT2$.

Mode 3 +

In this mode $MT2$ is still negative with respect to $MT1$ but the gate now is driven positive. Hence (10.20) applies. This means that p_{1b}-n_1 experiences a forward bias so that electrons are injected from n_1 across p_{1b} into n_{2b}. From there they flow into n_{2a} and turn on the $p_{1a}n_{2a}p_{2a}n_5$ SCR so that again there is conduction from $MT1$ to $MT2$.

These are the triggering and conducting mechanisms for the four operating modes. For further information on the physical operation and application of the triac the reader is referred to the sources listed at the end of this chapter.

10.6 UNIJUNCTION TRANSISTOR (UJT)

The unijunction transistor, also referred to as the double-base diode, is a *pn* junction device used in pulse and switching applications. One of its important applications is in generating a pulse of gate current to fire an SCR or triac.

The structure of this device is shown schematically in Fig. 10.16 along with its circuit symbol. In this device the p-region is heavily doped but the n-region is lightly doped so that the following features exist:

1. The n-region has substantial resistivity so that an interbase resistance R_{BB} of several kilohms exists between terminals $B2$ and $B1$.
2. Current flow across the *pn* junction consists almost entirely of injection of holes from the p-region into the n-region.
3. The injection of holes into the n-region can easily be high level injection, i.e., p_n comparable with or even greater than n_{no} near the point of injection.

The impact of these features upon the behavior of the device can be explained as follows.

Suppose that terminals $B2$ and $B1$ are connected to a 10 V source so that $V_{BB} = +10$ V, and suppose the structure of the device is such that the interbase resistance $R_{BB} = 2$ kΩ and point x in Fig. 10.16a lies halfway between $B1$ and $B2$. Then $I_{B2} = 5$ mA and $V_x = 5$ V where V_x is the potential at point x, i.e., the lower n-side edge of the junction. (All potentials are referred to terminal $B1$). The upper n-side edge (point y in Fig. 10.16a) of the junction is at a slightly higher potential, 5.2 V perhaps. This potential variation is due to the current I_{B2} flowing down through the n-region.

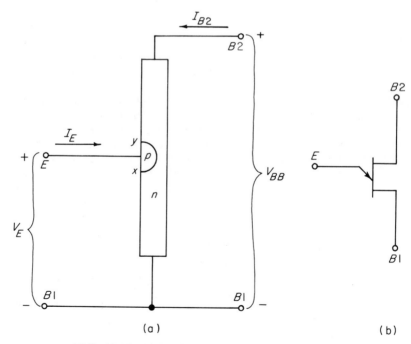

(a)   (b)

FIG. 10.16   (a) Schematic representation of the unijunction transistor and (b) its circuit symbol.

Consider now what happens as the emitter voltage V_E is increased from zero. For $V_E < 5.0$ V the entire pn junction is reverse biased and I_E is simply the reverse saturation current of the junction. As V_E exceeds 5.0 V the lower edge of the junction experiences forward bias and a positive current I_E flows. To continue the discussion assume that I_E and V_E are produced by an adjustable current source and let the device behavior be expressed in terms of I_E. As I_E is increased from zero, current first flows across the lower edge of the pn junction as just described.

This current produces a junction voltage V_J which, because it varies logarithmically with I_E, can be considered a constant, say 0.6 V for a silicon device. So long as I_E is quite small, 1 μA for example, the voltage V_x is unaffected and the emitter voltage V_E is thus $V_x + V_J = 5.6$ V. As I_E increases, however, the voltage V_x is affected by I_E in a rather unexpected way—V_x drops! The reason for this follows.

The emitter current produces an excess hole concentration Δp_n in the region immediately below point x. (The electric field due to V_{BB} ensures that no significant number of holes will diffuse into the upper section of the n-region. Thus holes are injected primarily at the lower edge of the junction and they move down, not up.) This excess hole concentration attracts an equal excess electron concentration Δn_n into the region immediately below point x. At an I_E value of perhaps 100 μA these excess concentrations become comparable with the equilibrium majority carrier concentration n_{no}. (The onset of this condition clearly depends on the magnitude of n_{no} and hence the doping in the n-region.) This means that the resistance of the region begins to be affected by the current I_E. The increase in carrier concentrations leads to increased conductivity and hence reduced resistance.

The effect of this can be seen with the aid of Fig. 10.17, a circuit model for the UJT. In this circuit model the interbase resistance R_{BB} is represented by three series-connected resistors. Resistors R_1 and R_2 together represent that portion of R_{BB} below the lower edge of the pn junction (point x in Fig. 10.16), while R_3 represents the remaining portion. Point y, the upper edge of the pn junction in Fig. 10.16, is represented as a tap on R_3. The two diodes in Fig. 10.17 account for the current-voltage characteristics of the pn junction. Variable resistor R_2 represents the portion of R_{BB} which decreases in resistance when the carrier concentrations increase as described above. When R_2 experiences this decrease, the voltage V_x drops and as a result the emitter voltage V_E drops below the 5.6 V it had previously.

As I_E is increased further the excess concentrations increase proportionally and further reduce resistance R_2. Eventually a point is reached where the drop in V_x due to the decrease of R_2 is offset by the increase in the voltage across R_1. Hence V_x and V_E reach minimums and then increase as I_E is increased still more.

This description can be quantified by analyzing the circuit model in Fig. 10.17. This analysis proceeds most easily if Thevenin's theorem

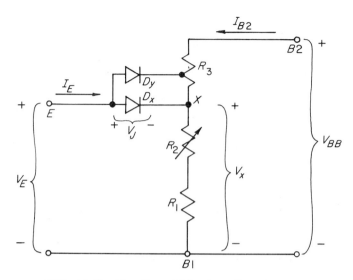

FIG. 10.17   Circuit model for the unijunction transistor in Fig. 10.16.

is applied to the V_{BB}-R_1-R_2-R_3 portion of the circuit so the simplified model in Fig. 10.18 is obtained.

From that circuit one immediately can write the following expression for V_E in terms of I_E.

$$V_E = V_J + I_E(R_1 + R_2)\|R_3 + V_{BB}(R_1 + R_2)/(R_1 + R_2 + R_3) \quad (10.22)$$

When I_E exceeds roughly 100 μA the dominant effect is the decrease in R_2 and the resultant decrease in the third term on the right side of this equation, the Thevenin voltage term. As I_E becomes increasingly large, R_2 becomes much smaller than R_1 and the Thevenin voltage becomes

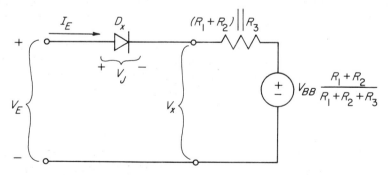

FIG. 10.18   An equivalent to the circuit of Fig. 10.17.

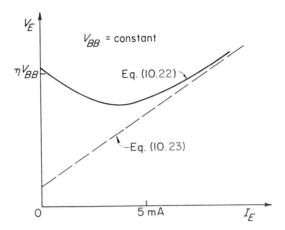

FIG. 10.19 Actual and limiting emitter characteristics for a typical unijunction transistor.

nearly constant. At the same time the Thevenin resistance also becomes nearly constant so that further increases in I_E result in noticeable increases in the term involving I_E and the Thevenin resistance. When this occurs V_E increases rather than decreases with increasing I_E. Since R_2 is approaching a negligible value, the V_E relationship is approaching (10.22) with $R_2 = 0$. Thus for large I_E one has

$$V_E \rightarrow V_J + I_E R_1 \| R_3 + V_{BB}[R_1/(R_1 + R_3)] \tag{10.23}$$

In Fig. 10.19 an actual I_E-V_E characteristic is plotted. Also shown as a dashed straight line is the limiting characteristic (10.23). In addition a new parameter, the *intrinsic standoff ratio* η, is introduced and implicitly defined within the figure. This ratio multiplied by the interbase voltage V_{BB} is the value the emitter voltage V_E must exceed for the *pn* junction to become forward biased. From Fig. 10.18 and/or (10.22) it is evident that η is simply the $(R_1 + R_2)/(R_1 + R_2 + R_3)$ ratio evaluated with R_2 not reduced by high level injection effects. Typical values for η lie in the range 0.4–0.8.

The form most commonly used to present the emitter characteristic, V_E vs I_E as in Fig. 10.19, follows logically from the physical relationship. At the same time comparison with the I-V characteristics of other devices described in this text is facilitated by plotting I_E as a function of V_E as in Fig. 10.20.

10.7 *pin* DIODES

A *pin* is a junction diode with an intrinsic layer interposed between the p- and n-materials, as indicated in Fig. 10.21. At low frequencies this device exhibits I-V characteristics like those of an ordinary

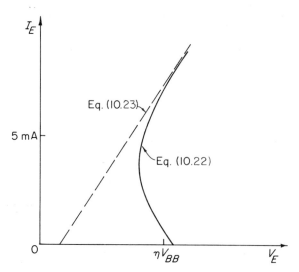

FIG. 10.20   The UJT emitter characteristic of Fig.
10.19 replotted with emitter voltage as the abscissa.

pn junction. It conducts well in the forward direction and blocks exceptionally well in the reverse direction. By making the i-layer length L large it is possible to apply very large reverse voltages before attaining peak electric fields large enough to cause avalanche breakdown.

Of greater interest than this is the behavior of the device at high frequencies from 1 MHz to 1 GHz (microwave frequencies). If we superimpose DC bias conditions and high-frequency AC signals we find that (1) for DC reverse bias the AC impedance of the device is that of a fixed capacitance in series with a fixed resistance—there is no variation of R and C with AC or DC voltage, and (2) for DC forward bias the AC impedance is that of a controllable linear resistor (the resistance varies inversely with the DC current but exhibits a linear i_{ac}-v_{ac} characteristic even for fairly large AC signals).

The reverse voltage and forward current required to attain this behavior depend on the length L of the intrinsic layer (see Fig. 10.21). To study the physical principles underlying these unique characteristics of the *pin*, consider first the case where the i-layer length L is comparatively long. This situation and the corresponding energy band diagram,

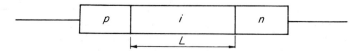

FIG. 10.21   General structure of the *pin* diode.

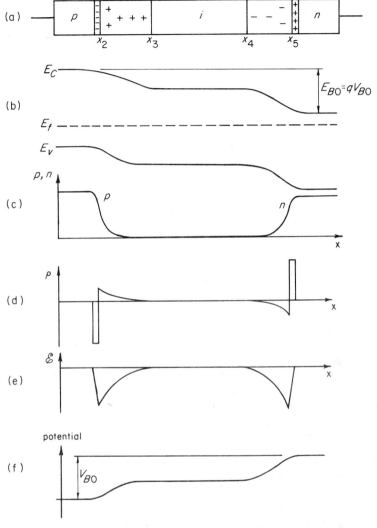

FIG. 10.22   (a) Long i-layer *pin* diode, (b) energy
band diagram, (c) *p* and *n* distributions, (d) space
charge distribution, (e) electric field distribution, and
(f) potential distribution.

carrier distributions, space charge distribution, electric field distribution, and potential distribution (all for the thermal equilibrium condition) are shown in Fig. 10.22. The Fermi level E_f in (b) must be constant
since the system is specified to be in thermal equilibrium. The positions
of the neutral p- and n-regions relative to the Fermi level are dictated

by the impurity concentrations; see (5.52) and (5.53) and Fig. 7.4. The band edges E_c and E_v must therefore make downward transitions across the p-layer space charge region, through the i-layer, and across the n-layer space charge region, with the exact manner depending on the space charge density in the i-layer.

At the left side of the i-layer there are more holes than electrons because holes have diffused in from the p-material. Some holes have recombined with electrons so that $p_o > n_i > n_o$ holds in the left portion of the i-layer. Since $p > n$ there is a net space charge density $\rho = q(p_o - n_o)$. This space charge region extends far enough into the i-layer for the total positive charge to match the negative charge in the p-layer space charge region (see Fig. 10.22d). Thus the electric field reaches a negative maximum at the *pi* boundary, x_2 in Fig. 10.22a, and returns to zero at x_3. An analogous situation occurs at the *ni* boundary. Electrons diffuse into the i-layer producing $n_o > n_i > p_o$ thereby giving a negative space charge in the right portion of the i-layer. This combined with the positive charge in the n-layer space charge region gives an electric field in the neighborhood of the *ni* boundary as shown in Fig. 10.22e. Thus the i-layer consists of three regions: (1) a positively charged region between x_2 and x_3, (2) a neutral region between x_3 and x_4, and (3) a negatively charged region between x_4 and x_5. The neutral i-region behaves like a resistor of length $x_4 - x_3$. This *pin* diode thus can be regarded as a *pi* diode, a resistor, and an *in* diode. What properties do the *pi* and *in* diodes have? The *pi* diode behaves approximately like a *pn* junction in which the n-material is very lightly doped. Current flow, whether in forward or reverse bias, is due almost entirely to holes. The reverse saturation current is larger than in a conventional *pn* junction diode because it is proportional to n_i (the hole concentration at x_3) rather than p_{no} as in a *pn* junction. Thus the silicon *pi* diode exhibits a smaller forward voltage drop than does a silicon *pn* diode, and probably smaller than does a germanium *pn* diode. Similar remarks hold for the *in* diode. Typically the *pi* diode shows a forward drop of perhaps 0.1 V. The total forward drop of the *pin* diode thus consists of these two small components plus the drop across the i-layer resistance.

As stated earlier, this resistance is controllable. When forward bias is applied there is an additional injection of holes and electrons into the i-layer, increasing the space charge there. Both the forward bias and the increased charge lead to a shortening of the space charge regions. Forward bias reduces the barrier voltages of the *pi* and *in* junctions, thus requiring lower electric fields and less charge and producing narrower space charge regions. The increased charge accentuates the effect. Thus the length of the neutral i-region increases slightly. Injection into this neutral i-region also occurs, causing the hole and electron concentrations in the neutral i-region to be increased above n_i. Hence the conductivity of this region increases which means the resistance decreases approximately in inverse proportion to the forward current. The total forward voltage drop V_F of the *pin* diode is

$$V_F = V_{pi} + I_r R_i + V_{ni}$$

But since R_i varies inversely with the forward current I_F, the $I_F R_i$ term is independent of current (so long as I_F is large enough to produce $p = n \gg n_i$ in the resistor). Hence V_F is not a linear function of I_F but is almost a constant not significantly different from V_F of a silicon *pn* junction (0.6–1 V depending on current level).

If the DC current-voltage graph is not linear, why is the high-frequency characteristic linear? The resistance of the neutral i-layer depends on the p and n values. Expressing the resistance in terms of p, n, area A, and $L_R = x_4 - x_3$ (and pretending for simplicity that $\mu_h = \mu_e = \mu$) we have $R_i = L_R/[q\mu(p + n)A]$. It is convenient to refer to an effective charge Q_i given by $q(p + n)L_R A$.[8] This charge is a measure of the total number of carriers available for carrying current in the resistor. In terms of Q_i the resistance R_i becomes

$$R_i = L_R^2/\mu Q_i$$

Thus the resistance varies inversely with Q_i. The effective charge Q_i in turn depends on the current in a manner analogous to the stored charge q_s in an ordinary *pn* diode (see Sec. 7.5). Thus one finds that

$$i_F = Q_i/\tau_i + dQ_i/dt \tag{10.24}$$

where τ_i is the lifetime of Q_i and i_F is the instantaneous forward current through the diode.

Now consider the case where i_F consists of a DC current I_F plus an AC current $I_{ac} \cos \omega t$, i.e.,

$$i_F = I_F + I_{ac} \cos \omega t \tag{10.25}$$

Solving (10.24) with the above expression for i_F yields

$$Q_i = \tau_i I_F + \tau_i I_{ac}[1 + (\omega \tau_i)^2]^{-1/2} \cos[\omega t - \tan^{-1}(\omega \tau_i)] \tag{10.26}$$

As expected the effective charge consists of a DC term and an AC term. This in turn implies some AC variation of resistance R_i. However if the frequency of the sinusoid is high enough, the variations in Q_i and R_i are negligible even when the peak AC current I_{ac} is comparable to or even larger than the DC forward current I_F. Specifically if $(\omega \tau_i)^2 \gg 1$ and $I_{ac}/\omega \tau_i \ll I_F$, then the second term on the right side of (10.26) is much smaller than the first, leading to

$$Q_i \simeq \tau_i I_F = \text{constant}$$

$$R_i \simeq L_R^2/\mu \tau_i I_F = \text{constant}$$

---

8. Hewlett Packard Co., Applications of *PIN* Diodes.

This resistance does not account for the total voltage drop. There are also the voltages V_{pi} and V_{ni} across the pi and ni diodes. Those diodes also exhibit frequency dependence due to charge storage. At the frequencies where R_i is essentially constant, the charge storage effects cause these diodes to behave as AC short circuits. Thus the high-frequency AC impedance is simply a linear resistance controlled by the DC forward current I_F.

What occurs when reverse bias is applied? In terms of the geometry in Fig. 10.22a the applied electric field is directed from right to left, tending to sweep holes back into the p-layer and electrons back into the n-layer. Thus the charge Q_i is removed from the neutral i-layer and the space charge densities in the i-layer are reduced. However the space charge requirements actually have increased. The applied voltage increases the widths of the p- and n-layer space charge regions, thus increasing the charges there. If the space charges in the i-layer are to match these, the boundaries x_3 and x_4 must move toward the center of the i-layer. Thus the neutral portion of the i-layer (the R_i portion) will be shortened. With only a moderate amount of reverse bias it will shrink to zero—the two space charge regions will meet.

Figure 10.23 presents the electric field distribution for (a) forward bias, (b) zero bias, (c) moderate reverse bias, and (d) larger reverse bias. Part (a) of the figure shows the forward bias case, with various space charge regions all narrow and a positive field in the neutral i-layer. Part (b) is a duplication of Fig. 10.22e. Part (c) shows the moderate reverse bias case with all space charge regions widened and the i-layer regions just meeting. Part (d) shows the case of larger reverse bias with the hole and electron space charge densities in the i-layer reduced to the point that they cannot provide enough charge to match the charges in the p- and n-layer space charge regions, and thus the pi and ni diodes no longer are individually neutral. Charge neutrality now holds only for the pin diode as a whole, with some electric flux lines traversing the entire distance from the n-layer to the p-layer. Thus as before the field reaches a negative maximum at x_2, but decreases only slightly in the left half of the i-layer because there is only a small charge there. It then increases negatively and finally returns to zero because of the positive space charge in the n-layer. Thus with substantial reverse bias there is an almost constant field in the entire i-layer. This field has swept out almost all the holes and electrons so that the i-layer is essentially a depletion layer and hence acts like an insulator.

The electrical characteristic of the device in reverse bias is similar to that of a capacitor. The capacitance is exactly analogous to the SCL capacitance discussed in Sec. 7.6.2 for the ordinary pn junction. The thickness of the dielectric W in (7.46) is the i-layer length L plus the small thicknesses of the p- and n-layer space charge regions. By use of large impurity concentrations these latter thicknesses can be made

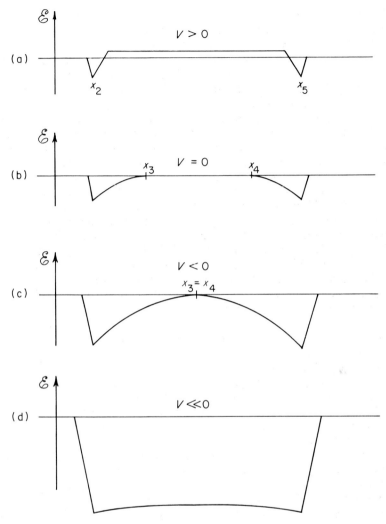

FIG. 10.23   Electric field distributions in the *pin*
diode of Fig. 10.22 for (a) forward bias, (b) zero bias,
(c) moderate reverse bias, and (d) large reverse bias.

negligible so that the capacitance is simply $C_j = \epsilon A/L$. Thus so long as
the reverse bias is sufficient to sweep the i-layer free of mobile charges
the *pin* diode behaves like a fixed small capacitance with magnitude independent of the applied voltage.

The above analysis began with the assumption that the i-layer is
comparatively long. What changes occur if it is shorter? If it is short

enough the i-layer can be fully depleted even at zero bias. Then a neutral region in the i-layer does not appear until sufficient forward bias is
applied. When the injection of holes and electrons into the i-layer becomes substantial, the space charge densities there become large enough
to match the doped layer space charges, thus bringing the electric field
to zero at the center of the i-layer. For still larger forward biases the
space charge densities increase more and the neutral region widens to
form the resistor R_i. Once that condition is attained the previous
analysis applies. The electric field distributions for a short i-layer diode
under various bias conditions are given in Fig. 10.24. Comparing Figs.

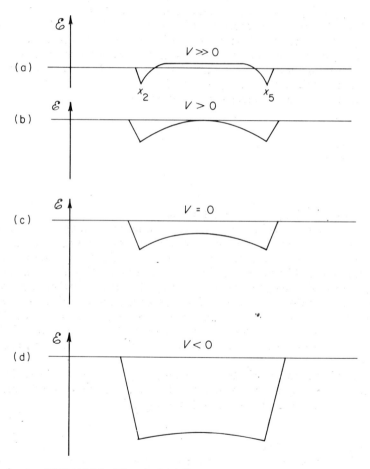

FIG. 10.24   Electric field distributions for a *pin* diode
with short i-layer with (a) $V \gg 0$, (b) $V > 0$, (c) $V =$
0, and (d) $V < 0$.

10.23 and 10.24 we see that the limiting cases (a) and (d) are essentially the same. Substantial forward bias gives a neutral i-region with resistance controlled by current. Substantial reverse bias produces a depleted i-layer and the device behaves as a fixed capacitor. The long and short devices differ mainly in their behavior under slight forward and slight reverse bias conditions.

In conclusion, the *pin* diode can be modeled as an ordinary *pn* junction at low frequencies and by the pair of circuit models in Fig. 10.25 at high frequencies. Two elements R_p and R_n not yet discussed have been added to the models. These represent the ohmic resistances of the p- and n-layer neutral regions. As R_i is decreased by increasing I_F these resistances eventually become an important part of the total device resistance. For reverse bias these resistances are important if the frequency is high enough to result in $1/\omega C_i < R_p + R_n$.

The AC resistance characteristic for a typical *pin* diode is shown in Fig. 10.26. As stated above the AC resistance decreases with increasing DC current. The dependence is not precisely an inverse proportionality however. The straight line in Fig. 10.26 obeys the following empirical relationship, $R_{ac} = 0.2/I_F^{0.8}$.

Other typical parameters for this diode are

breakdown voltage $V_{BR} \geq 100$ V
reverse bias capacitance $C_j = 0.3$ pF
effective lifetime $\tau_i = 1.3\ \mu$s
residual series resistance $R_s = 1.5\ \Omega$

10.8   IMPATT AND GUNN DIODES

Microwave oscillators are often produced by combining microwave resonators (passive components functionally similar to lumped inductor-capacitor circuits) with certain kinds of semiconductor diodes. The diodes used are devices that exhibit high-frequency impedance with negative resistance, thus generating rather than dissipating AC power. The device does not create energy, of course. Energy from some DC supply is converted to AC form by the device. The device absorbs power from the DC source and returns part of this power to the external circuit in AC form. The remainder is dissipated as heat.

Several types of diodes that exhibit negative resistance to high-frequency AC signals are available. These include the IMPATT diode and the Gunn diode discussed in this section.

10.8.1   IMPATT Diode

The name IMPATT is an acronym for IMPact ionization Avalanche Transit Time, which refers to the fact that the IMPATT diode combines avalanche multiplication with carrier transit time to produce

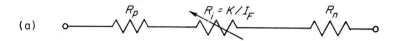

(a)

(b)

FIG. 10.25   High-frequency circuit models for the
pin diode in (a) forward bias and (b) reverse bias.

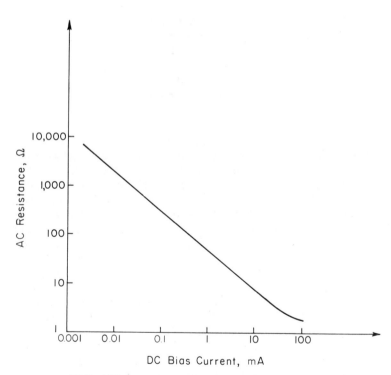

FIG. 10.26   Representative *rf* resistance characteristic of a *pin* diode. (Adapted from data for the
Hewlett-Packard model 5082-3080)

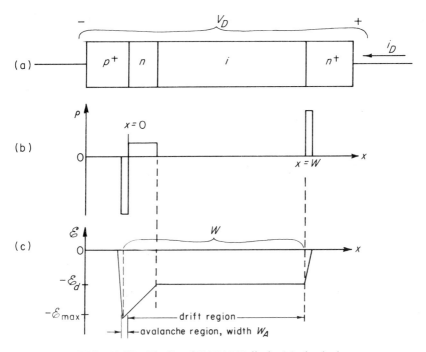

FIG. 10.27   The Read IMPATT diode: (a) physical
structure, (b) space charge density, and (c) electric field
distribution.

the needed negative AC resistance. To examine this combination we
consider the IMPATT diode structure proposed by Read in 1958.[9] This
structure, a p^+nin^+ configuration, is shown in Fig. 10.27 along with the
space charge and field distributions resulting when a voltage with the
indicated polarity is applied. (The analogous n^+pin^+ structure could
equally well be selected.) In (c) of that figure we see that the electric
field reaches a negative maximum $-\mathcal{E}_{max}$ at the interface between the
p^+- and n-layers, moves to a smaller negative value $-\mathcal{E}_d$ at the edge of
the n-layer, remains constant across the i-layer, and then goes to zero
in the n^+-layer. If a direct current much larger than diode saturation
current I_s is applied to the diode in the negative direction (see Fig.
10.27a), the total voltage across the diode will be large enough for
avalanche breakdown to occur. The avalanching occurs where the field
is largest, i.e., at and near the p^+n boundary, the narrow section in
Fig. 10.27c labeled "avalanche region." The remaining part of the
n-layer, where the field is not large enough to produce significant avalanche multiplication, and the entire i-layer together comprise the drift

9. Read, A Proposed High-Frequency Negative Resistance Diode, p. 401.

region labeled in Fig. 10.27c, so named because electrons "created" by avalanche multiplication drift across this region under the influence of the electric field. To explain the existence of a negative AC resistance we shall examine both the avalanche and drift regions.

Consider the avalanche region. A static model of avalanche breakdown is presented in Sec. 7.7.1. We now develop the corresponding dynamic model to investigate the time-dependent features of avalanche multiplication. Using the notation of Sec. 7.7.1 we assume N_1 primary carriers per second enter the avalanche region. If T_1 represents the average time a primary carrier spends in this region, then the total number of primary carriers in the avalanche region at any time is $N_1 T_1$. Likewise there are N_2 secondary pairs produced per second within the avalanche region; if T_2 represents the average time required for a hole-electron pair to emerge from the region, then the total number of secondary pairs is $N_2 T_2$. The flow of the primary carriers comprises the diode saturation current I_s so that we have

$$I_s = qN_1 \tag{10.27}$$

The flow of secondary pairs comprises a current designated i_A. In terms of N_2 this is

$$i_A = qN_2 \tag{10.28}$$

Equation (10.28) indicates that to predict the time dependence of the avalanche current i_A we must study N_2, or equivalently $N_2 T_2$. Consider therefore the differential equation governing $N_2 T_2$. We refer in Sec. 7.7.1 to the probabilities P_1 and P_2 of primary carriers and secondary pairs producing new secondary pairs. If there are $N_1 T_1$ primary carriers in the region and each has a probability P_1 of generating a secondary pair, then the number of new secondary pairs generated is $P_1 N_1 T_1$. This occurs during the time T_1 so the rate of generation is $P_1 N_1 T_1 / T_1 = P_1 N_1$. Similarly the secondary pairs generate additional pairs at a rate $P_2 N_2$. At the same time secondary pairs are continually being removed from the avalanche region at a rate N_2. Computing the net rate of change of $N_2 T_2$ we have $d(N_2 T_2)/dt = P_1 N_1 + P_2 N_2 - N_2$. Since T_2 is a constant this can be rewritten as

$$T_2 \frac{dN_2}{dt} = P_1 N_1 + (P_2 - 1)N_2 \tag{10.29}$$

If we now use (10.27) and (10.28) to express (10.29) in terms of currents we obtain

$$T_2 \frac{di_A}{dt} = P_1 I_s + (P_2 - 1)i_A \tag{10.30}$$

By (7.55) and (7.56) the probability P_2 is empirically given by

$$P_2 = (v_A / V_A)^m \tag{10.31}$$

where v_A is the voltage across the avalanche region, V_A is the avalanche breakdown voltage and m is an empirical constant. [The negative sign in (7.55) is eliminated here because the sign convention in Fig. 10.27 is opposite to that used for I and V in Sec. 7.7.1.] Since we are interested in the case where v_A is time dependent, let this voltage be expressed as the sum of a DC voltage V_0 and a time-varying voltage v_1, that is, $v_A = V_0 + v_1$. Using this, (10.31) yields the following expression for P_2:

$$P_2 = [(V_0 + v_1)/V_A]^m = (V_0/V_A)^m(1 + v_1/V_0)^m \qquad (10.32)$$

Now let us make a small signal assumption, namely $|v_1/V_0| \ll 1$ so that this expression may be approximated as

$$P_2 = (V_0/V_A)^m(1 + mv_1/V_0) = P_0 + \alpha v_1 \qquad (10.33)$$

where $P_0 = (V_0/V_A)^m$ and $\alpha = (V_0/V_A)^m(m/V_0)$. The avalanche current i_A is likewise composed of a DC term I_0 and a time-varying term i_1, that is,

$$i_A = I_0 + i_1 \qquad (10.34)$$

If (10.30), (10.33), and (10.34) are combined we obtain

$$T_2 \frac{d(I_0 + i_1)}{dt} = P_1 I_s + (P_0 - 1 + \alpha v_1)(I_0 + i_1) \qquad (10.35)$$

We now make an additional small signal assumption that i_1 is small enough to justify ignoring the term $\alpha v_1 i_1$ that arises when the second term on the right side of (10.35) is expanded. Thus we have

$$T_2 \frac{di_1}{dt} = P_1 I_s + (P_0 - 1)I_0 + (P_0 - 1)i_1 + \alpha v_1 I_0 \qquad (10.36)$$

If we now specify that i_1 and v_1 are sinusoidal, i.e., $i_1 = I_1 \exp(j\omega t)$ and $v_1 = V_1 \exp(j\omega t)$, then (10.36) separates into the following DC and AC equations:

$$0 = P_1 I_s + (P_0 - 1)I_0 \qquad (10.37)$$

$$j\omega T_2 I_1 \exp(j\omega t) = (P_0 - 1)I_1 \exp(j\omega t) + \alpha I_0 V_1 \exp(j\omega t) \qquad (10.38)$$

If (10.37) is solved for I_0 we obtain

$$I_0 = P_1 I_s/(1 - P_0) \qquad (10.39)$$

This is almost the same as the total DC current through the diode. To obtain that current, called I_s' in Sec. 7.7.1, we add I_s to I_0 and obtain an equation like (7.55) except that P_0 appears in place of P_2. But P_0 is simply the DC value of P_2 so the results would in fact be identical. As a practical matter I_0 can be considered equal to the total DC current since I_s is very small by comparison with I_0.

In the AC equation (10.38), the quantity $P_0 - 1$ appears. If (10.39) is used to express that quantity in terms of I_0, then (10.38) may be rewritten as

$$I_1 = \alpha I_0 V_1 / [\, j\omega T_2 + (P_1 I_s / I_0)]$$
$$= V_1 / [\, j\omega (T_2 / \alpha I_0) + (P_1 I_s / \alpha I_0^2)] \tag{10.40}$$

The denominator in (10.40) has the dimension of impedance, and more specifically is of the form $j\omega L_A + R_A$. At the frequencies where this device is used the inductive term completely overshadows the resistive term. Thus (10.40) can be rewritten simply as

$$I_1 = V_1 / j\omega L_A \tag{10.41}$$

where $L_A = T_2 / \alpha I_0$. From (10.41) it is evident that the AC avalanche current I_1 lags 90° behind the AC avalanche voltage V_1. The significance of this is seen later.

The current I_1 is not the only AC current associated with the avalanche region. A displacement current also exists due to the time-varying electric field in the avalanche region.

A displacement current I_2 is a capacitive current and here is related to the geometrical capacitance of the avalanche region,

$$C_A = \epsilon A / W_A \tag{10.42}$$

where ϵ is the electric permittivity, A is the cross-sectional area, and W_A is the thickness of the avalanche region. The total AC current is thus $I_1 + I_2$, and it can be modeled in circuit form by C_A in shunt with L_A as shown in Fig. 10.28.

The circuit model of Fig. 10.28 and the development leading to it summarize the current-voltage relationships of the avalanche region. We now find the corresponding relationships for the drift region. Consider the current relationship at the left edge of the drift region, i.e., at the boundary between the avalanche and drift regions ($x = 0$ in Fig.

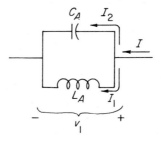

FIG. 10.28   Circuit model for the AC behavior of the avalanche region of an IMPATT diode.

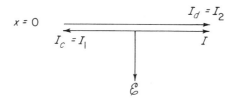

FIG. 10.29   The phasor diagram at $x = 0$, the avalanche drift boundary, in an IMPATT diode.

10.27). This relationship can be calculated from Fig. 10.28 by applying the current divider law.

$$I_1 = I\{(1/j\omega L_A)/[(1/j\omega L_A) + j\omega C_A]\} = I/(1 - \omega^2 L_A C_A) \qquad (10.43)$$

$$I_2 = I\{(j\omega C_A)/[(1/j\omega L_A) + j\omega C_A]\} = I(-\omega^2 L_A C_A)/(1 - \omega^2 L_A C_A) \qquad (10.44)$$

These equations show that either I_1 or I_2 is in phase with I and the other is out of phase. We see later that the situation yielding negative AC resistance is where I_1 is out of phase and I_2 is in phase which occurs for $\omega^2 L_A C_A > 1$. For discussion we arbitrarily select $\omega^2 L_A C_A = 2$, for which (10.43) and (10.44) yield $I_1 = -I$ and $I_2 = +2I$.

Currents I_1 and I_2 are the conduction and displacement currents for the avalanche region and also the left boundary conditions for the drift region, i.e., $I_c(0) = I_1$ and $I_d(0) = I_2$. Using phasor diagrams to portray the various relationships in the drift region yields the diagram of Fig. 10.29 for $x = 0$. In this figure we show the three currents and also the electric field intensity $\mathcal{E}(x)$ because the integral of $\mathcal{E}(x)$ determines the voltage V_d across the drift region. The AC field is, in general, related to the AC displacement current by

$$\mathcal{E}(x) = I_d(x)/j\omega\epsilon A \qquad (10.45)$$

This equation shows that the electric field $\mathcal{E}(x)$ lags 90° behind the displacement current $I_d(x)$, as shown in Fig. 10.29.

To find the voltage V_d, the electric field intensity must be expressed as a function of distance. Equation (10.45) indicates that this will be known if the x-dependence of the displacement current $I_d(x)$ can be found, and $I_d(x)$ can be found from the x-dependence of the conduction current $I_c(x)$ via the continuity relationship $I = I_c(x) + I_d(x)$ because I does not vary with x.

We thus turn to the conduction current in the drift region. As electrons emerge from the right side of the avalanche region they experience a reduced but still substantial field that levels off at $-\mathcal{E}_d$. This causes the electrons to travel across the drift region with a velocity v_d which, surprisingly, is independent of the electric field intensity. The

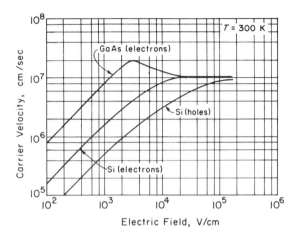

FIG. 10.30   Carrier drift velocities as a function of
electric field intensity for holes and electrons in silicon,
and electrons in gallium arsenide. (Adapted from
Sze, *Semiconductor Devices*, p. 59)

field dependence of the carrier drift velocities in silicon and gallium
arsenide are shown in Fig. 10.30.

In that figure we see that the drift velocity is proportional to field
intensity at low fields (say below 10^3 V/cm), thus agreeing with the
equation $v_d = \mu \mathcal{E}$, but that it becomes constant at high fields (say above
2×10^4 V/cm). [Note: The unusual shape of the GaAs curve is studied
later in conjunction with discussion of the Gunn diode.] This constant
value (roughly 10^7 cm/s) is known as the scattering-limited velocity because it is the value to which scattering (the various collision processes)
limits the average velocity of a carrier in the presence of large electric
fields.

The fact that the electrons drift at the scattering-limited velocity
means their transit time across the drift region is fixed, i.e., it does not
vary with the sinusoidal variations in the electric field. Therefore the
conduction current variations at any point x in the drift region are
precisely the same as those at $x = 0$ except that they are delayed in time
by $\Delta t = x/v_d$. This time delay translates to a phase delay $\omega \Delta t = \omega x/v_d$.
Thus the conduction current $I_c(x)$ is simply the value I_1 (at $x = 0$)
times a delay factor $\exp(-j\omega x/v_d)$, i.e.,

$$I_c(x) = I_1 \exp(-j\omega x/v_d) \qquad (10.46)$$

Given this equation and the continuity relationship

$$I_d(x) = I - I_c(x) \qquad (10.47)$$

we can construct the phasor diagrams for various values of x. This is

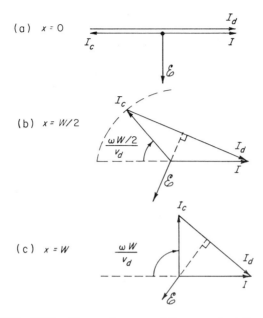

FIG. 10.31 Phasor diagrams of the current relationships in the drift region of an IMPATT diode at (a) $x = 0$, (b) $x = W/2$, and (c) $x = W$.

done in Fig. 10.31 for $x = 0$, $x = W/2$, and $x = W$. For illustration we have chosen the case where $\omega W/v_d = 90°$, i.e., where the total transit time across the drift region is one-quarter of the period of the sinusoidal signal. Figure 10.31a repeats Fig. 10.29. In (b) and (c) we find I_c unchanged in magnitude but shifted by an appropriate delay angle $\omega x/v_d$ in accordance with (10.46). The phasor $I_d(x)$ in each case runs from the tip of $I_c(x)$ to the tip of I, thus satisfying (10.47). Finally the phasor $\mathcal{E}(x)$ is perpendicular to $I_d(x)$ and lagging, as required by (10.45). Observe that $\mathcal{E}(x)$ varies in both magnitude and phase because $I_d(x)$ is required to do so. The average $\mathcal{E}(x)$ over the entire drift region can be used to find the drift region voltage V_d. This is easily seen as follows.

$$V_d = \int_0^W \mathcal{E}(x)\,dx = W\left[(1/W)\int_0^W \mathcal{E}(x)\,dx\right] = W\mathcal{E}_{av} \qquad (10.48)$$

An exact computation of $\mathcal{E}_{av}$ requires evaluation of the integral in (10.48) and is not difficult. However, let us estimate the result. The magnitude and phase of $\mathcal{E}(x)$ vary from (a) to (c) in Fig. 10.31. The average $\mathcal{E}(x)$ has some intermediate magnitude and phase comparable to the values it has at $x = W/2$, as shown in Fig. 10.31b. The phasor

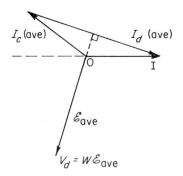

FIG. 10.32   Phasor diagram for the drift region of an
IMPATT diode.

diagram for the drift region is thus similar to Fig. 10.31b, with the addition of the voltage V_d, as shown in Fig. 10.32. From this figure it is evident that $\mathcal{E}_{av}$, and hence V_d, is behind the current I by more than 90°. Hence V_d/I has a real negative component, i.e., the AC resistance is negative as stated earlier in this section.

The impedance V_d/I is easily calculated. If (10.46) is substituted into (10.47), the latter is substituted into (10.45), and the resulting expression for $\mathcal{E}(x)$ is then substituted into (10.48) we obtain

$$V_d = (1/j\omega\epsilon A) \int_0^W [I - I_1 \exp(-j\omega x/v_d)]\, dx$$

If the integral is evaluated and (10.43) is then used to eliminate I_1, we have

$$V_d = \frac{I}{j\omega C_d} + \frac{I[1 - \exp(-j\omega T_d)]}{\omega^2 C_d T_d (1 - \omega^2 L_A C_A)}$$

where $C_d \equiv \epsilon A/W$ = drift region geometrical capacitance and $T_d \equiv W/v_d$ = drift region transit time. Finally, dividing V_d by I to find the impedance Z_d and using the Euler identity to convert the exponential to sine-cosine form yields

$$Z_d = \frac{V_d}{I} = \frac{1 - \cos(\omega T_d)}{(\omega C_d)(\omega T_d)(1 - \omega^2 L_A C_A)} + \frac{1}{j\omega C_d}$$
$$- \frac{\sin(\omega T_d)}{(j\omega C_d)(\omega T_d)(1 - \omega^2 L_A C_A)} \qquad (10.49)$$

For $\omega^2 L_A C_A > 1$ this expression yields the promised negative AC resistance. Also for that case both reactive terms are capacitive, assuming $\sin(\omega T_d) > 0$.

The complete AC circuit model for the IMPATT diode is drawn

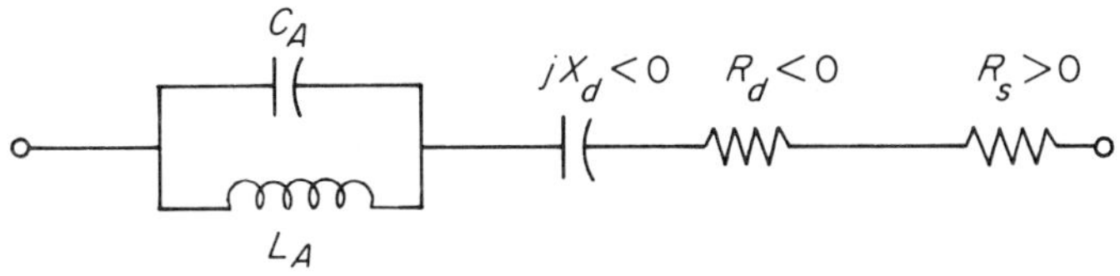

FIG. 10.33 Small signal AC circuit model for the IMPATT diode operated with $\omega^2 L_A C_A > 1$.

in Fig. 10.33. Elements C_A and L_A represent the avalanche region. At the frequencies where negative resistance appears, i.e., $\omega > (1/L_A C_A)^{1/2}$, the net impedance of these two parallel elements is capacitive. The capacitive element labeled jX_d represents the two imaginary terms in (10.49). It is not a simple capacitance because its reactance does not vary as ω^{-1}; the reactance is negative at the frequencies of interest, however, so the capacitor symbol is appropriate. Element R_d represents the negative resistance term in (10.49) while R_s represents the small positive ohmic resistance of the neutral p^+- and n^+- layers.

A word of caution is needed regarding (10.49). The impedance there applies only to the small signal case. In practice the IMPATT diode is used under large signal conditions so this equation may not be in quantitative agreement with results actually obtained. However, the principles set forth do apply under large signal conditions. There are complications in both the avalanche and drift regions causing substantial departures from the small signal model. The interested reader is urged to consult the references listed at the end of this chapter for discussion of the large signal behavior of the IMPATT diode.

10.8.2 Gunn Diode

The Gunn diode is a negative resistance device used for producing microwave oscillations. The Gunn diode is not a junction device but a bulk device, i.e., a device utilizing the properties of the interior of a semiconducting layer rather than the properties of its interface with another semiconducting layer. While Gunn diodes can be made with several different semiconductors, gallium arsenide (GaAs) is by far the most widely used, and the discussion here is framed in terms of this material. The device structure is similar to an ordinary resistor; see Fig. 10.34. In fact at voltages such that $\mathcal{E} < 10^3$ V/cm the device acts as a resistor. In Fig. 10.30 we have drift velocity versus electric field intensity plotted. For $\mathcal{E} < 10^3$ V/cm, the electron drift velocity in GaAs is proportional to the electric field so that the device follows Ohm's law.

As the voltage is increased the electric field increases to the point that $\mathcal{E} > 3 \times 10^3$ V/cm with the unusual result that the drift velocity decreases with increasing field. This means that the conduction current

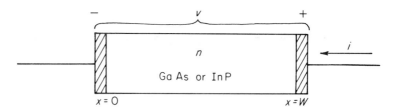

FIG. 10.34   Basic structure of the Gunn diode.

decreases with increasing field, precisely the requirement for a negative AC resistance.

The explanation of decreasing current with increasing field involves the quantum structure of the conduction band in GaAs. The details lie beyond the scope of this text, but a general explanation follows. The electric field accelerates the conduction electrons, thus increasing their average energy so they lie higher in the conduction band than in thermal equilibrium. In GaAs a large portion of the quantum states laying at these higher energies is characterized by large values of effective mass m_e^*. Increased effective mass means decreased mobility so that less drift velocity results from the increased electric field. In other words, as the electrons are accelerated to higher total velocities (higher kinetic energy) they are scattered so much by quantum mechanical interactions that the organized or directed component of their velocity diminishes.

Considering the field dependence of the drift velocity, what current-voltage characteristic should we expect from GaAs? The current is given by qnv_dA, i.e., the product of the particle charge, the particle concentration, the drift velocity, and the device cross-sectional area. Assuming n is constant, the current varies in exactly the same way as the velocity. If the electric field is uniform ($\mathcal{E} = V/W$) then the I-V characteristic has the same shape as the v_d-$\mathcal{E}$ characteristic. If the DC voltage is then chosen to place operation on the negative slope portion of the I-V curve, the incremental relationship between current and voltage is

$$\frac{\Delta i}{\Delta v} \sim \frac{\partial i}{\partial v} = -\left| \frac{\partial i}{\partial v} \right| < 0$$

Thus the AC voltage and the AC conduction current are 180° out of phase and the device acts as an AC negative resistance. By using this negative resistance to cancel the positive resistance of the external resonant circuit, sinusoidal steady-state oscillation can be obtained. This is one way the Gunn diode is used to produce microwave power.

The above discussion is based on the assumption that the electric field is uniform. This assumption is correct if (1) the GaAs sample is uniformly doped with impurities and (2) the external circuit resonates

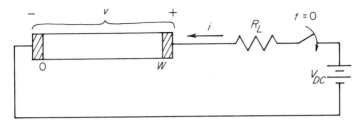

FIG. 10.35 Gunn diode with resistive load.

at a frequency much higher than v_d/W, the reciprocal of the transit time—the time for an electron to travel the length of the diode. This latter requirement prevents the development of major nonuniformities in the field distribution (discussed in more detail below) and results in sinusoidal oscillation at the resonant frequency.

If the resonant frequency of the external circuitry is reduced toward v_d/W or if the resonator is replaced by a resistive load, the operation of the diode changes. The diode current still varies periodically, but in a nonsinusoidal manner. With a resonant load the period of the variations is determined by the resonator but efficiency is poor because not all the AC power is concentrated at the fundamental frequency. With a resistive load the period of oscillation is the transit time W/v_d.

To see what is happening in this case consider the following. Let the diode be connected as shown in Fig. 10.35. Let the supply voltage V_{DC} be just large enough to produce an average field of 3×10^3 V in the diode when the circuit is energized at $t = 0$ (by closing the switch in Fig. 10.35). This value of the field corresponds to the peak in the velocity-field characteristic. At $t = 0$ the field is almost uniform throughout the device. The electrons are in their normal quantum states so that the conductivity has its normal value. By Ohm's law ($\mathcal{E} = J/\sigma$ in microscopic form) the field is thus the same everywhere except near the ohmic contacts. Energy barriers and corresponding built-in fields are, at the metal-semiconductor interfaces, identical in nature with those associated with the contact potentials V_{C1} and V_{C2} of the *pn* diode in Fig. 7.6. Because of these built-in fields we say the total field is *almost* uniform at $t = 0$. Clearly there are nonuniformities near $x = 0$ and $x = W$.

Assume that in the Gunn diode the metal used for the contact is such that the built-in electric field is directed *from* the semiconductor *to* the metal. Since the applied field in Fig. 10.35 is directed from right to left, the applied and built-in fields add at $x = 0$ and subtract at $x = W$. This means we have $\mathcal{E} > 3 \times 10^3$ V/cm at $x = 0$ and $\mathcal{E} \leq 3 \times 10^3$ V/cm elsewhere. What does this imply? At $x = 0$ the electrons are accelerated enough for them to reach the decreasing mobility portion of the velocity-field characteristic of Fig. 10.30. This in turn implies increased resistivity; the region near $x = 0$ will take up more than its

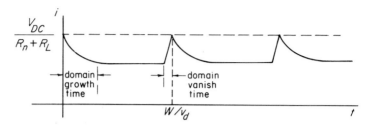

FIG. 10.36   Conduction current waveform for the
Gunn diode circuit of Fig. 10.35.

normal share of the applied voltage. But that means an even larger field
there and a lower field elsewhere. This in turn leads to further lowering
of the mobility near $x = 0$ and further increase of the resistivity there,
etc. The situation thus compounds itself and a narrow high field region
develops taking up a substantial portion of the total applied voltage.
This region is commonly known as a *high field domain*. This domain
does not remain fixed in position. The electrons in the region drift to
the right at the scattering-limited velocity; hence the domain moves
across the device. When it arrives at $x = W$ it vanishes since it cannot
propagate out into the metal. As it vanishes the field must rise again
elsewhere to approximately $3 \times 10^3 \, \text{V/cm}$. This in turn raises the field
at $x = 0$ above $3 \times 10^3 \, \text{V/cm}$ and initiates a new high field domain.
What current flows as a result of the above events? At $t = 0$ the conduction current is given by Ohm's law $i = V_{DC}/(R_L + R_n)$ where R_n
is the resistance computed using the normal electron mobility. As the
high field domain builds up, the field outside the domain is reduced and
hence the conduction current drops. Then as the domain reaches $x = W$
and vanishes, full voltage is again applied to $R_n + R_L$ and the current
rises rapidly to the original value again. The conduction current waveform thus appears as shown in Fig. 10.36.

This discussion of the physical behavior of the Gunn diode is
highly simplified. The references listed at the end of the chapter may be
consulted for further explanation and analysis of the various modes of
operation the Gunn diode exhibits.

10.9   PHOTORESISTORS

A photoresistor is a resistor with resistance depending on the intensity and the spectrum of whatever light is caused to fall on the
device. It is fabricated by placing ohmic contacts on opposite ends of a
piece of intrinsic or lightly doped semiconductor. In general this device
has a conductance G given by $G = \sigma A/L$, where σ is the conductivity
of the material, A is its cross-sectional area, and L is its length. Using
(6.10) to relate σ to the carrier concentrations, the conductance ex-

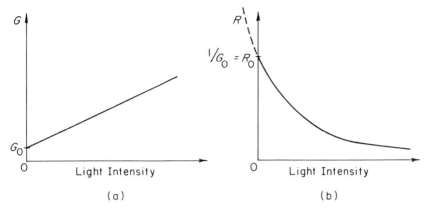

FIG. 10.37 Photoresistor light sensitivity characteristics.

pression becomes

$$G = qA(\mu_e n + \mu_h p)/L$$

In the absence of light, n and p have equilibrium values n_o and p_o. When light is applied hole-electron pairs are generated (assuming photons with energy greater than E_g are present) so that n and p both increase by Δn. Hence the conductance is given by

$$G = qA(\mu_e n_o + \mu_h p_o)/L + qA(\mu_e + \mu_h)\Delta n/L \qquad (10.50)$$

where $G_o = qA(\mu_e n_o + \mu_h p_o)/L$, the conductance in the absence of light, and $\Delta G = qA(\mu_e + \mu_h)\Delta n/L$, the conductance increase due to the applied light. If the spectral content of the light is constant, ΔG is proportional to the light intensity. Hence G varies linearly with light intensity and the resistance $R = 1/G$ varies hyperbolically. Plots of G and R are shown in Fig. 10.37.

Photoresistors are used in a variety of ways in light-sensitive switching applications, such as turning on a yard light at sunset and turning it off again at sunrise, and in light-measuring applications.

10.10 PHOTO DIODES AND PHOTO TRANSISTORS

Photo diodes and photo transistors are conventional junction devices housed in cases having a window to admit light. The admitted light strongly affects the current flowing through the diode or transistor, because the photons of light generate hole-electron pairs in and near the SCL of the diode junction or the transistor collector junction (provided the photon energy hc/λ is E_g or greater). To see how this comes about, consider first the diode.

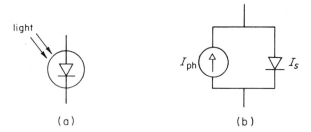

FIG. 10.38 (a) Photo diode circuit symbol and (b) its circuit model.

Generation of hole-electron pairs just outside the SCL of the diode causes a major increase in the minority carrier concentrations n_p and p_n, which means that the flows F_1 and F_4 in Fig. 7.9 are greatly increased. However the flows F_2 and F_3 are unaffected because the photo-generated majority carriers have insufficient kinetic energy to surmount the energy barrier. As a result the reverse component of diode current, I_s in (7.18), becomes $-(I_s + I'_{ph})$ while the forward component remains $I_s \exp(q V_d / kT)$, where I'_{ph} is the current due to the increases in F_1 and F_4. In addition there is photogeneration of hole-electron pairs within the SCL. The electric field in the SCL sweeps the electrons toward the n-side and the holes toward the p-side. Thus another reverse component of diode current $-I''_{ph}$ is produced. Combining all these components the photo diode current-voltage relationship is thus

$$
\begin{aligned}
I &= I_s \exp(q V_d / kT) - (I_s + I'_{ph}) - I''_{ph} \\
  &= I_s[\exp(q V_d / kT) - 1] - I_{ph}
\end{aligned}
\tag{10.51}
$$

where $I_{ph} = I'_{ph} + I''_{ph}$ is the diode photo current.

Equation (10.51) suggests a simple circuit model for the photo diode. This is shown in Fig. 10.38 with the circuit symbol for the device. The diode symbol in Fig. 10.38b represents a simple *pn* junction with reverse saturation current I_s. All the photo effects are accounted for by the photocurrent generator I_{ph}. This photocurrent is proportional to the light intensity and depends on the spectral content of the light. A representative value for I_{ph} might be 1 mA at an illumination level of 40 mW/cm^2.

The photo transistor combines the current-producing properties of the photo diode with the current gain properties of the transistor. The collector-base junction serves simultaneously as the photocurrent source and the transistor collector junction. The photocurrent I_{ph} has the effect of supplementing the external base current, as shown in Fig. 10.39b where a circuit model for the photo transistor is given. Since the

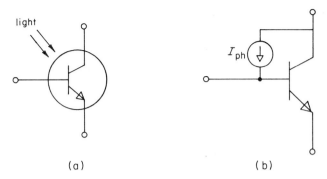

FIG. 10.39   (a) Photo transistor circuit symbol and
(b) its circuit model.

transistor might exhibit a current gain of 50, then an amplified photo-current of 50 mA at 40 mW/cm² illumination is typical.[10]

Photo diodes and photo transistors have uses similar to photoresistors and are preferred in many applications because a light-controlled current source is often more convenient than a light-controlled resistance.

10.11   LIGHT-EMITTING DIODES (LED)

The light-emitting diode (LED) is a *pn* junction device that complements the photo diode. When the photo diode is illuminated, it conducts current. When forward current is passed through the LED it emits light. This light emission results from recombination of hole-electron pairs in and near the SCL of the *pn* junction. When an electron drops toward the valence band it releases an energy ΔE equal to the drop in quantum state energy (this follows from conservation of energy). The electron may give up the energy ΔE by either radiating a photon of energy $h\nu = \Delta E$ or transferring ΔE to the lattice, thereby increasing its vibrational energy and hence raising its temperature. The law of conservation of momentum determines which possibility occurs. The initial momentum is that corresponding to the initial quantum state of the electron. The final momentum is the sum of the photon momentum h/λ and the momentum corresponding to the final quantum state of the electron. Since the photon momentum is extremely small we find that the initial and final electron momenta must be essentially equal, placing a considerable restriction on the possible recombinations for which photon emission can occur.

---

10. Grafham and Hey, *SCR Manual*, p. 411.

Assume for the moment that recombination occurs by a direct transition from the conduction band to the valence band (*direct* recombination). Most conduction electrons are found within a few kT of the bottom of the conduction band E_c, and most holes are found within a few kT of the top of the valence band E_v. Hence the quantum states near E_c must have momenta matching those of quantum states near E_v if substantial numbers of photon-producing recombinations are to occur. If one must go many kT into the conduction band to find quantum states that are momentum-compatible with states near E_v, then few photon-producing recombinations occur because there are few electrons in quantum states many kT above E_c. Likewise if one must go many kT into the valence band to find states compatible with those near E_c, few photon-producing recombinations occur because there are few holes many kT below E_v. We thus conclude that (1) direct recombination produces significant light output only if the quantum states near E_c are momentum-compatible with those near E_v, and (2) the photon energy in that case is roughly E_g, i.e., between E_g and E_g plus a few kT.

In silicon and germanium the quantum states near E_c are not momentum-compatible with those near E_v. Consequently no significant light output is obtained by direct recombination in silicon or germanium. Furthermore, the photons would fall in the deep infrared range. In Table 10.1 the photon energies for red, yellow, green, and blue light are given. From these values it is evident that $E_g = 1.9\,eV$ or more is required for visible light to be obtained. Silicon and germanium, with energy gap values of 1.1 eV and 0.66 eV, respectively, fall far short of this requirement.

A semiconductor in which the required momentum-compatibility does exist is gallium arsenide (GaAs), one of the III-V semiconductors (so called because gallium and arsenic come from Groups III and V, respectively, of the periodic table). The energy gap for GaAs is 1.43 eV. This falls in the infrared range, but not so far as to be useless. While not visible to the human eye, light with $h\nu \simeq 1.43$ eV is quite visible to a silicon photo diode. Thus GaAs may be used for light-emitting diodes intended not for visual display purposes but as components in electronic communication, instrumentation, or control systems.

Table 10.1.   Visible light photon wavelength and energy.

Color	λ(nm)	$h\nu$(eV)
red	650	1.9
yellow	570	2.2
green	510	2.4
blue	470	2.6

Next consider recombination as a multiple-step process (*indirect* recombination). Suppose that an electron near E_c drops into a vacant acceptor state and then later into a hole. If the acceptor state is momentum-compatible with the state near E_c then that two-step recombination process results in emission of a photon. Similarly an electron near E_c might drop into a donor state and then later into a hole; if the donor state is momentum-compatible with the hole state then again a photon is emitted. There could also be three-step recombination: from near E_c to a donor state, from the donor state to an acceptor state, and then from the acceptor state to a hole. If momentum-compatibility exists the donor-acceptor step produces a photon.

"Deep lying" impurity states can also play a role. These are quantum states lying well above E_v but well below E_c; they are introduced by introduction of impurities other than those normally used as donor or acceptor dopants. An electron near E_c can then make a two-, three-, or four-step transition to a hole in the valence band. If one of these steps involves states with compatible momenta, that step produces a photon.

The energy change for a photon-producing step in any of the above multiple-step recombinations is either roughly equal to E_g— when only donor and acceptor states are involved—or significantly less than E_g—when deep lying states are involved.

Thus depending on the semiconductor and impurities involved, several photon energies less than or equal to E_g can be produced when multiple-step recombinations are significant.

The efficiency of a light-emitting diode depends on the ratio of photon-emitting recombinations to total recombinations. Since pairs of quantum states with unequal momenta are more numerous than pairs with equal momenta, most recombinations are nonemitting and efficiency is relatively low, i.e., a few percent or less, especially in silicon and germanium. Because of this and because the photons are not in a useful energy range, these materials have not been developed as light emitters.

To obtain visible light output it is clear that an LED must be made from a material with E_g of approximately 2 eV or greater (see Table 10.1). The most promising materials appear to be gallium phosphide (GaP) and gallium arsenide phosphide ($GaAs_{1-x}P_x$). The latter is a modified form of gallium arsenide in which a fraction x of the arsenic atoms are replaced by phosphorous atoms. The result is a semiconductor with the energy gap in the desired range and in which, for $x < 1$, photons are produced by direct (one-step) recombinations. The gap increases from 1.43 eV at $x = 0$ for GaAs to 2.24 eV at $x = 1$ for GaP.

Gallium phosphide does not have compatible momenta for photon-producing direct recombinations. However by use of suitable impurities effective light production via multiple-step recombinations is obtained. As a result GaP and GaAsP light-emitting diodes with red,

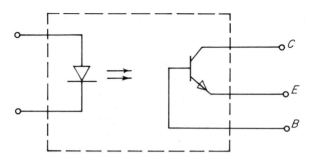

FIG. 10.40   Symbolic representation of LED combined with photo transistor to form optical coupler.

yellow, or green light outputs are commercially available. Even though
the efficiency is inherently low (as in incandescent lamps) the DC current required to produce useful light output from these devices is
quite reasonable, of the order of 10 mA.

10.12   OPTICAL COUPLERS

The optical coupler is a four-terminal device formed by placing
an LED and a photo transistor in one encapsulation as shown in
Fig. 10.40. When current is applied to the LED (input) terminals, light
is produced which is directed to the photo transistor. The photo transistor then, provided it is appropriately biased, produces an output current controlled directly by the current applied to the LED terminals.
Electrically the LED and photo transistor are completely separate.
Thus electrical isolation between input and output terminals of many
megohms of resistance and thousands of volts of breakdown capability
is possible.

The current transfer ratio of an optical coupler is not large because
of the low efficiency of the LED. Nevertheless, because of the current
gain of the photo transistor, the overall current transfer ratio can still
be 1–10 or more.

10.13   INTEGRATED CIRCUITS

An integrated circuit (IC) is an electronic component in which
techniques of device fabrication are used to create an entire electronic circuit, such as an amplifier or digital logic circuit, in a volume
often no larger than that occupied by one encapsulated diode or transistor. It stands in contrast with circuits composed of discrete components, i.e., individually packaged diodes, transistors, resistors, etc. The
most widely used ICs are the monolithic integrated circuits, in which
all components are fabricated within one piece of silicon. Other types

include thin-film, thick-film, and hybrid ICs; for description and discussion of these consult the references at the end of the chapter. Here
we discuss only the monolithic IC.

Integrated circuits are often referred to as microminiature circuits.
The key to this microminiaturization is the elimination of separate
chips, cases, and leads for each individual diode, transistor, resistor,
and capacitor in the circuit being fabricated. Instead the components
are all fabricated within one chip of silicon, the necessary interconnections are made by means of an etched metal layer on the surface of the
chip (see Chap. 9), only those connections needed externally are brought
out as accessible leads, and one case is used for the entire circuit. In a
discrete transistor only a small fraction of the total space used actually
involves the working volume of the transistor itself. Most of the space
is taken by the peripheral areas of the silicon chip, the leads, and the
case; thus discrete components make extremely inefficient use of space.
They also make inefficient use of materials and production time since
an entire IC can be produced with only slightly more material and time
than required for one discrete transistor.

Integrated circuits have added new considerations to electronic
circuit design. In discrete design, resistors are used widely because
they are inexpensive. In IC design they are avoided when possible because resistances of more than a few $k\Omega$ require a larger chip area than
a transistor. This area consideration is important from two standpoints.
It is obviously important in large scale integration (LSI) where complex
circuits, such as the central processor for a digital computer involving
thousands of transistors, resistors, etc., are produced on a single chip.

Even in small scale integration it is important. In any slice of crystalline silicon there are imperfections that degrade or ruin circuit performance if they fall within one of the devices in the circuit. Suppose
that a given slice of silicon has a surface area A_s and contains N_I
imperfections. If the area required for one circuit is A_c, the slice will
yield a number of circuits $N_c = A_s/A_c$. Now compare the number of
circuits with the number of imperfections, i.e., compare N_c with N_I. If
$N_c < N_I$ we shall have an average of more than one imperfection per
circuit. Our chances of finding a circuit without an imperfection are not
good and hence the expected production yield is low. A low yield raises
the cost per good circuit. On the other hand if $N_c \gg N_I$ we shall find a
high percentage of good circuits and the cost per good circuit drops
tremendously. Since N_c varies inversely with A_c, it is clear that circuits
should be designed using the smallest practical area to maximize production yield and minimize cost.

Returning to the unique considerations involved in electronic circuit design for ICs, we find that resistors should not be used abundantly
because of their area penalty. The same restraint applies to capacitors
with even greater emphasis. Capacitances larger than about 30 or 40 pF
are prohibitive because of the area required. Even this size capacitance

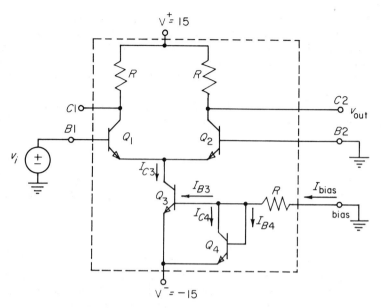

FIG. 10.41   Integrated differential amplifier with
typical external connections.

is extravagant; many transistors could be fabricated in the same area!
It would seem that the designer is severely boxed in because not many
resistors (at least of the many-kilohm variety) and no capacitors should
be used. However there is another side to the story. In discrete circuit
design circuits requiring matched transistors, diodes, etc., are avoided
because procurement of such matched components is very costly. In
integrated circuit design, on the other hand, one can assume a ready
supply of as many matched components as required! They are all made
simultaneously from identical masks (see Chap. 9), so close matching
of device characteristics is an automatic result of the IC fabrication
process.

Consider one simple example: an integrated differential amplifier.
The circuit diagram of the amplifier is shown inside the dotted lines in
Fig. 10.41. Outside the lines are the external connections required for
operation of the circuit.

Let us examine the operation of this circuit and note particularly
the use of matched device characteristics. Consider first the operation
of Q_3, Q_4, and the resistor R connected between ground and the base
of Q_4. This combination is designed to produce a well-defined direct
current at the collector of Q_3. Using (8.56) that current is given by

$$I_{C3} = \alpha_F I_{ES}[\exp(q V_{BE}/kT) - 1] \tag{10.52}$$

We assume $I_{CS}[\exp(qV_{BC}/kT) - 1]$ to be negligible. Notice that transistor Q_4 has exactly the same applied V_{BE} as Q_3 because their base-emitter junctions are connected directly in parallel. Hence (10.52) also gives I_{C4}, the collector current of Q_4. Observe that Kirchhoff's current law relates I_{C4} to I_{bias}, the current through the resistor R, in the following manner: $I_{bias} = I_{C4} + I_{B4} + I_{B3}$.

Noting that $I_{B4} = I_{C4}/\beta_{F4}$, $I_{B3} = I_{C3}/\beta_{F3}$, and neglecting collector junction saturation current effects—the $-(1 + \beta_F)I_{co}[\exp(qV_{BC}/kT) - 1]$ term in (8.58)—we have

$$I_{bias} = I_{C4} + I_{C4}/\beta_{F4} + I_{C3}/\beta_{F3} \tag{10.53}$$

But we have already noted that I_{C4} and I_{C3} are both given by (10.52) because $\alpha_F I_{ES}$ is the same for both transistors (within a small tolerance). Hence $I_{C4} = I_{C3}$ and (10.53) yields

$$I_{bias} = I_{C3}(1 + 1/\beta_{F4} + 1/\beta F_3)$$

$$I_{C3} = I_{bias}/(1 + 1/\beta_{F4} + 1/\beta_{F3}) \simeq I_{bias} \tag{10.54}$$

The approximation in (10.54) is based on the reasonable assumption that β_{F3} and β_{F4} are large so their reciprocals may be neglected in comparison with unity. We thus find whatever current is caused to flow in resistor R is duplicated or mirrored in the collector of transistor Q_3. The combination Q_3-Q_4 is often called a "current mirror" because of this characteristic.

The current through R is easily calculated. The potential at the right terminal of R is zero. The potential at the left terminal is $-15 + V_{BE}$. Hence $I_{bias} = [0 - (-15 + V_{BE})]/R = (15 - V_{BE})/R$. The value of V_{BE} depends upon I_{bias}. However the dependence is logarithmic and one can guess that $V_{BE} \simeq 0.7 \pm 0.1$ V. Hence

$$I_{bias} = 14.3 \, V/R \pm 0.1 \, V/R \tag{10.55}$$

This equation shows that I_{bias} is not sensitive to the exact value of V_{BE}.

Consider next the Q_1-Q_2-R-R combination. The collector current of Q_3 has the value I_{bias}, as seen in (10.54). This current divides in some fashion between the emitters of Q_1 and Q_2. Let $v_i = 0$ for calculation of the bias conditions. With this condition imposed, we have identical base-emitter voltages applied to Q_1 and Q_2. If Q_1 and Q_2 are matched then their emitter currents must be equal. Hence

$$I_{E1} = I_{E2} = -I_{bias}/2$$

The corresponding collector currents are then (neglecting I_{co} again)

$$I_{C1} = I_{C2} = \alpha_F I_{bias}/2$$

The DC voltages at the collectors of Q_1 and Q_2 are

$$V_C = 15 - RI_C = 15 - R\alpha_F I_{bias}/2 \tag{10.56}$$

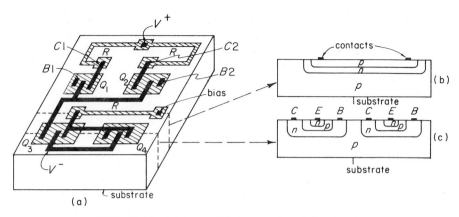

FIG. 10.42 (a) A possible integration of the circuit of Fig. 10.41, (b) cross-sectional view of the bias resistor, and (c) cross-sectional view of *npn* transistors Q_3 and Q_4.

Assuming the two collector resistors are matched (as implied by the use of the same label R for both), then the two transistors have identical DC operating conditions. Furthermore the collector voltages are insensitive to production variations in R so long as all three Rs are equal. This is because I_{bias} varies inversely with R so that R disappears from the expression for V_C when I_{bias} is related to the external bias conditions. Thus using (10.55) to substitute for I_{bias} in (10.56) we obtain

$$V_C = 15 - R\alpha_F(14.3 \text{ V}/R \pm 0.1 \text{ V}/R)(1/2)$$
$$= 15 - \alpha_F(7.15 \pm 0.05)$$
$$\simeq (15 - 7.15) \pm 0.05 \qquad (\alpha_F \simeq 1)$$

Thus the DC collector voltages of Q_1 and Q_2 are well defined with both transistors operating in the active region.

Consider now the fabrication of this circuit. Figure 10.42 shows perspective and cross-sectional views of a possible integration of the amplifier of Fig. 10.41. The hatched areas in (a) represent the regions within the silicon chip occupied by the transistors and resistors. The solid black bars in (a) represent metal contacts to and interconnections among the devices making up the circuit. All four transistors have the emitter contact in the center. Transistors Q_2, Q_3, and Q_4 have collector contacts on the left and base contacts on the right. Transistor Q_1 has a reverse orientation. Note in (b) and (c) that the entire circuit is formed upon a p-type substrate that serves not only as a mechanical foundation for the IC but also provides electrical isolation between devices. The substrate is internally connected to the most negative point in the circuit, V^- in this example. This ensures that all junctions between substrate and n-regions in the device are reverse biased so that they act as insulators providing the required isolation between devices. Figure 10.42c shows a cross-sectional view of transistors Q_3 and Q_4, including the placement of the contacts. Figure 10.42b shows one of the integrated resistors and its contacts. The conducting path for the resistor is through p-material contacted by the metal. The n-layer is required to separate the resistor from the substrate. P-type resistors of high resistivity material are used so that excessive lengths are not required to obtain the required resistance. [Recall that R = (resistivity) × (length)/(area).] When the *npn* transistors are made, a lightly doped p-layer is created during the formation of the base. Since this is the only step involving lightly doped material, the resistors and the transistor bases are made simultaneously. The n-layer underlying the resistor is formed at the same time as the transistor collector region.

This example illustrates some general features of monolithic integration of electronic circuits. Junction transistors (normally *npn*) are formed in rectangular regions within a substrate layer. Resistors are formed as long narrow conductors, either straight or not, from the same material used in the base regions of the transistors. A layer of metal, chemically etched into the desired pattern, makes contact to the terminals of the various resistors and transistors and provides the appropriate circuit "wiring."

Before concluding the present discussion we note certain "parasitic" elements present in any monolithic IC. Each transistor is isolated from other elements and from the neutral part of the substrate by the reverse biased junction between the substrate and the collector. A space charge layer capacitance is associated with this *pn* junction so that the high-frequency behavior of the circuit is affected by a capacitance connected effectively from the collector to AC ground. Furthermore this reverse biased junction can act as a collector for holes. Thus if the base-collector junction of Q_3 or Q_4 in Fig. 10.42c becomes forward biased, holes will be injected into the n-layer and some might diffuse across to the collector-substrate junction and be collected there. If that happens the *npn* collector current will be reduced from its expected value and circuit misfunction will occur. To prevent this the n-layer should be several diffusion lengths thick. On the other hand this base-collector-substrate *pnp* transistor, the substrate *pnp*, can sometimes be put to good use. If the circuit being integrated requires a *pnp* transistor with collector connected directly to V^-, then the substrate *pnp* may be used.

A parasitic effect also is associated with an integrated resistor. More specifically, there is a distributed capacitance from the resistor body to AC ground consisting of two SCL capacitances in series, those of the two *pn* junctions in Fig. 10.42b.

One might think that a substrate *pnp* effect exists since there is an obvious *pnp* structure present in Fig. 10.42b. Note however that no connection is made to the n-layer. Therefore zero base current is provided to the "base" of this *pnp* and hence negligible "collector" and "emitter" currents flow.

This introduction to monolithic integrated circuits is very brief, partly because there is little new to say. The individual elements within the IC have already been treated. Even the parasitic effects are describable in terms of what has gone before. Thus at the introductory level we conclude by pointing out that nearly all the devices discussed earlier can be used as elements in an IC. This is especially true of the MOSFETs. The MOSFET can be fabricated in even less area than an *npn* or *pnp* bipolar junction transistor (BJT). For this reason MOSFETs are the principal components in many large scale integrated digital circuits (LSI) such as central processors and memories. One or two such LSI circuits, for example, form the entire computational structure of a hand-held scientific calculator.

The fabrication steps used in making monolithic ICs are discussed in Chap. 9. For information on the design of integrated circuits the references listed at the end of the present chapter may be consulted.

REFERENCES

Field Effect Transistors

Angelo, E. C., Jr. 1969. *Electronics: BJTs, FETs, and Microcircuits.* McGraw-Hill, New York. Chaps. 6, 7.

Grove, A. S. 1967. *Physics and Technology of Semiconductor Devices.* Wiley, New York. Chaps. 8, 11.

Kano, K. 1972. *Physical and Solid State Electronics.* Addison-Wesley, Reading, Mass. Chaps. 10, 11.

Middlebrook, R. D. 1963. A Simple Derivation of Field-Effect Transistor Characteristics. *Proc. IEEE* 51:1146–47.

IMPATT and Gunn Diodes

Kano. *Physical and Solid State Electronics.* Pp. 174–79, 363–74.

Read, W. T. 1958. A Proposed High-Frequency Negative Resistance Diode. *Bell Syst. Tech. J.* 37:401.

Soohoo, R. F. 1971. *Microwave Electronics.* Addison-Wesley, Reading, Mass. Chap. 12.

Streetman, B. G. 1972. *Solid State Electronic Devices.* Prentice-Hall, Englewood Cliffs, N.J. Pp. 418–35.

Sze, S. M. 1969. *Physics of Semiconductor Devices.* Wiley, New York. Chaps. 5, 14.

van der Ziel, A. 1968. *Solid State Physical Electronics.* Prentice-Hall, Englewood Cliffs, N.J. Pp. 453–59.

Watson, H. A. 1969. *Microwave Semiconductor Devices and Their Applications.* McGraw-Hill. Chaps. 15, 16.

Integrated Circuits
Meyer, C. S.; Lynn, D. K.; and Hamilton, D. J., eds. 1968. *Analysis and Design of Integrated Circuits.* McGraw-Hill, New York.

Sorkin, R. 1970. *Integrated Electronics.* New York. McGraw-Hill, New York.

Stern, L. 1968. *Fundamentals of Integrated Circuits.* Hayden, New York.

Warner, R. M., Jr., and Fordemwalt, J. N. 1965. *Integrated Circuits.* McGraw-Hill, New York.

Light-Emitting Diodes
Bergh, A.A., and Dean, P. J. Light-Emitting Diodes. *Proc. IEEE* 60(1972): 156–223.

Streetman. *Solid State Electronic Devices.* Pp. 239–44.

Thomas, D. G. 1968. Electroluminescence. *Physics Today* 21:43–48.

Photoresistors, Photo Diodes, and Photo Transistors
Streetman. *Solid State Electronic Devices.* Pp. 232–39.

Sze. *Semiconductor Devices.* Pp. 653–83.

van der Ziel. *Solid State Physical Electronics.* Chapt. 11, pp. 401–7.

pin Diodes
Hewlett-Packard Co. Applications of *PIN* Diodes. (Appl. note 922) Hewlett-Packard. Palo Alto, Calif.

van der Ziel. *Solid State Physical Electronics.* Pp. 317–23, 411–12.

Watson. *Microwave Semiconductor Devices.* Chaps. 9, 10.

*pnpn*s and Triacs
Bedford, B. D., and Hoft, R. G. 1964. *Principles of Inverter Circuits.* Wiley, New York.

Grafham, D. R., and Hey, J. C. 1972. *SCR Manual, 5th ed.* General Electric, Rectifier Components Dept. Auburn, N.Y.

Murray, R., Jr., 1963. *SCR Designers' Handbook.* Westinghouse Electric Corp., Semiconductor Div. Youngwood, Pa. Pp. 1.3–1.11.

RCA. 1971. *Solid-State Power Circuits.* Radio Corp. Am., Solid State Div. Somerville, N.J.

Sze. *Semiconductor Devices.* Chap. 7.

Index

Alpha, 225, 260–64
Avalanche
  breakdown, 196–99, 203, 209
  multiplication
    IMPATT diode, 344–46
    junction diode, 196–99
    junction transistor, 225–28, 257
    pnpn, 324

Bands, conduction and valence, 73–78, 97–101, 108–9, 148, 149
Barrier
  energy, 170
  layer, 171. *See also* Space charge layer
  potential, 170
  voltage, 175–76
Base, 220
Base transport factor, 226
Beta, 227–29, 260–64
Bias, forward and reverse, 176–77
Blackbody radiation, 10–12, 29

Capacitance
  diffusion, 252
  parasitic, 365
  space charge layer, 192–95, 248
Carrier
  energy distribution, *pn* junction, 173–74, 179, 214–17
  spatial distribution
    pin diode, 335
    pn junction, 180
    pnp transistor, 235, 239
Carrier concentration
  excess, 152. *See also* Injection
  intrinsic, 90, 114
    temperature dependence, 114, 115
    values, 115, 163
  n-type material, 88–89, 91–93

p-type material, 89, 93
  thermal equilibrium, 90–91
Carriers
  energetic, 179, 214–17
  majority, 80
  minority, 80
    suppression, 91
  primary, 197
  secondary, 197
Channel, 311
Charge, stored
  junction diode, 186–88
  junction transistor, 234–50
Circuit
  common-base, 225
  common-emitter, 227–28
  equivalent. *See* Model, circuit
  hybrid-pi, 250–56, 259–60
  integrated (IC), 360–66
Collector, 220
Collisions, 134
Compton effect, 20–25, 29
Concentration
  carrier. *See* Carrier concentration
  electron and hole
    distribution in energy, 108–10
    quantum-mechanical calculation, 110–13
    temperature dependence, 123–24
    thermal equilibrium, 88–93, 125
Conductivity, 5, 130
  hole, electron, 132
  and impurities, 79–86
  temperature dependence, 6, 85–86, 138
Conductor, 74, 75, 76
Constant
  dielectric, values, 163
  diffusion, 141, 148, 163, 226, 227, 298
  lattice, 71–72
  separation, 34, 35
Contact potential, 173, 175

369